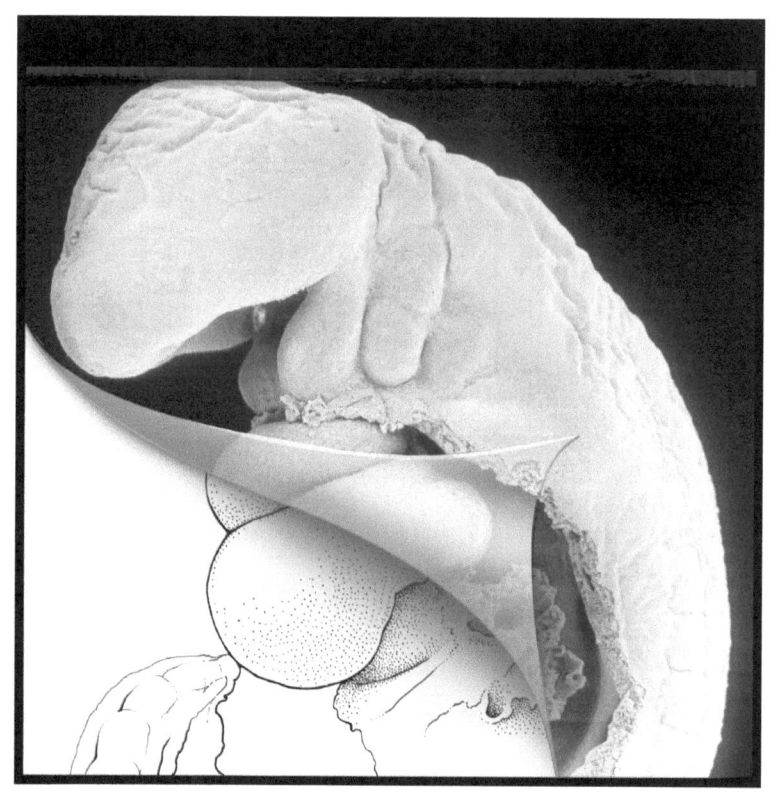

Steding's and Virágh's
Scanning Electron
Microscopy Atlas of the
Developing Human Heart

Steding's and Virágh's Scanning Electron Microscopy Atlas of the Developing Human Heart

Roelof-Jan Oostra
Gerd Steding
Wout H. Lamers
Antoon F. M. Moorman

 Springer

Roelof-Jan Oostra
Department of Anatomy and Embryology
Academic Medical Centre
Amsterdam, The Netherlands

Gerd Steding
Department of Embryology
Georg-August-Universität
Göttingen, Germany

Wout H. Lamers
Department of Anatomy and Embryology
Academic Medical Centre
Amsterdam, The Netherlands

Antoon F. M. Moorman
Department of Anatomy and Embryology
Academic Medical Centre
Amsterdam, The Netherlands

Library of Congress Control Number: 2006933726

ISBN-10: 0-387-36942-6
ISBN-13: 978-0-387-36942-2
Printed on acid-free paper.

9 8 7 6 5 4 3 2 1

springer.com

Contents

Preface and acknowledgments

Morphogenesis of the embryonic heart in humans and other higher vertebrates is a complex process which involves an intricate program of tissue remodeling. In particular, the process of septation, as a result of which right and left cardiac chambers become separated, continues to fascinate scientists for over a century now. Thanks to the recent advances in molecular biology, especially in immunohistochemistry and (whole mount) in situ hybridization, it has become increasingly possible to investigate the biological processes that effectuate cardiac morphogenesis. As a consequence, molecular and biochemical scientists urgently require an updated morphological reference of cardiac embryology for topographic correlation of the results of their experiments, which, in the end, must lead to a better understanding of normal and of abnormal heart development.

This atlas contains about 180 scanning electron microscopy (SEM) pictures, together with several explanatory figures, showing the essence of human cardiac development. Apart from serving a unique overview on cardiac development in the human embryo, this atlas enables the projection of experimental results in animals to the human situation. The material for this atlas is largely based on the collection of Prof. dr Gerd Steding, with additional material from the late Prof. dr Szabolcs Virágh. The differences in approaches and specific interests guarantee the diversity in images which is necessary to give a complete and extensive exposure of all spatial and temporal aspects of human cardiac development, as presented in this atlas.

Embryos were staged according to the Carnegie classification. However, it should be taken into consideration that the cardiac developmental state varies individually even in embryos of the same stage. A table is appended that summarizes the hallmarks in human cardiac morphogenesis during the various developmental stages. The development of the heart in the human embryo is known only from material collected through spontaneous miscarriages and legally terminated pregnancies. Thus, obtaining material with a gestational age of less than three weeks that is suitable for scanning electron microscopy is nowadays virtually impossible. Therefore, although heart development commences at stage 9 (20–21 days p.c.), the youngest embryos we dispose of are from stage 11 (23–25 days p.c.).

The first chapter comprises an illustrated textual overview of the early developmental stages in the vertebrate embryo and the formation of the primitive heart tube up to the stage of compartment formation. The subsequent chapters comprise the SEM pictures, which start off at Carnegie stage 11, i.e., when looping has completed. Each chapter begins with a concise description of the relevant developmental events followed by the SEM pictures. The text and the pictures are intended to be separately comprehendible, i.e., the text, which mostly represents the current opinions, should merely give a "backbone" to the reader, whereas the SEM pictures together with their legends speak for themselves. All photographs are accompanied by line drawings that carry the legends, thus leaving the pictures themselves untouched. A list of terms we used to describe the structures we encountered is appended. We found these terms to be the most appropriately usable, although we realize that some of them may be controversial. We refrained from using adjectives such as "embryonic" and "primitive," which we consider to be superfluous when describing developmental morphology, although we are well aware of the fact that several mature cardiac structures are only partially represented by their embryonic synonyms. Following the initial orientation of the heart tube in human and animal embryos, we used the terms "anterior" and "posterior" with reference to the outflow and inflows parts respectively. The terms we used to describe the various angles, section planes, and topographic relations are summarized in the figures below (Figures 0 A, B).

With this atlas we hope to have succeeded in our intentions to make a readily accessible reference aid for scientists working in the fields of molecular, biochemical, genetic, and morphological investigation of cardiac development. Additionally, we believe that this atlas may serve as a helpful tool in the cardiological education of medical students, clinicians, pathologists, and geneticists.

We wish to express our gratitude to all who contributed to the completion of this atlas, in paticular, the following people:

At the Department of Embryology, Georg-August-Universität, Göttingen, Germany:

Mr. Hans-Georg Sydow for his untiring and conscientious efforts in collecting and preparing the specimens for scanning electron microscopy, his inimitable skill in the complicated setting-up of the microinstruments for dissection and for his valuable support in the solution of laborious technical problems with the scanning electron microscope.
Mrs. Kirsten Falk-Stietenroth for the photographic work she carried out in the darkroom with unsurpassable care, great dedication and her own very special aesthetic aptitude.
Mrs. Anja Aue for archiving the specimens and photographs, which she carried out with great care, thus playing an important role in the maintenance of order and in keeping the records straight.
Dr. Jörg Männer, who, during his time as acting head of the Department of Embryology, generously provided the opportunities to allow the authors to complete this book in familiar surroundings.

At the Department of Pathology, National Health Centre, Budapest, Hungary:

Mr. Gyula Szabó, photographer; Mr. József Farsang EM-emgineer; Ms. Margit Stark, technician; and the late Mrs. Ilona Kennedy, technician, all of whom assisted Prof. Dr. Virágh in making the EM specimens and photographs.
Dr. Gabriella Arató, former collegue of Prof. Dr. Virágh, who generously assisted in collecting the materials and took care of his heritage.

At the Department of Anatomy and Embryology, Academic Medical Centre, University of Amsterdam, The Netherlands:

Mrs. Lara Laghetto (Visualmedics) for making the drawings of the depicted specimens with meticulous precision and for the additional illustrations, which beautifully clarify the intricate processes of cardiac septation.

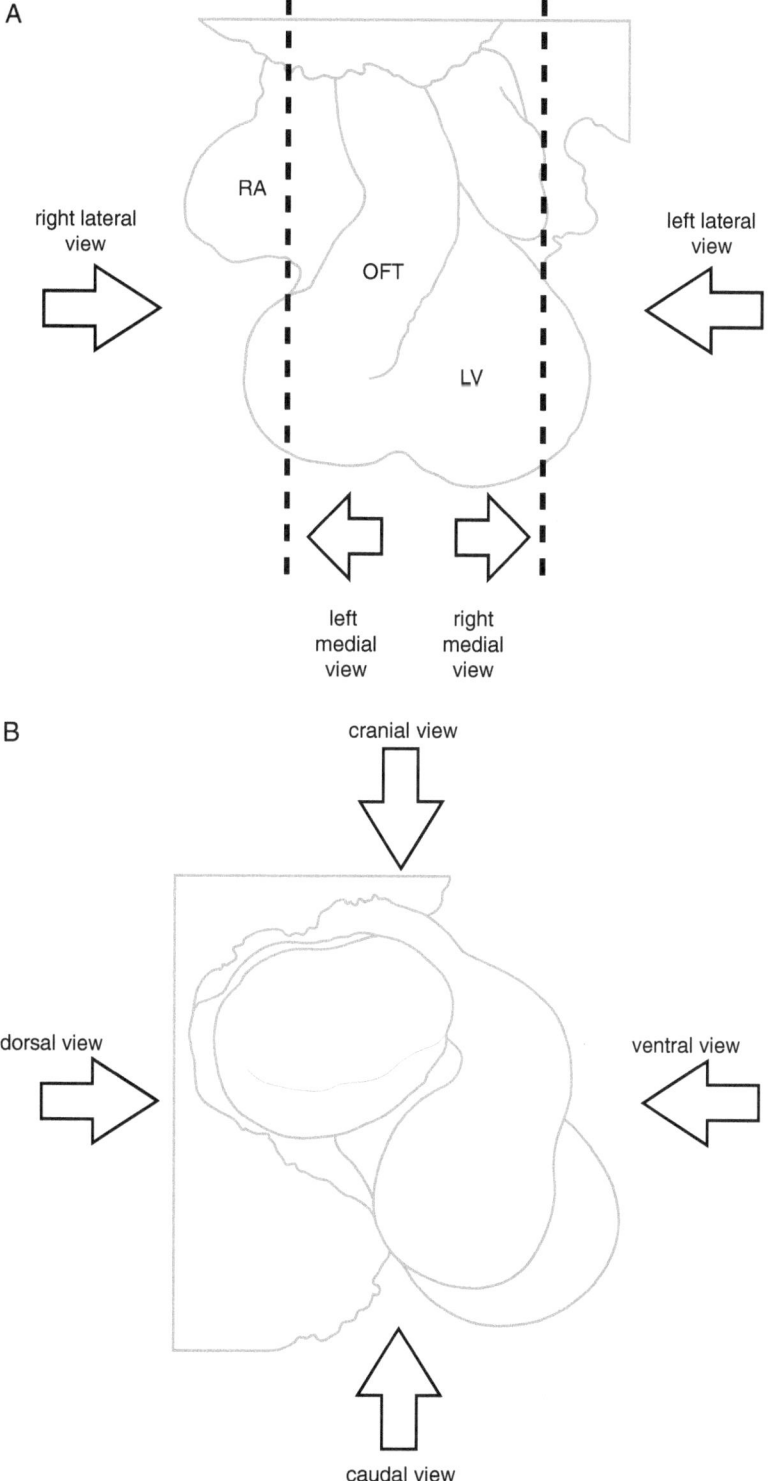

Figures 0 A, B Terminology used to describe the angles, section planes and topographic relations.

Mr. Cees Hersbach and Mr. Cars Gravemeijer for scanning and archiving the numerous photographs that were used in making this atlas.

Last but certainly not least we wish to thank Drs. R.H. Anderson, A.E. Becker, B Christ, V.M. Christoffels, F. de Jong and M.B.J. van den Hoff for their helpful discussions.

Ths making of this atlas was financially supported by the Netherlands Organization of Scientific Research (NWO) and the Hungarian Scientific Research fund (OTKA).

In Memoriam

In March 2001, Prof. Dr. Szabolcs Virágh passed away. Dr. Virágh, pathologist at the former Imre Haynal University (presently the National Health Centre) in Budapest, Hungary, was one of the instigators and driving forces in the making of this atlas. His enormous collection of scanning electron micrographs concerning the developing human heart in various embryonic stages, dating back from the early 1980s onward, initiated the idea of making an atlas out of it. Realizing that his material did not cover all aspects of human cardiac development, he readily agreed with Prof. Dr. Steding to join in. Dr. Virágh's expertise, enthusiasm, dedication, and, not in the least, his social skills inspired the co-workers in this project to continue despite several drawbacks. Sadly, he will never to see the results of his efforts. We dedicate this atlas to his memory.

1
Introduction

THE EARLIEST STAGES OF CARDIAC DEVELOPMENT

The morphogenesis of the four-chambered heart is one of the most intricate processes in higher vertebrate embryology, which involves a program of gene expression, differential growth, spatial organization, and cell movement. Since diffusion of nutrients from the surrounding tissues, which nourishes the rapidly growing embryo in its earliest stages, soon becomes insufficient, the embryonic cardiovascular system is the first functioning organ to appear. Thus, a primitive but functioning circulation with a beating heart is already accomplished during the beginning of the fourth week of development. During development, the primitive single-circuited tubular heart must evolve into a four-chambered double-circuited structure, while it is already committed to its lifelong task, i.e. maintaining circulation. This requires profound and complex remodeling, which is difficult to comprehend and makes great demands on one's spatial insight. With the advent of molecular technology a new era in cardiac embryonic research has begun and the mechanisms involved in the sequential processes of cardiac development are now starting to become unraveled.

During the third week of development (stage 7, 16 days p.c.), ingressing epiblast cells spread in various directions over the embryonic disc between the former epiblast and the hypoblast, thus giving rise to the third embryonic layer: the intraembryonic mesoderm. During stage 8 (17–19 days p.c.), two areas of mesoderm in each half of the embryonic disc meet each other anterior to the stomatopharyngeal membrane and form an arch-shaped structure. The anterior part of this structure is dubbed the cardiogenic crescent (heart forming region). This is the area where the future heart will start to develop. In this arch-shaped band of mesoderm, small cavities appear. The adjacent mesodermal cells will be transformed into epithelial cells. These cavities coalesce and form the first intra-embryonic coelom, i.e. the pericardial cavity. This lumen separates the part of the lateral plate mesoderm that faces the ectoderm, the parietal (or somatic) mesoderm, from that apposed to the endoderm, the visceral (or splanchnic) mesoderm. When the first vacuoles coalesce, the cranial lumen, which becomes the pericardial cavity, expands in caudal direction, forming the pleuro-peritoneal ducts (coelomic ducts) that connect to the peritoneal cavity. The cranial most rim of mesoderm in the embryonic disk will later contribute to the septum transversum. The visceral mesoderm that forms the floor of the pericardial cavity gives rise to the myocardium and endocardium.

At various sites in the extraembryonic mesoderm, and later also the intraembryonic mesoderm, mesenchymal cells appear that form vacuolated masses and cords. These cells known as angioblasts give rise to both blood cells and to a layer of endothelial cells that encloses the blood islands, a process known as vasculogenesis [Poole and Coffin, 1989]. These endothelial cavities and strings fuse to form primitive vessels. Thus, in the intraembryonic visceral and parietal mesoderm, the outlines of the major systemic arteries and veins appear on each side of the embryonic midline. Close to the notochord the two dorsal aortae are formed, whereas the venous plexuses are situated more laterally in the body wall. In the same manner, angioblasts in the area of the cardiogenic crescent, formed by the cardiogenic plate, give rise to the primitive endocardial plexus [Viragh et al., 1989]. These angioblastic islands coalesce and form a plexus in the midline of the myocardial mantle. The branches of this plexus coalesce and form the unpaired endocardial tube which acts as anastomoses between the rostral ends of the dorsal aortae and the venous plexuses (Figures 1 A–E). Gene expression studies in chicken and mouse embryos have shown that this coalescence takes place at the site that, at a later stage, will contribute to the formation of the left ventricle. The parts of the heart tube that will later on develop into the right ventricle and outflow tract are added later at the arterial end of the heart tube by the so-called secondary or anterior heart-forming region [Kelly et al., 2001; Mjaatvedt et al.; 2001; Waldo et al., 2001]. In between the endocardial tube and the myocardial mantle a glycosamin rich extracellular layer is present which is generated by the cardiogenic plate. This material is known as cardiac jelly, which at this stage is acellular (see Chapter 5). Shortly after the primitive heart tube has been formed, the first cardiac contractions can be seen in the region where the future ventricles will develop, even before the circulation is completely closed.

LOOPING OF THE HEART TUBE

Following the formation of the heart tube, two more or less simultaneously occurring processes accompany the formation of the primitive heart tube. Firstly, during neurulation, which commences at stage 9 (19–21 days p.c.), the embryonic disk flexes and folds along both its transverse and longitudinal axes, resulting in head and tail folds and lateral folds. As a results of the head fold, the most anteriorly positioned structures, being the stomatopharyngeal membrane, the septum transversum, and the primitive heart, curve ventrally at an angle of more than 180° and acquire their definite position in front of the foregut. Secondly, the heart tube starts to loop at the beginning of stage 10 (21–23 days p.c.), a process that in man, as well as in most vertebrate species, already commences before coalescence of the endothelial plexus has formed the unpaired cardiac lumen. Seen from its eventual position ventral to the foregut, the first loop to appear in the primitive heart tube is found in the region where the ventricles develop and causes the tube to curve in dextroventral position; it is dubbed the D(extro)-loop or ventricular loop. The second loop occurs in the region of the future atria and the atrioventricular connection and proceeds in the opposite direction, thus causing a levodorsal curving of the heart tube; it can be dubbed the atrial loop the two loops result in an S-shaped configuration of the heart, both in its ventral and lateral aspects. Subsequently, the ventricular loop bulges over the atrial loop, and twists to the right. As a result, the initial left and right sides of the ventricular loop will become the ventral and dorsal sides respectively (Figures 1 F–L).

It has been debated to what extent extrinsic and intrinsic factors are responsible for the initiation, proceeding and completion of normal cardiac looping. Manasek and Monroe [1972] investigated the morphogenesis in asystolic hearts of live chicken embryos. In contrast to the current opinion at the time, they found that "pre-looped" hearts of HH stage 10 embryos undergo normal looping during 5 hours of potas-

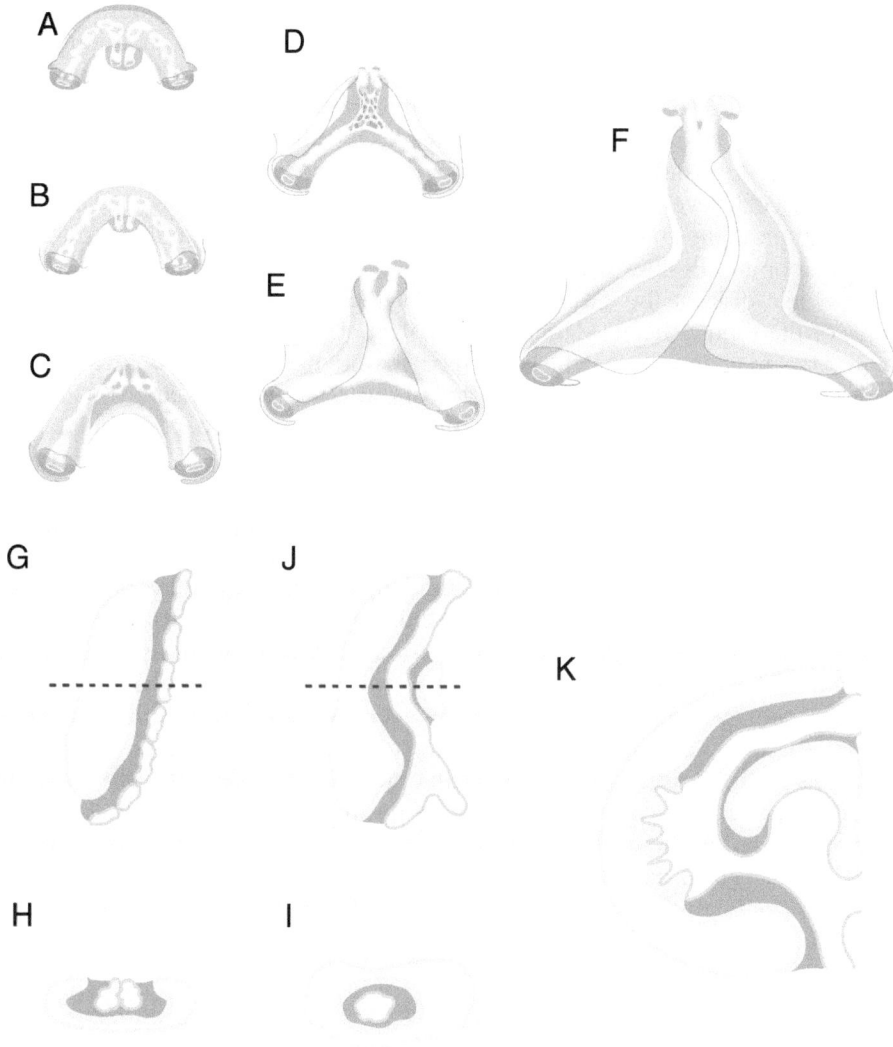

FIGURE 1   **A–F** Formation of the heart tube in the heart forming region during folding of the embryonic disc (dorsal views), involving the endocardial plexus and tubes (light grey), cardiac jelly (dark grey) and the myocardial layer which is continuous with the pericardial lining (transparent sheet). **G–K** Formation and looping of the heart tube (cranial and left lateral views) and its protrusion in the pericardial cavity (white), involving the endocardial plexus and tubes (light grey), cardiac jelly (dark grey) and the myocardial layer which is continuous with the pericardial lining (medium gray).

sium induced cardioplegia and they therefore concluded that normal looping of the heart does not require either cardiac perfusion or contraction. Manning and McLachlan [1990] examined explanted hearts of HH stage 8–10 chicken embryos and found that normal looping occurred in almost all cases, thus supporting the assumption that cardiac looping is an intrinsic process. On the other hand, Hogers et al. [1997, 1999] recently studied the effects of ligation of vitellinous veins on cardiac morphogenesis in HH stage 17 chicken embryos and found that long term ligation, irrespective of which vitellinous vein was clipped, resulted in a spectrum of cardiovascular malformations, which they, at least partially attributed to impaired looping of the heart tube. Resuming the results of all forementioned studies, it seems plausible to assume that cardiac looping is in essence intrinsically controlled i.e. at a molecular level but that intracardiac blood flow patterns may have a profound effect on the eventual morphological outcome, especially during later stages of cardiac looping. Besides this, it has been suggested that longitudinal flexion of the embryonic disk, at the site of the head or the neck is essential for a proper looping of the tubular heart. Männer et al. [1995] observed that experimental prevention of cranial flexion in chicken embryos did not interfere with a normal looping pattern, whereas different studies show that interference with cervical flexion may lead to cardiac anomalies that are based on defective looping [Männer et al., 1993; Kosaki et al., 1996]. It must be noted however, that cranial and cervical flexion in chick embryos are temporally separated processes, whereas in mammals the two occur much more simultaneously.

During the process of looping the heart tube projects into the pericardial cavity but remains connected, initially over its entire length, with the midline of the dorsal body wall by means of the dorsal mesocardium. Subsequently, this mesocardium becomes very thin, perforates and disappears almost completely, except for the atrial part, which continues to be connected to the embryonic body wall by a pedicle formed by the epithelial bridge between pericardium and the heart that contains scarce mesenchyme: the persisting dorsal mesocardium or heart stalk [Webb, 1998]. The thus arisen dorsal communication, between the left and right sides of the pericardial cavity and known as the transverse pericardial sinus, can still be recognized in the mature heart. It should be noted that in chicken embryos the cardiogenic plate, including the intraembryonic coelom that gives rise to the pericardial cavity, remains separated in two lateral parts until folding of the embryonic disc has completed, hence a ventral mesocardium is temporarily present.

Outlines of external development

BLOOD FLOW IN THE TUBULAR HEART

At stage 11, the heart tube has looped completely and despite the fact that it has lost its left-right symmetry, it can still be considered a homogeneous structure from both morphological and functional points of view. The embryonic cardiomyocytes, derived from the cardiogenic plate mesoderm, form a layer, which is dubbed primary myocardium. Impulse propagation and the subsequent contraction waves, which initially have a peristaltoid form, run from the inflow to the outflow end of the heart tube, i.e. in postero-anterior direction. The presence of cardiac jelly guarantees adequate propulsion of blood. From the outset on, pacemaker activity is dominant at the inflow end of the heart tube, although coupling of excitation and contraction is first achieved in the future ventricular area [Van Mierop 1967]. Which mechanisms are responsible for the pacemaker dominance of the inflow end is as yet unknown but it may well be related to the anteroposterior differentiation of the heart tube as a whole, in which retinoic acid signaling plays a quintessential role [Xavier-Neto et al. 2001]. Moreover, many molecular factors involved in early cardiac development [reviewed by e.g. Franco et al. 1998 and Xavier-Neto et al. 2001] exhibit an antero-posterior expression gradient and thus a gradual change of electrochemical properties along the heart tube.

Different blood flows can already be observed soon after looping of the heart tube has completed, i.e. long before physical septation of the embryonic heart is initiated. It has been hypothesized that these flow patterns not only mold the developing heart tube but play a crucial role in the septation processes as well. Many studies have been performed in the past in chicken embryos to elucidate the stream patterns in the early looped heart [e.g. Bremer 1932, Jaffee 1965, Rychter and Lemez 1965, Leyhanne 1969]. Yoshida et al. [1983] performed microangiography with methylene blue injections in live chick embryos and found two consistent blood stream patterns through the heart from Hamilton-Hamburger (HH) stage 14 on. They observed that one of the streams, which runs a ventral intracardiac course, goes to the left branchial arteries, whereas the other one, which runs dorsally, drains onto the right branchial arteries. Steding and Seidl [1990] noticed in chicken embryos that the circular lumen of the tubular heart achieves a halter shape during contraction, thus dynamically bring about two separated blood streams. However, although the flow patterns described by these author groups differ considerably, they both indicated that the patterns they observed cannot explain the morphological characteristics in the development of the atrioventricular and outflow tract septa. They therefore concluded that intracardiac blood flow patterns are not primarily involved in the initiation of cardiac septation. Hogers et al. [1995]

performed labeling studies in stage HH 12–17 chicken embryos and observed flow patterns which again differed from those published by others, but they agreed with Yoshida et al. and Steding and Seidl on the absence of a hemodynamic explanation for the morphology of the outflow tract septum. It seems presently impossible to be conclusive about the correlation between early embryonic blood stream patterns and the subsequent septation of the heart, firstly because almost all hemodynamic studies disagree profoundly with respect to the precise routes of the intracardiac blood streams and their venous and arterial connections, and secondly because both the stream patterns themselves as well as their peripheral vascular connections, according to most of these studies, may change completely within the course of a single developmental stage.

BALLOONING OF THE CARDIAC COMPARTMENTS AND SUBSEQUENT DEVELOPMENT

In the looped heart, an inner (lesser) and outer (greater) curvature can be distinguished, which are important landmarks in the view of subsequent developmental events. The looping process itself is accompanied by a certain degree of torsion since fate map studies have indicated that the outer curvature is initially at the ventral side of the straight heart tube [De la Cruz 1999]. From stage 11 onward, four progressively enlarging balloon-shaped distensions appear at the outer curvature of the atrial and ventricular loops, which will become the cardiac compartments. These compartments expand from the heart tube and should therefore not be considered as segments of the heart tube itself. As a consequence, the inner curvature part is not involved in this process of chamber formation [Moorman & Christoffels, 2003]. It should be noted that the atrial compartments appear as parallel structures on either side of the outer curvature whereas the ventricular compartments are formed successively as serial distensions of the outer curvature. Because of the newly formed cardiac compartments, different parts of the original heart tube can now be identified at the outer curvature. These are the outflow tract at the anterior end, the inflow tract at the posterior end, and the atrioventricular canal in between the developing atrial and ventricular compartments. These parts remain connected with each other at the side of the inner curvature.

The externally visible features of subsequent cardiac development are mostly the results of intricate internal processes. Since they are defined to specific parts of the heart, they will be depicted and described in detail in the according chapters. Between stages 11 and 13 (28 days p.c.) the posterior most part of the inflow tract gradually shifts to the right, resulting in a sinus venosus that drains exclusively to the right atrium. During later development the myocardium that surrounds the sinus venosus and the dorsal mesocardium increasingly contributes to the formation of the dorsal parts of the right and left atria respectively [Soufan et al., 2004], whereas the embryonic atria themselves gradually loose their function in blood propulsion and become transformed into auricles. This process begins around stage 14 (32 days p.c.) but the different shapes of these auricles cannot be clearly appreciated until stage 17 (41 days p.c.). In the early post-looping stages, the atrioventricular canal is located predominantly on the left side of the heart, despite the fact that separate blood flows are already present (see above). During later stages the atrioventricular canal gradually shifts towards the right and becomes largely incorporated in the atria [Wessels et al., 1996]] until its position is merely indicated by the atrio-ventricular sulcus.

The ballooning ventricles, separated by an initially deep interventricular groove, differ in size from their first appearance during stage 11 onward but although the left ventricle is larger than the right one, it is not until stage 17 that the apex of the left ventricle projects beyond the apex of the right ventricle. From that stage onward, the primarily spherical shape of the ventricles changes, the right ventricle will become tetrahedral, the left one cylindric. The interventricular groove becomes less pronounced and by the time embryonic development has completed, the apical parts of the ventricles have formed a single contour. Externally visible development of the coronary arteries can be noted during stage 19 (47–48 days p.c.) by the appearance of a fine reticulum that covers the surface of the ventricles. Soon afterwards, the main vessels and their branches can be distinguished.

The outflow tract, which connects the ventricles with the aortic sac, initially forms a tube-like structure with a single lumen. The knick in this tube roughly separates the proximal part of the outflow tract (conus) from the distal part (truncus). Whether or not this knick represents a fixed anatomical landmark is not known. During stage 15 the regular convexity of the contour is gradually lost with the appearance of a spiralized longitudinal flattening. This flattening corresponds with the formation of endocardial ridges, which, especially in the distal part of the outflow tract, already start to fuse, thus creating two physically separated lumens. From stage 15 onward the myocardial mantle of the distal part of the outflow tract becomes patchy and starts to disappear, leaving a well recognizable and steadily retreating boundary between the proximal and distal parts by the end of stage 17. At this level, the semilunar valves will develop. The proximal part will form the aortic and pulmonary infundibulums and becomes gradually incorporated in the bases of the ventricles. By the end of stage 18, the distal part of the outflow tract has been transformed into the intrapericardial parts of the aorta and pulmonary trunk. The eventual mature contours of the heart as a whole are achieved during stages 19 (47–48 days p.c.) till the end of the embryonic period.

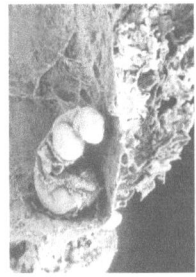

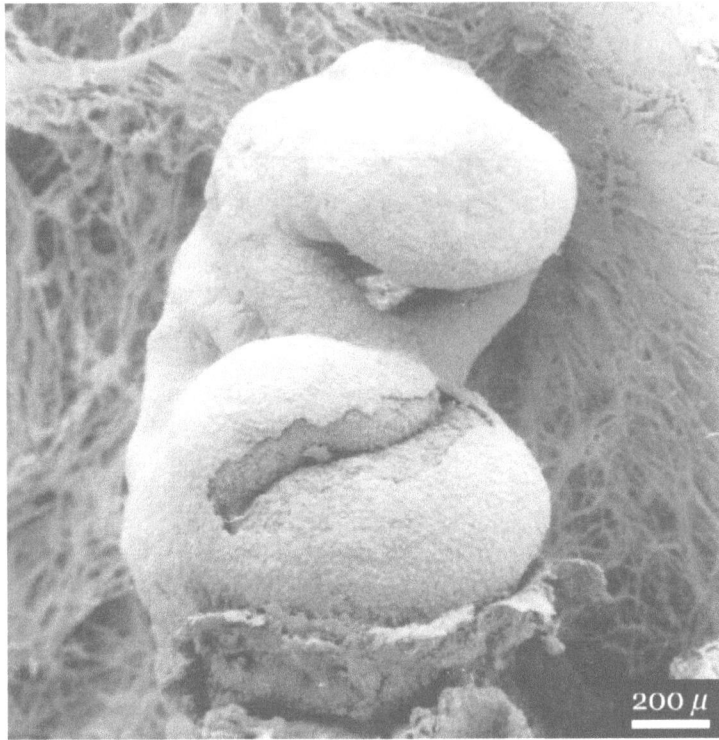

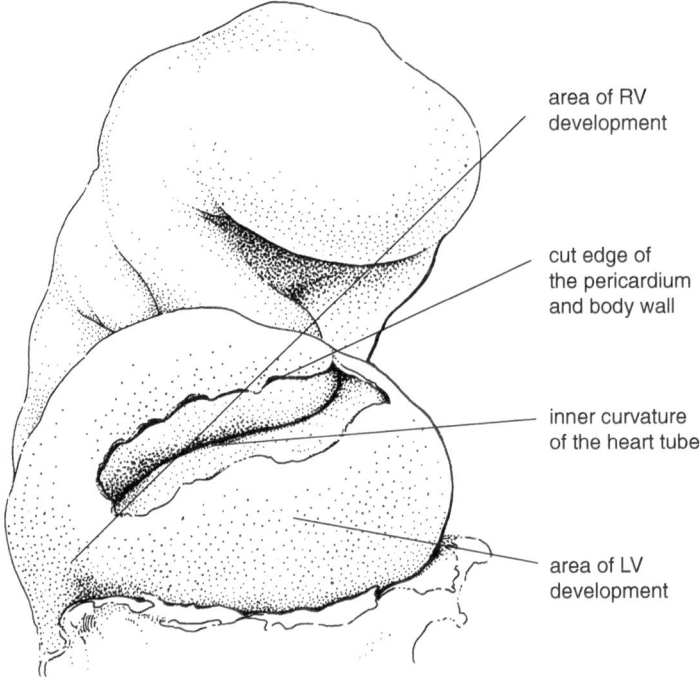

FIGURE 2.1   Complete embryo in situ (stage 11), ventral view. The yolk sac and the amnion are removed. The ventral body wall and the pericardium are opened.

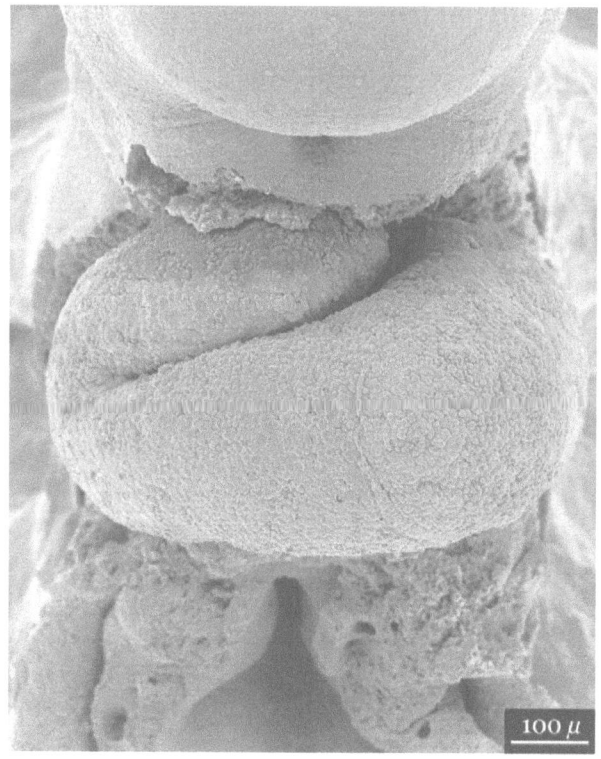

100 μ

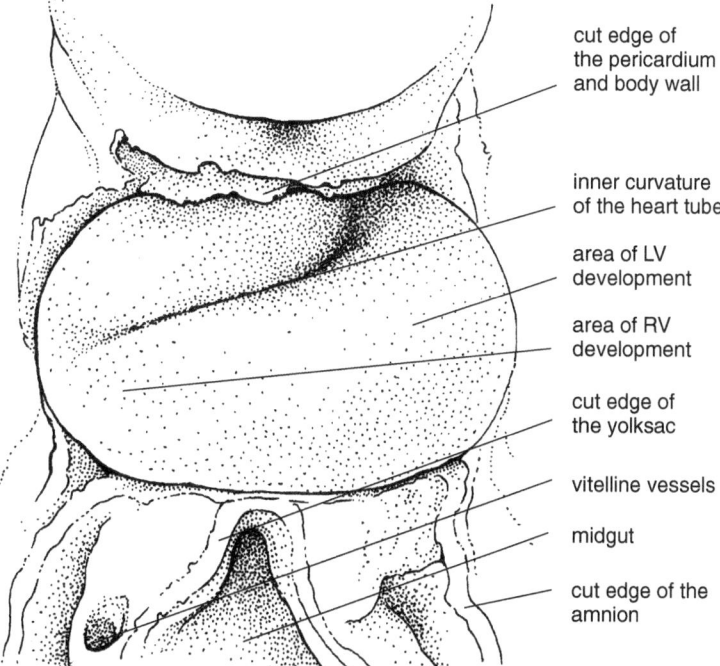

cut edge of
the pericardium
and body wall

inner curvature
of the heart tube

area of LV
development

area of RV
development

cut edge of
the yolksac

vitelline vessels

midgut

cut edge of the
amnion

FIGURES 2.2 and 2.3   Complete embryo in situ (stage 11), ventral
and left lateral views. The yolk sac, the amnion, the ventral body wall
and the pericardium are removed.

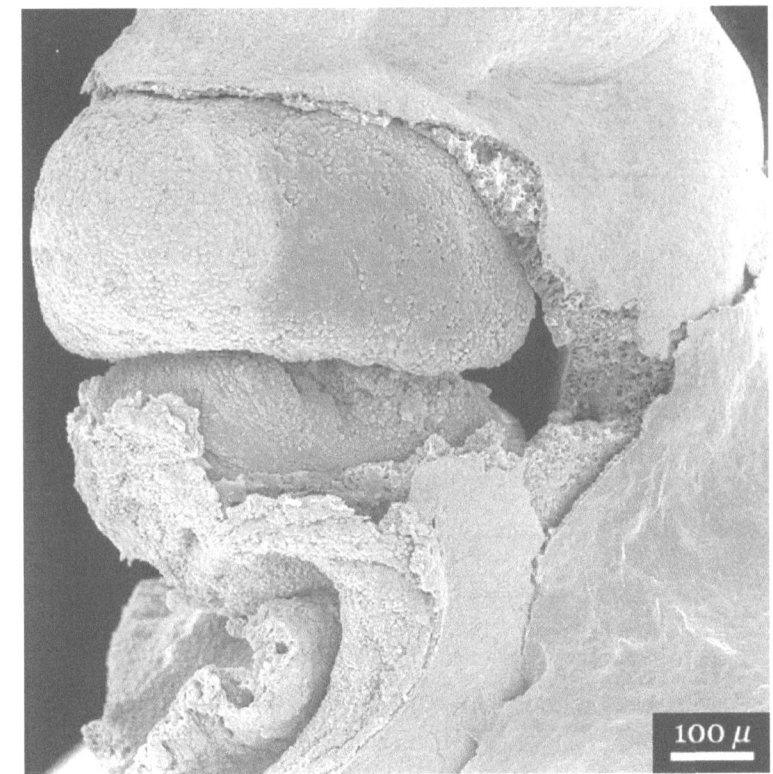

100 μ

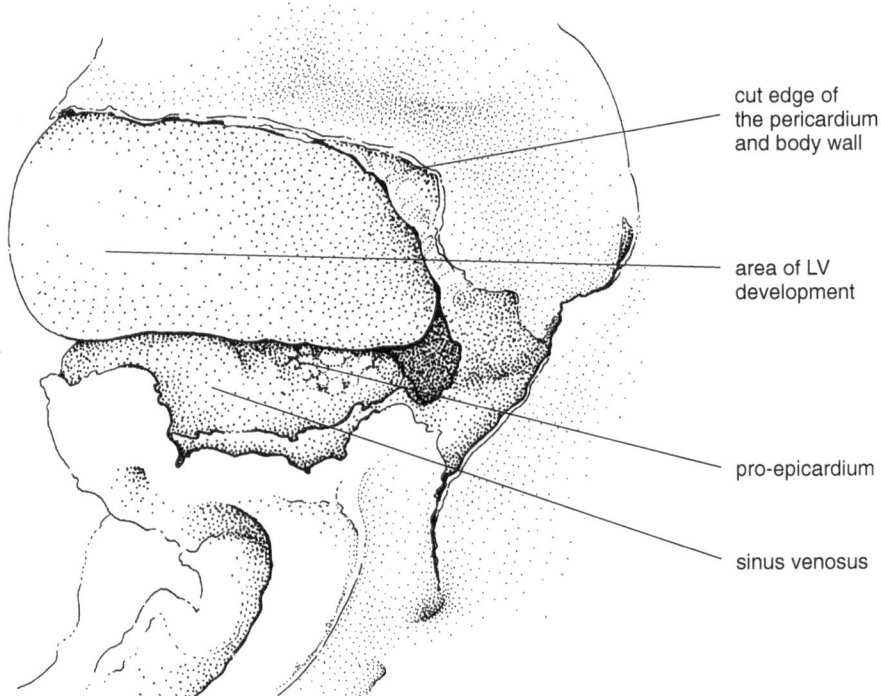

cut edge of
the pericardium
and body wall

area of LV
development

pro-epicardium

sinus venosus

FIGURES 2.2 and 2.3   *Continued*

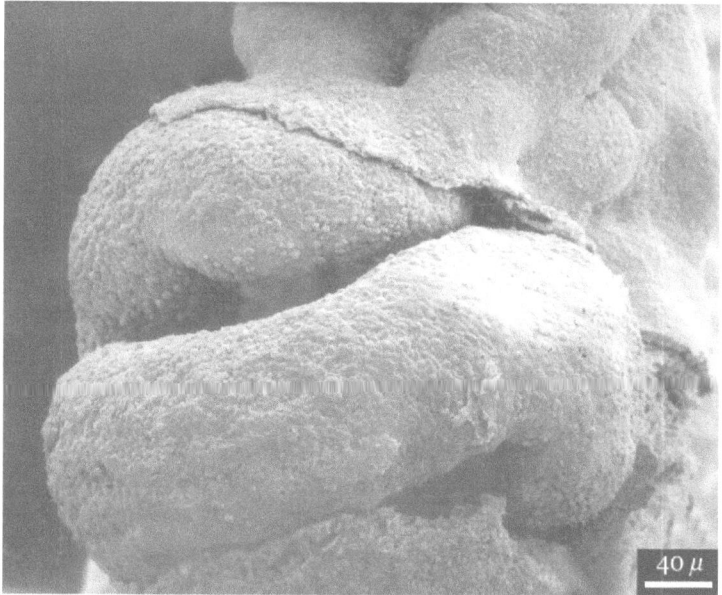

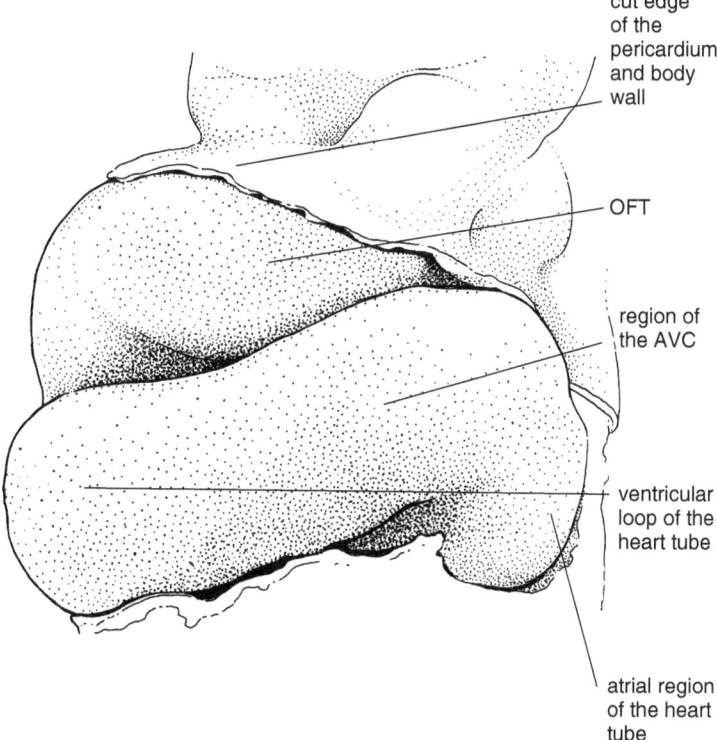

FIGURES 2.4 and 2.5   Complete embryo in situ (stage 11), ventral, left and right lateral views. The yolk sac, the amnion, the ventral body wall and the pericardium are removed. The heart tube has looped completely and the ventricular loop covers the atrial region. There are no externally visible signs of any compartments yet.

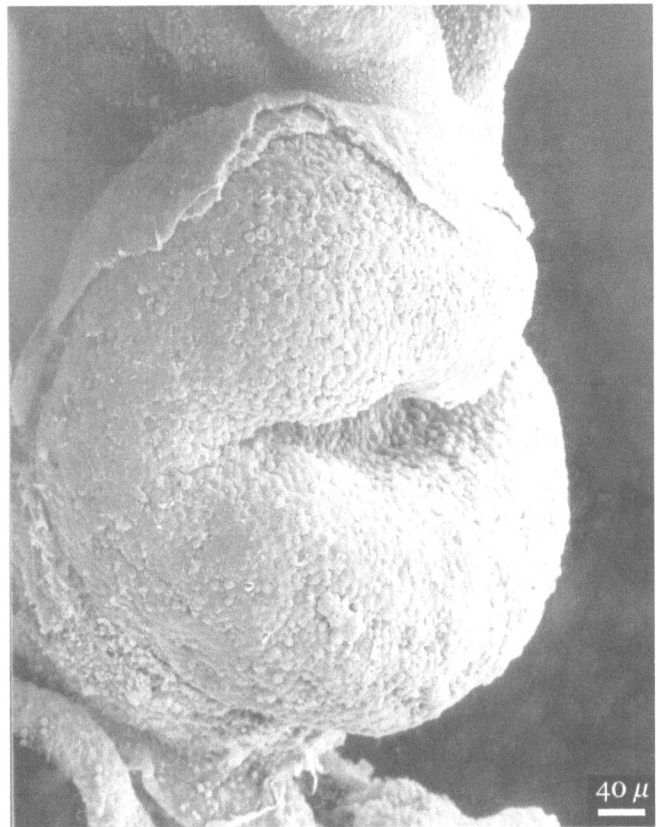

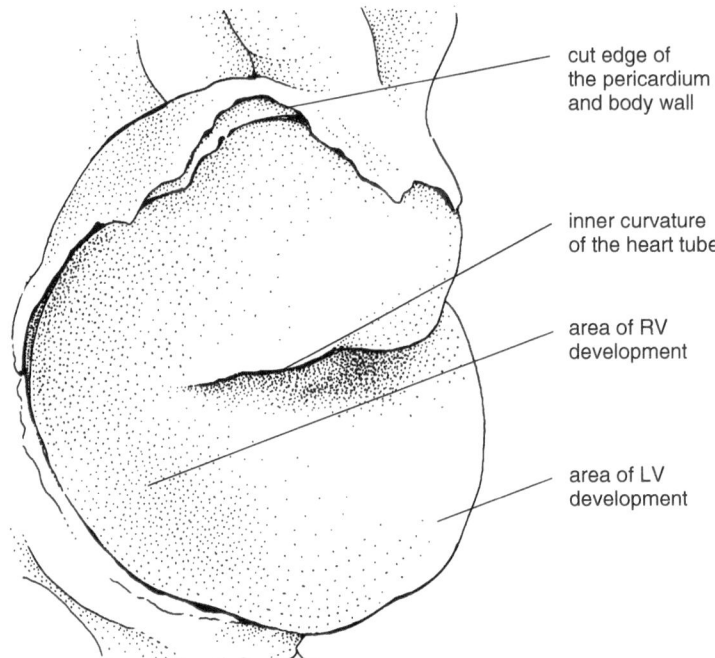

cut edge of
the pericardium
and body wall

inner curvature
of the heart tube

area of RV
development

area of LV
development

FIGURES 2.4 and 2.5   *Continued*

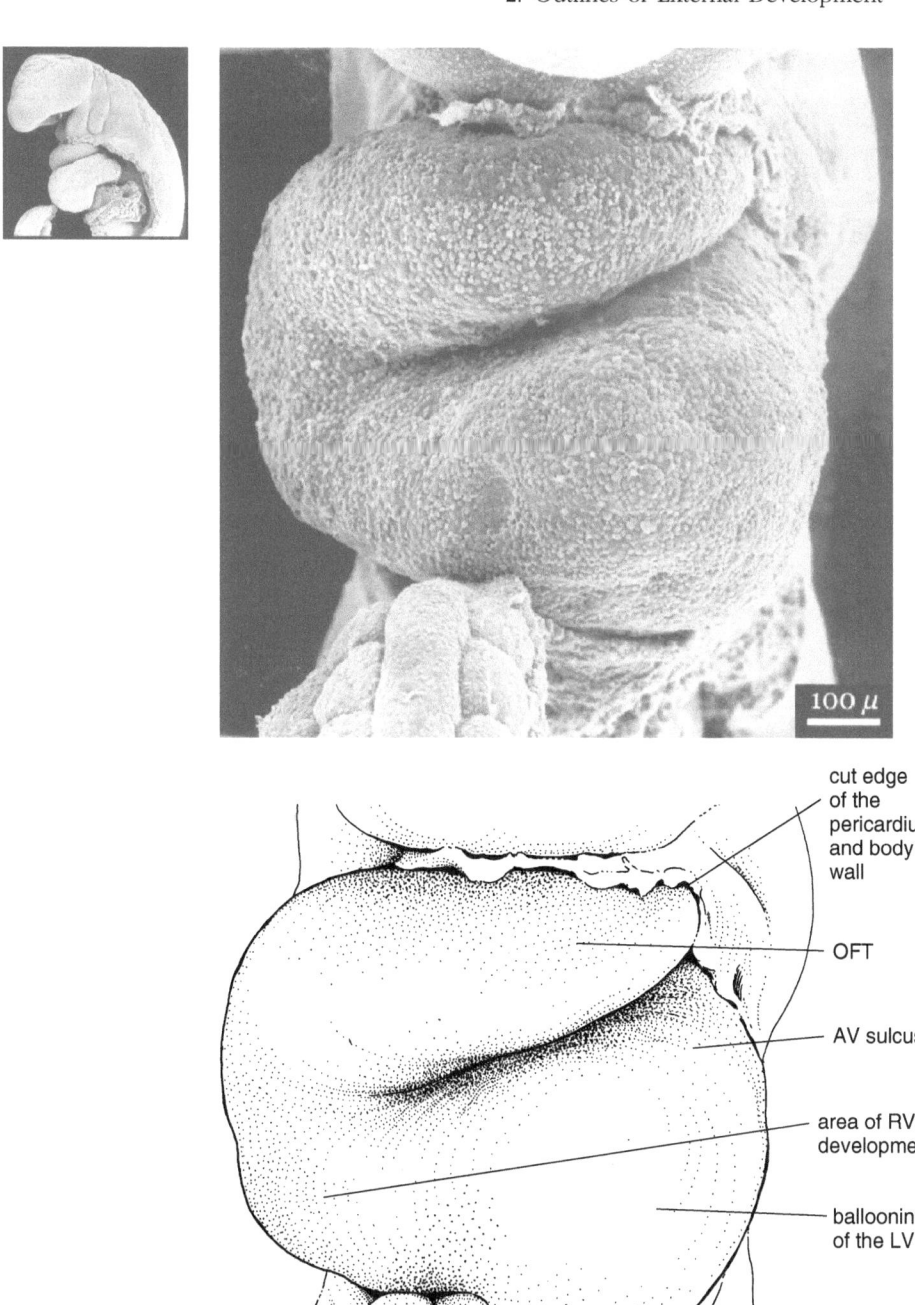

FIGURES 2.6-2.8   Complete heart in situ (stage 12), ventral, right and left lateral views. The ventral body wall and the pericardium are removed. The heart tube shows a dilatation at the posterior part of the left limb of the D-loop. This is the site where the LV will develop. Other compartments are still only very faintly recognisable externally.

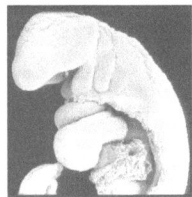

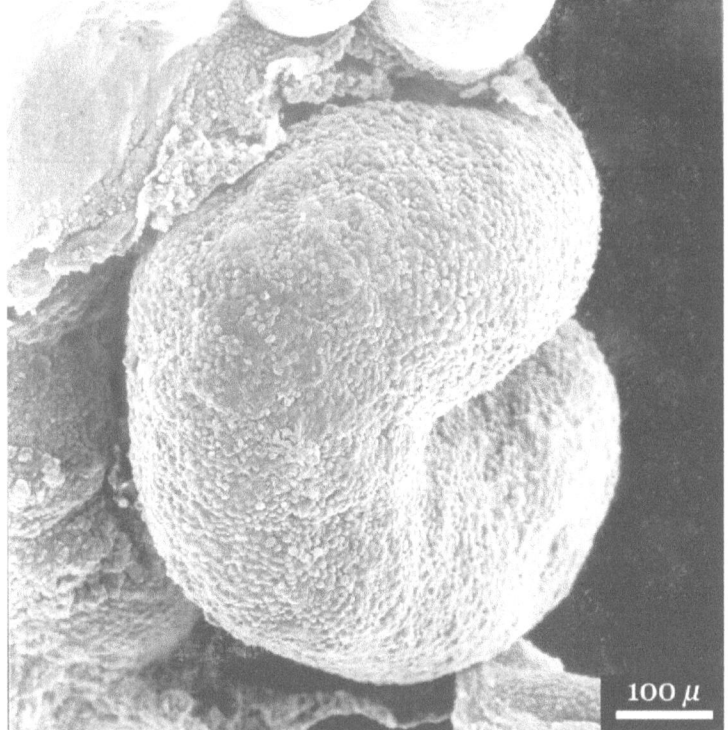

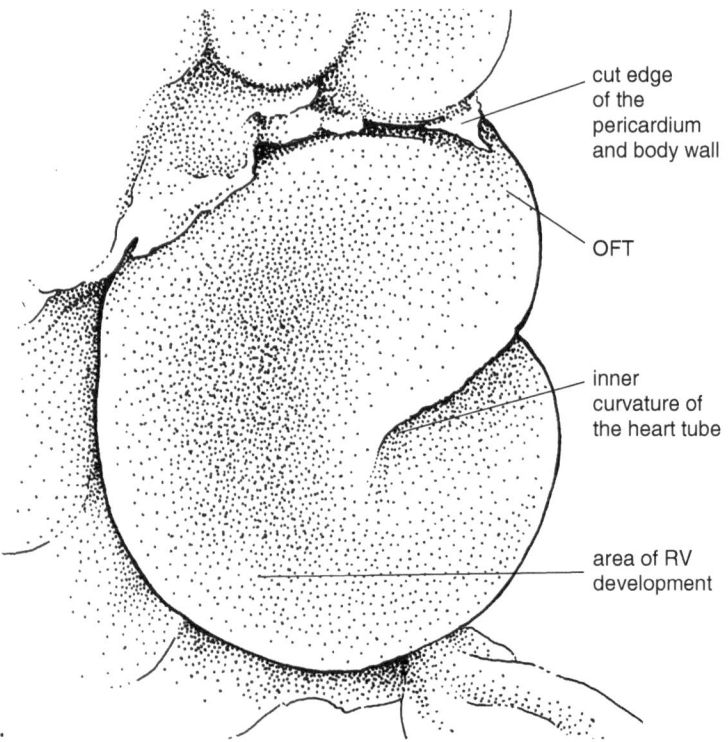

cut edge
of the
pericardium
and body wall

OFT

inner
curvature of
the heart tube

area of RV
development

FIGURES 2.6–2.8   *Continued*

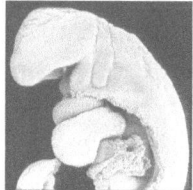

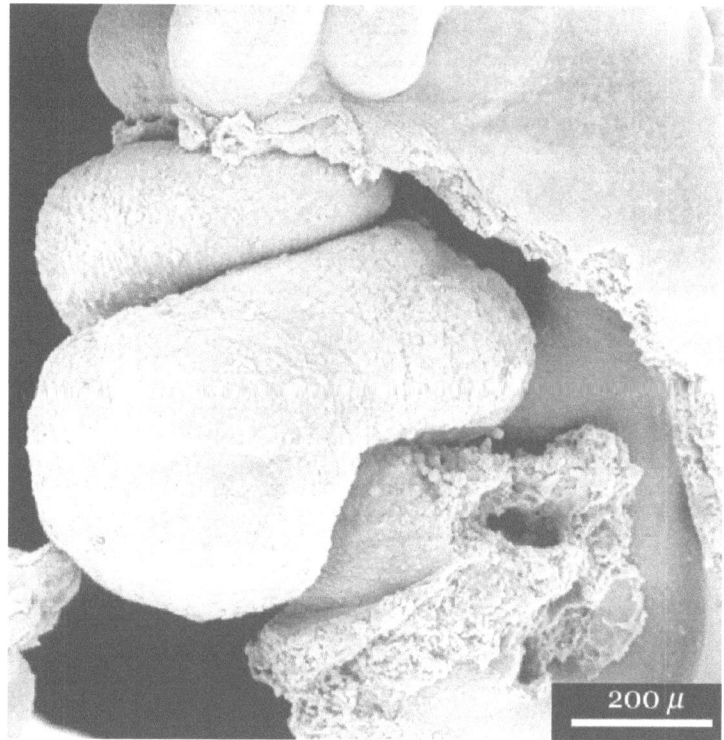

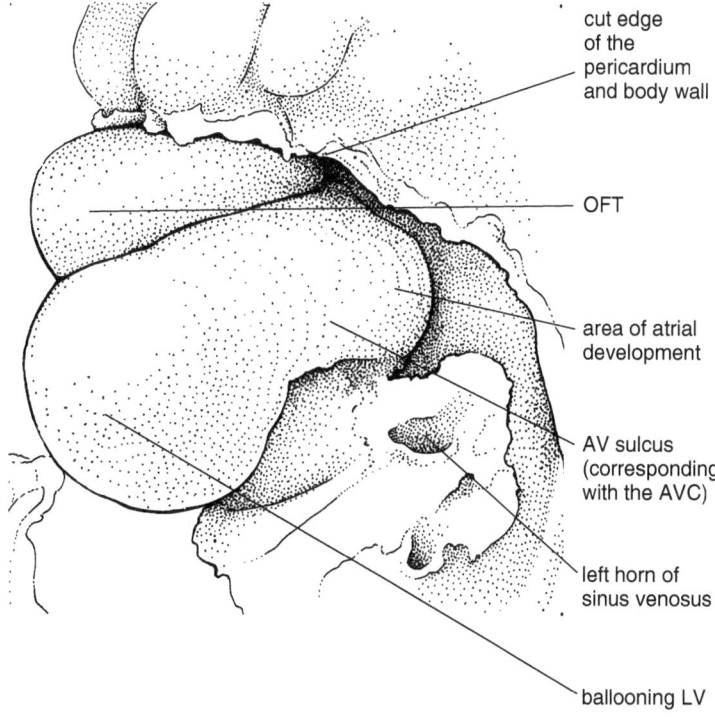

cut edge
of the
pericardium
and body wall

OFT

area of atrial
development

AV sulcus
(corresponding
with the AVC)

left horn of
sinus venosus

ballooning LV

FIGURES 2.6–2.8   *Continued*

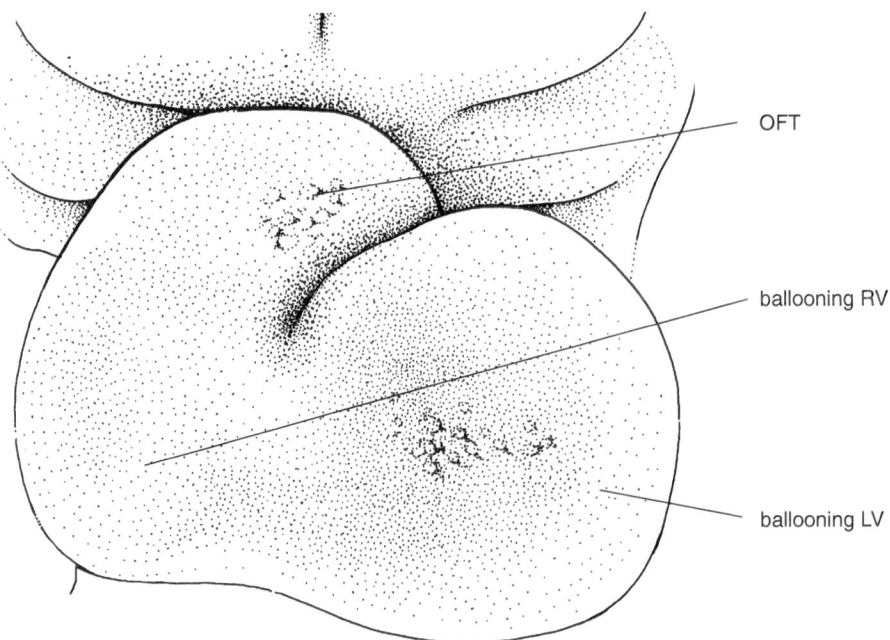

FIGURES 2.9–2.12   Complete heart in situ (stage 13), ventral, right and left lateral and caudal views. The ventral body wall and the pericardium are removed. Dilatations of the heart tube are seen at the sites of the developing ventricles and atria. The RV and LA are still markedly smaller than their contralateral counterparts. The outflow tract is markedly bent.

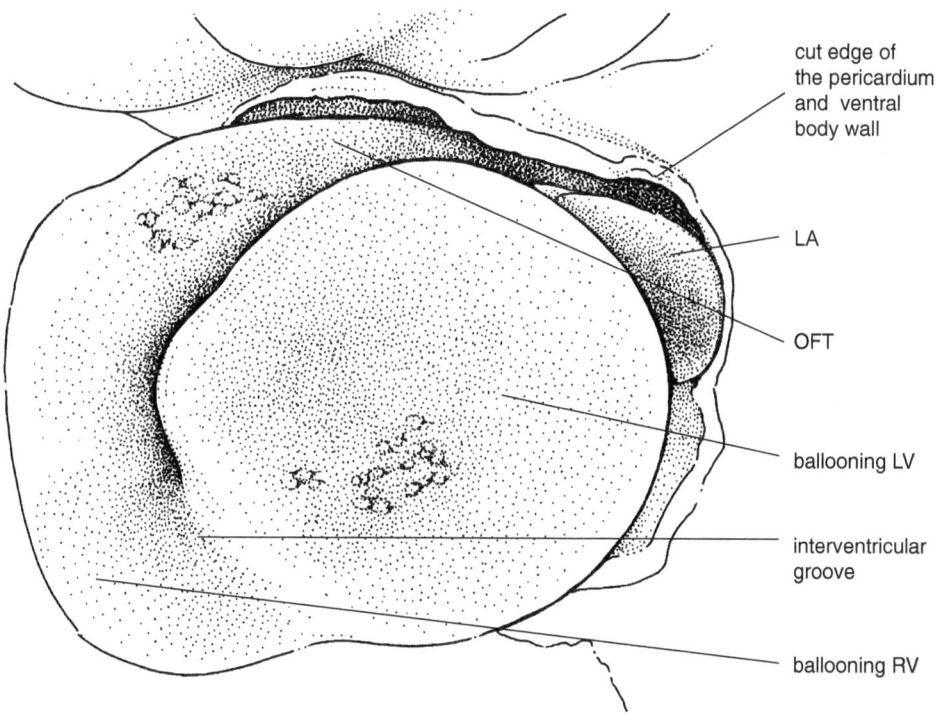

cut edge of
the pericardium
and ventral
body wall

LA

OFT

ballooning LV

interventricular
groove

ballooning RV

FIGURES 2.9–2.12   *Continued*

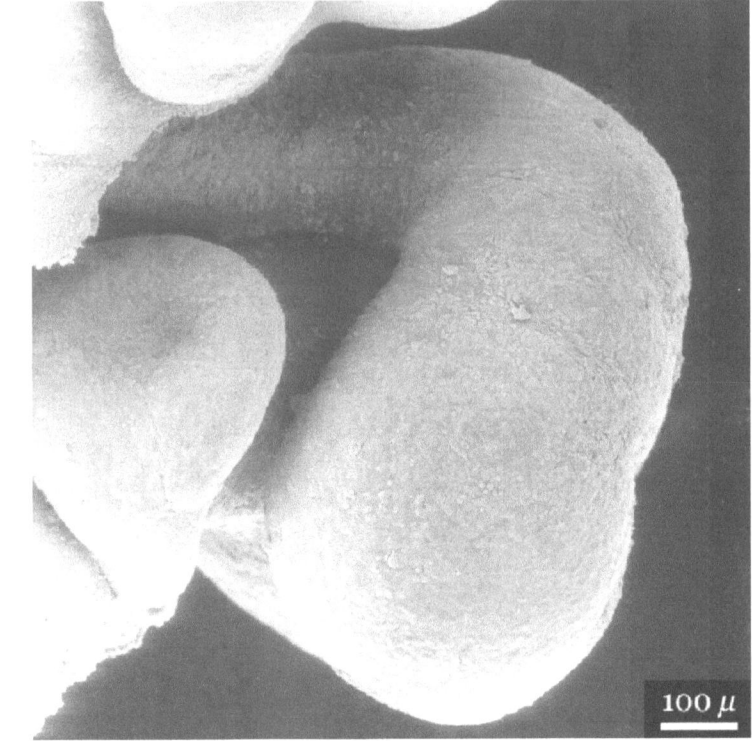

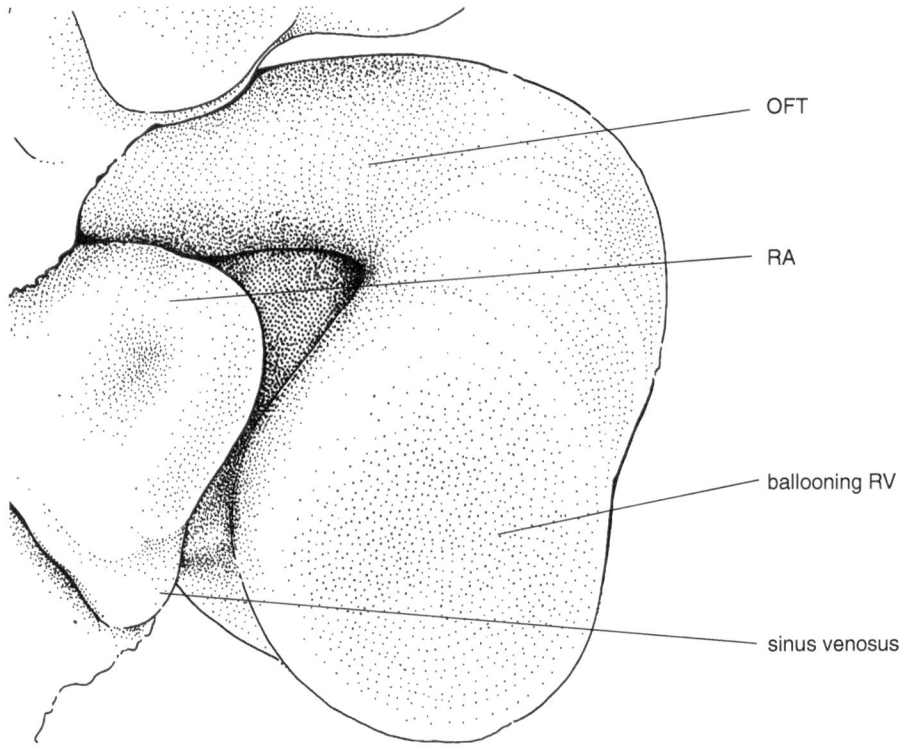

FIGURES 2.9–2.12   *Continued*

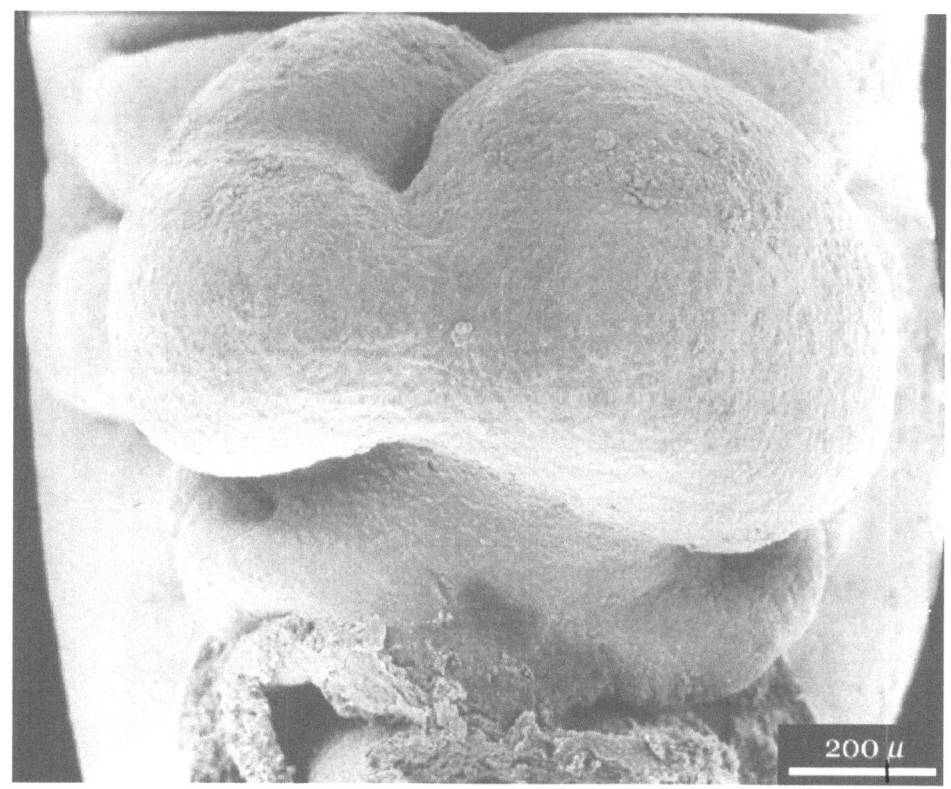

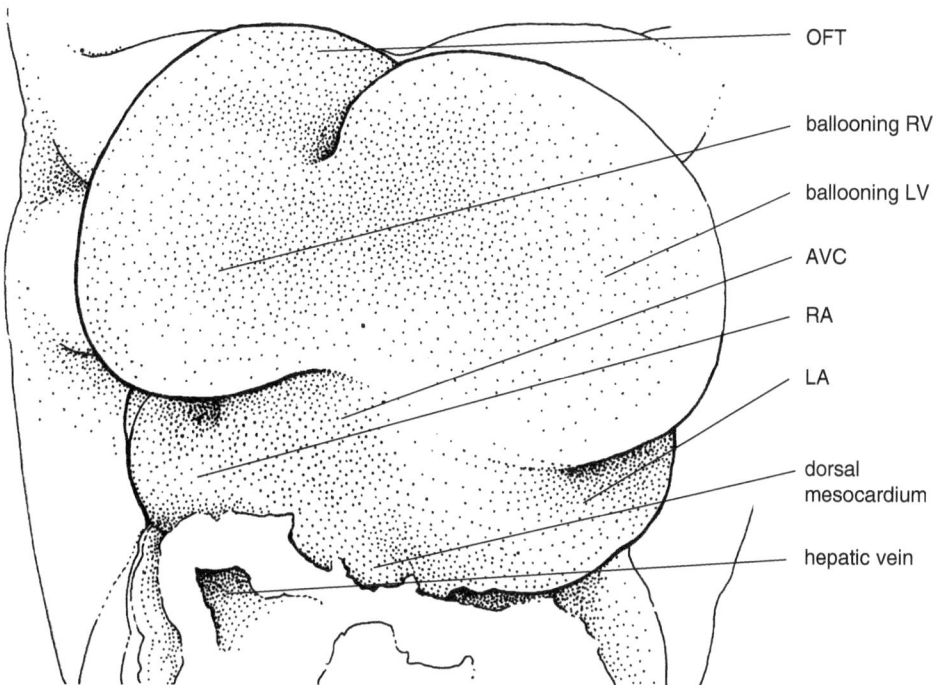

OFT

ballooning RV

ballooning LV

AVC

RA

LA

dorsal
mesocardium

hepatic vein

FIGURES 2.9–2.12   *Continued*

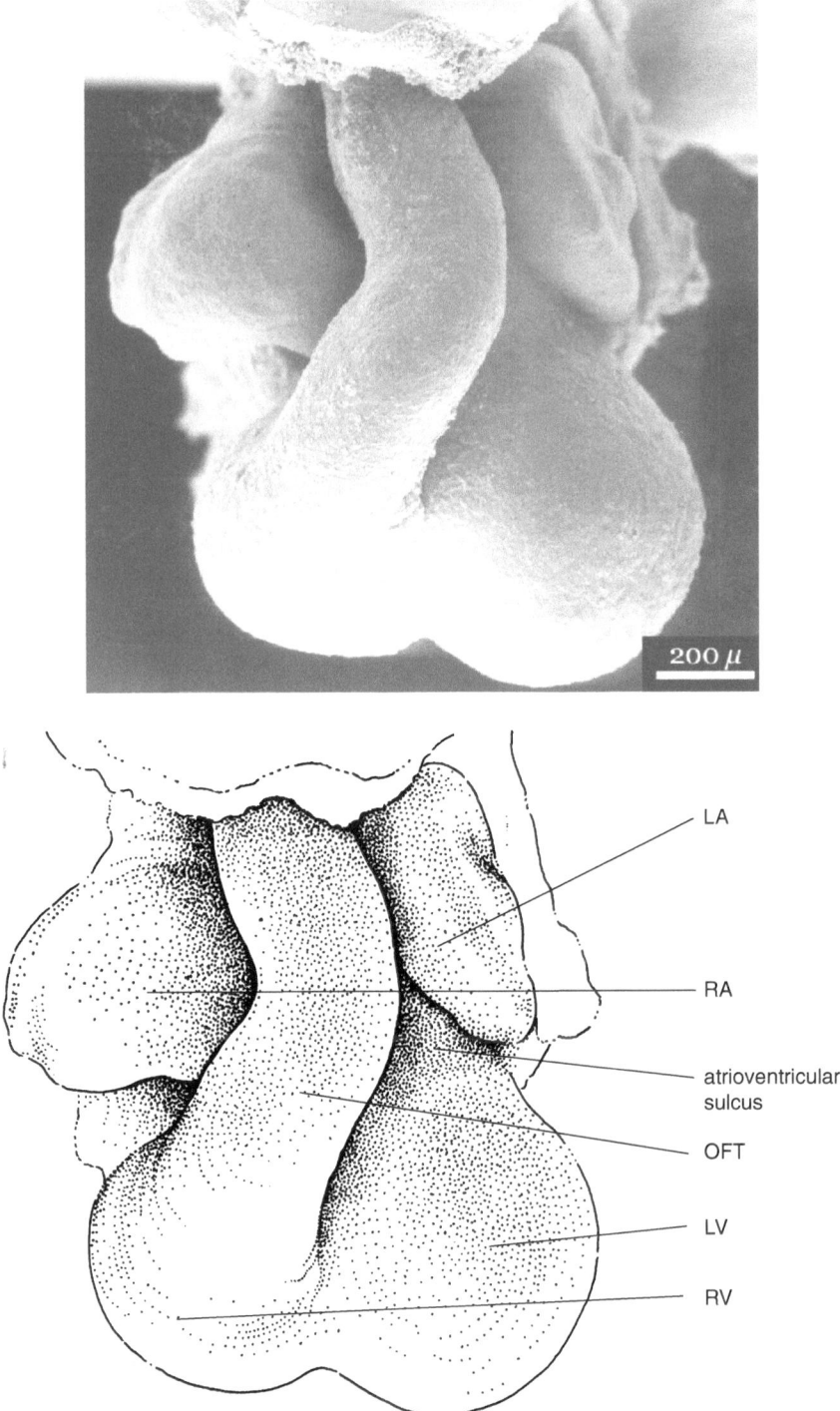

FIGURES 2.13–2.16   Complete heart in situ (stage 14), ventral cranial, ventral caudal, right and left lateral views. The ventral body wall and the pericardium are removed. The ballooning of the ventricles creates an interventricular groove. Parts of the atria, now equal in size, can be recognized as auricles.

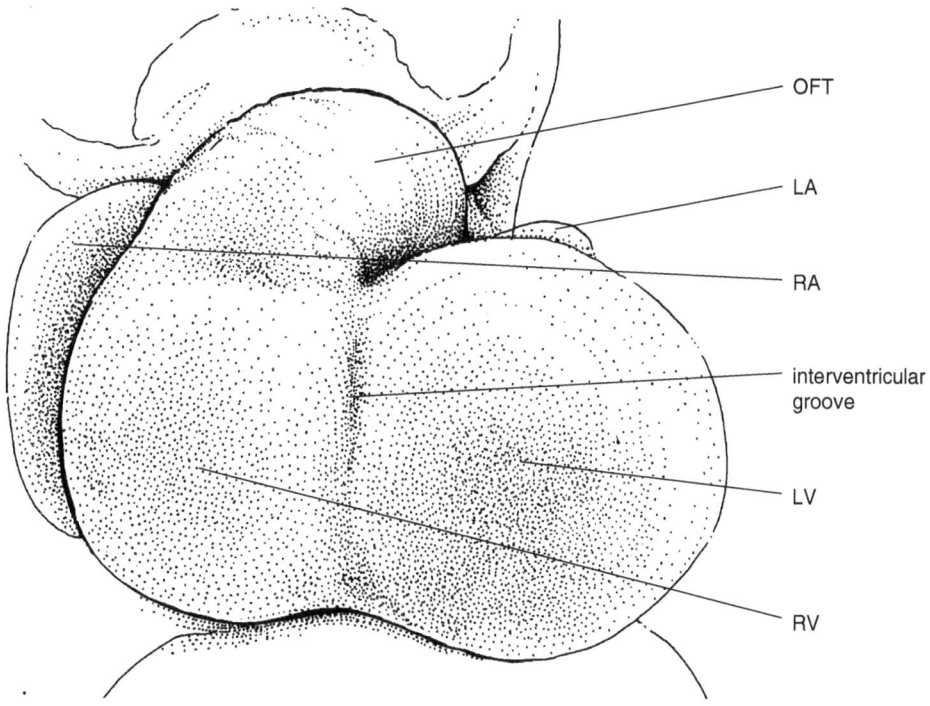

OFT

LA

RA

interventricular groove

LV

RV

FIGURES 2.13–2.16   *Continued*

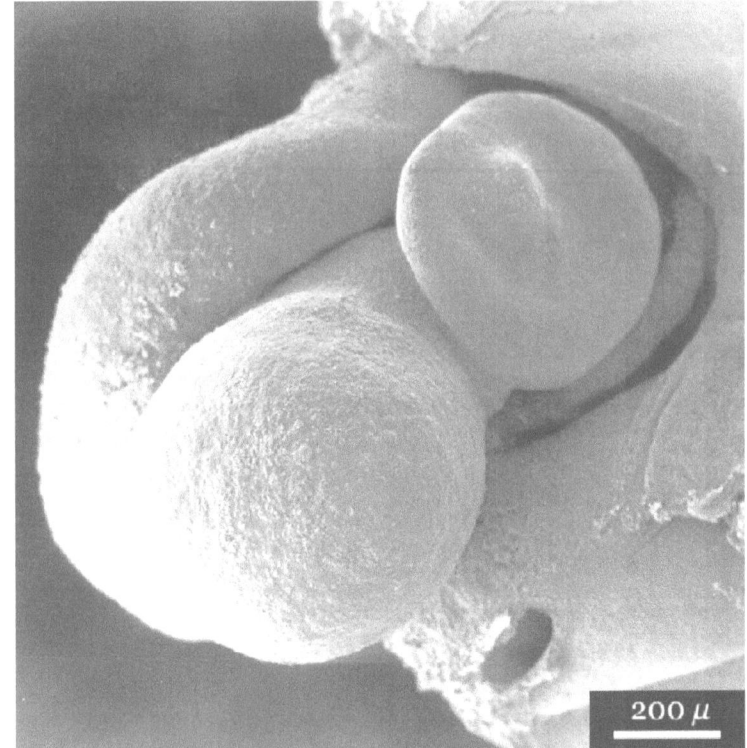

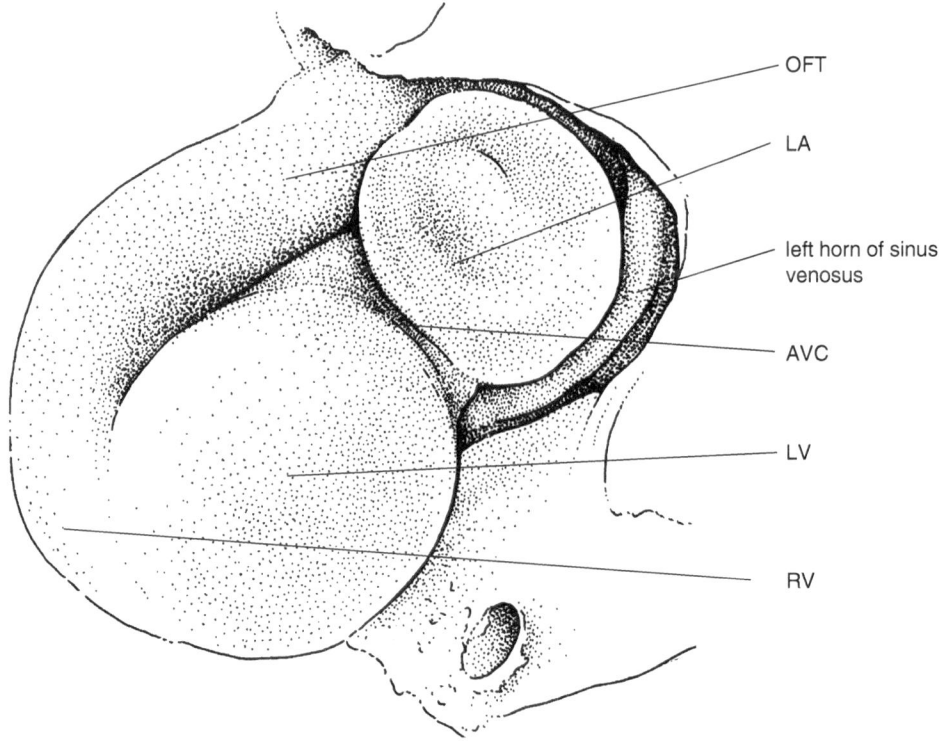

FIGURES 2.13–2.16   *Continued*

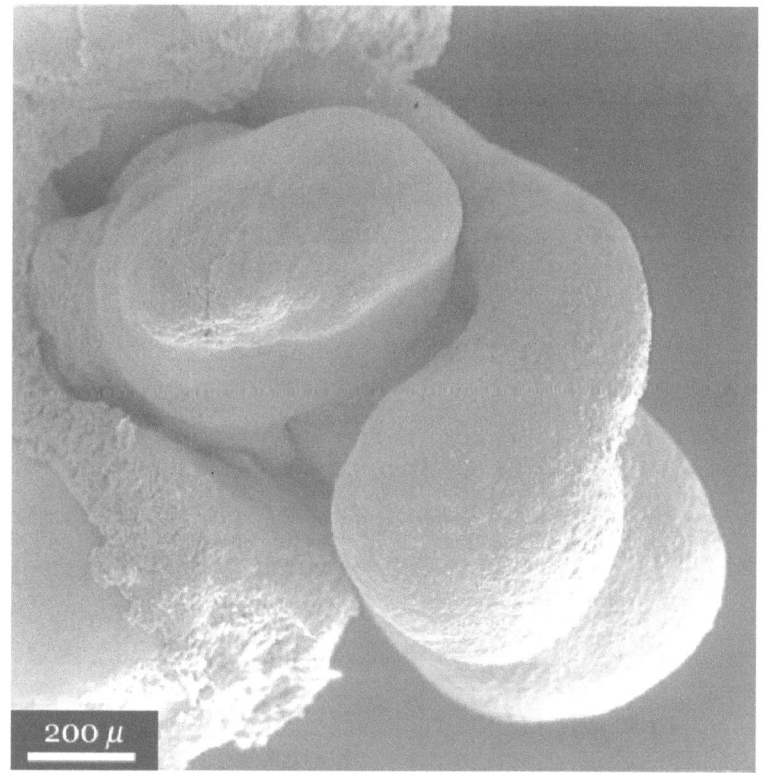

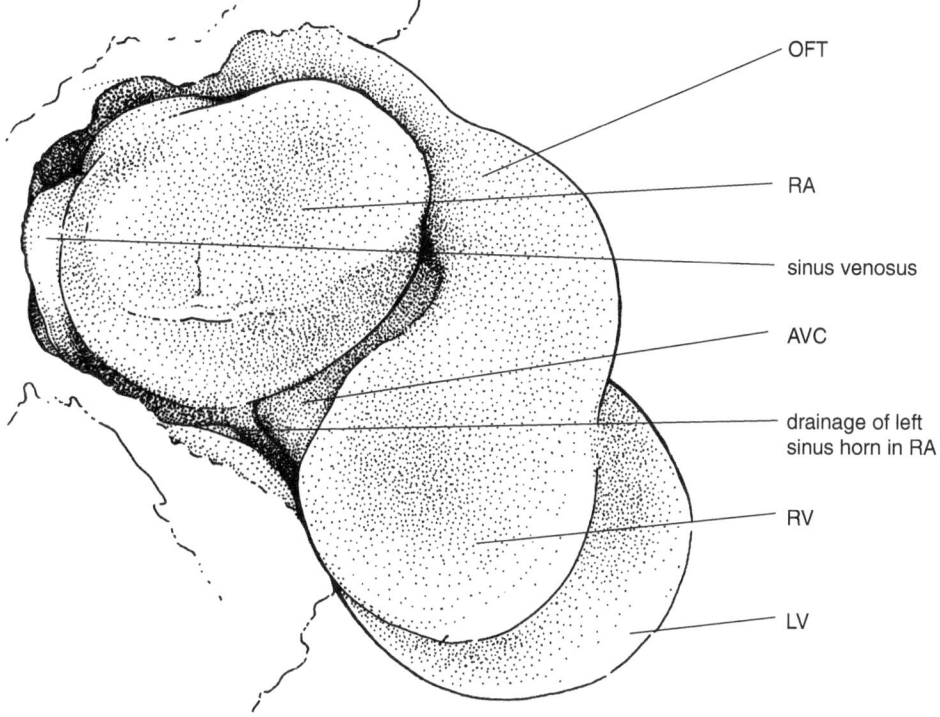

OFT

RA

sinus venosus

AVC

drainage of left
sinus horn in RA

RV

LV

200 μ

FIGURES 2.13–2.16   *Continued*

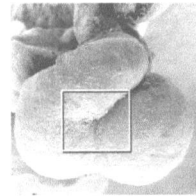

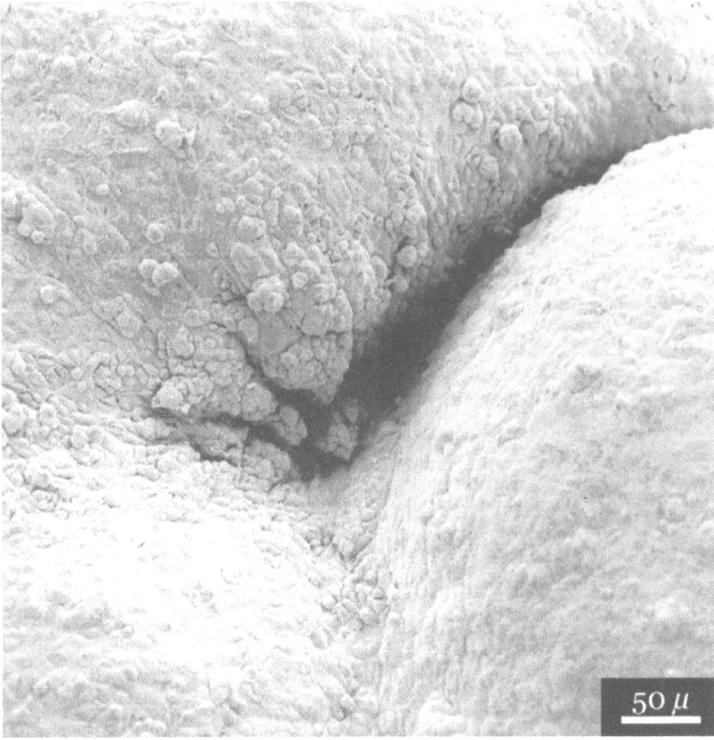

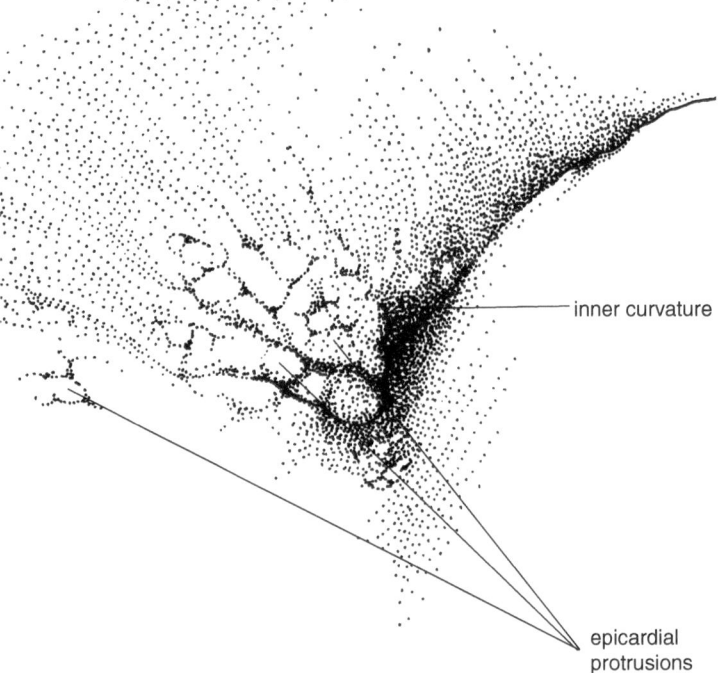

FIGURE 2.17   Complete heart in situ (stage 14), ventral view. The ventral body wall and the pericardium are removed. A thin layer of dispersed cells is visible in the area of the inner curvature.

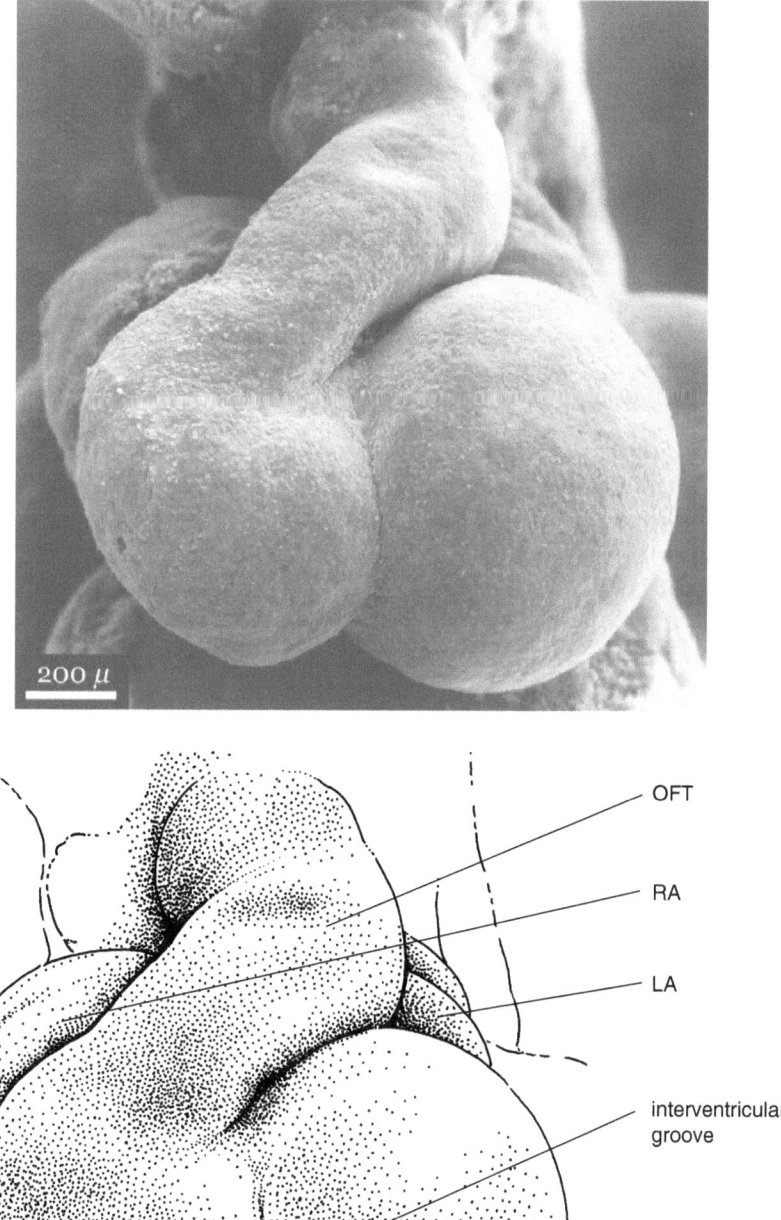

FIGURES 2.18–2.20   Complete heart in situ (stage 15), ventral, right and left view. The ventral body wall and the pericardium are removed. The outflow tract shows areas of irregular flattening as an external indication of septation.

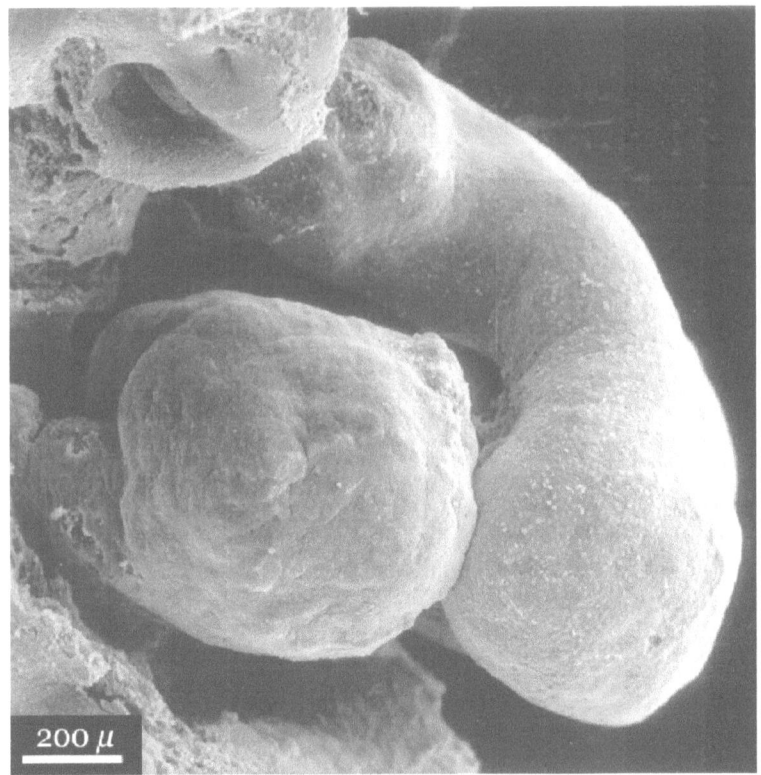

200 μ

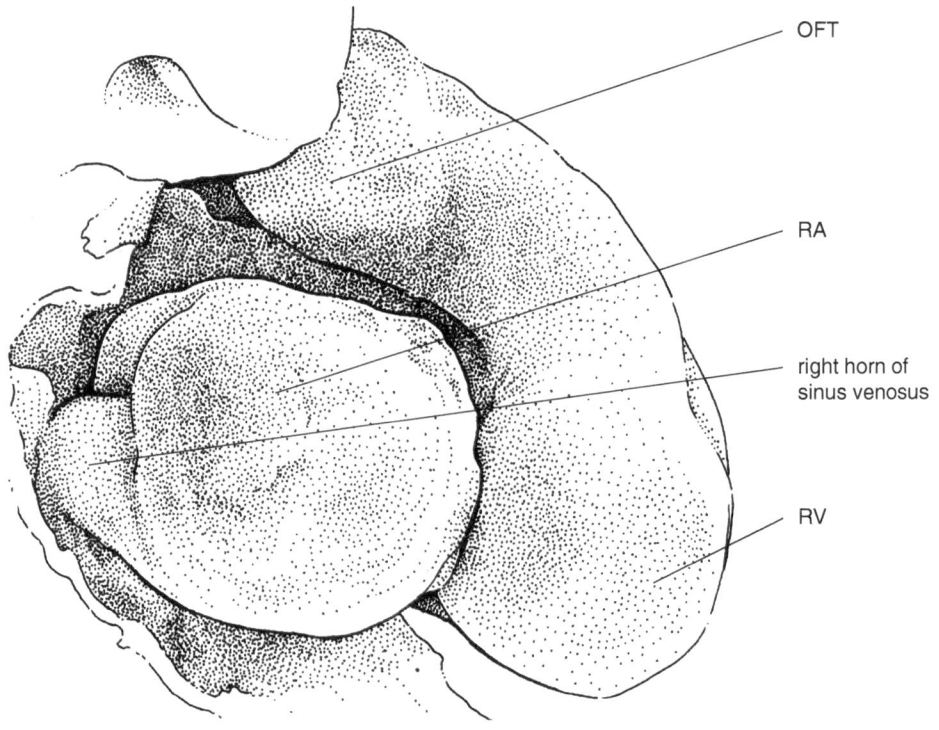

OFT

RA

right horn of
sinus venosus

RV

FIGURES 2.18–2.20   *Continued*

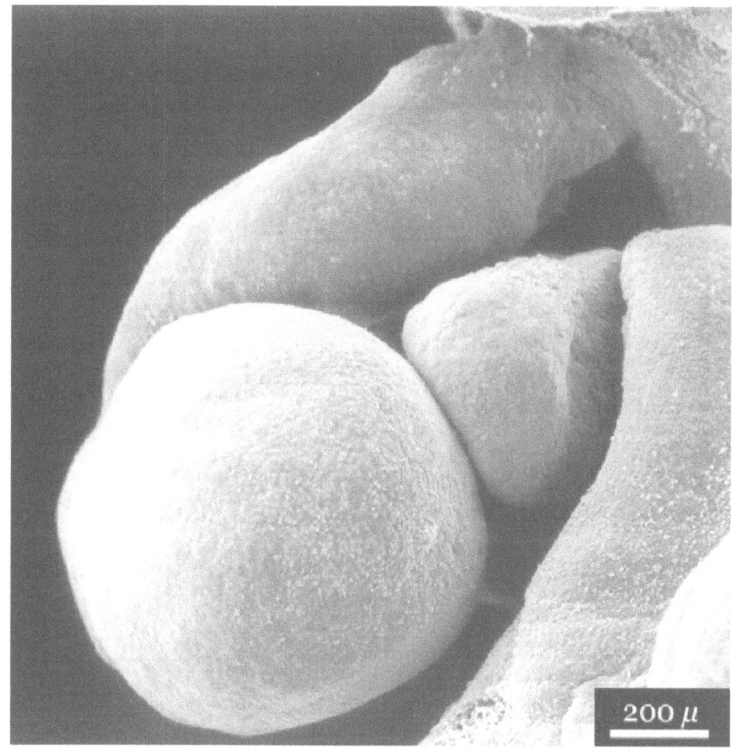

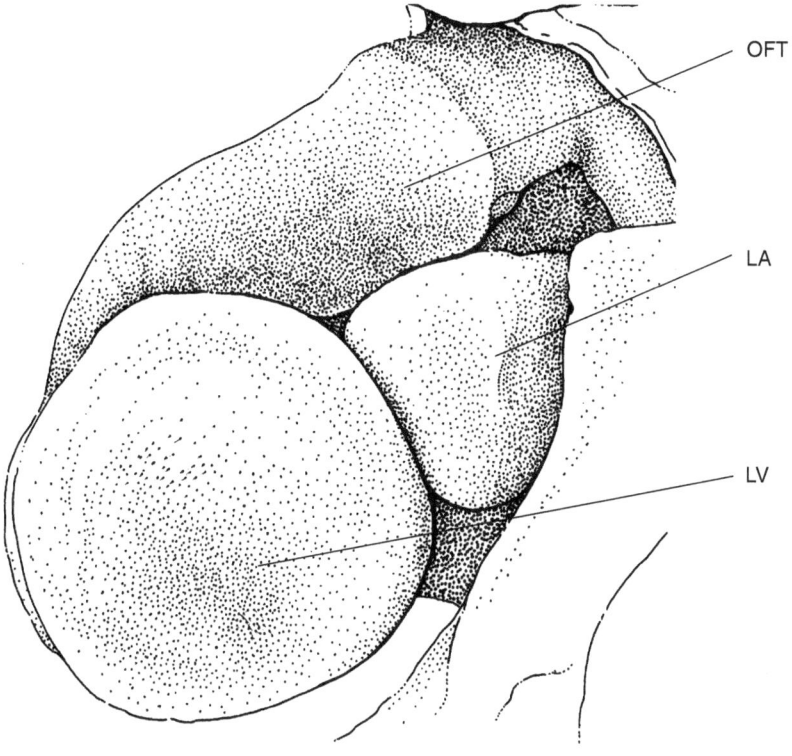

FIGURES 2.18–2.20   *Continued*

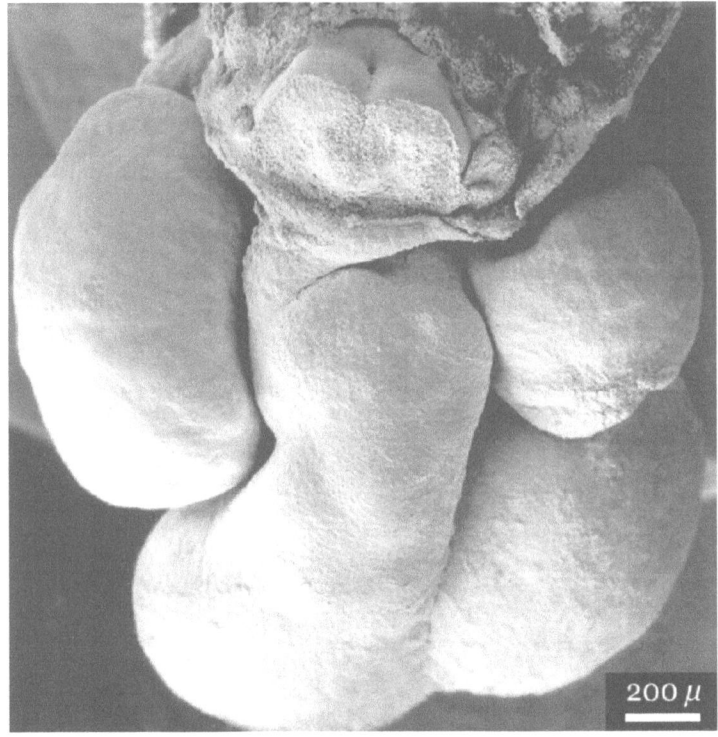

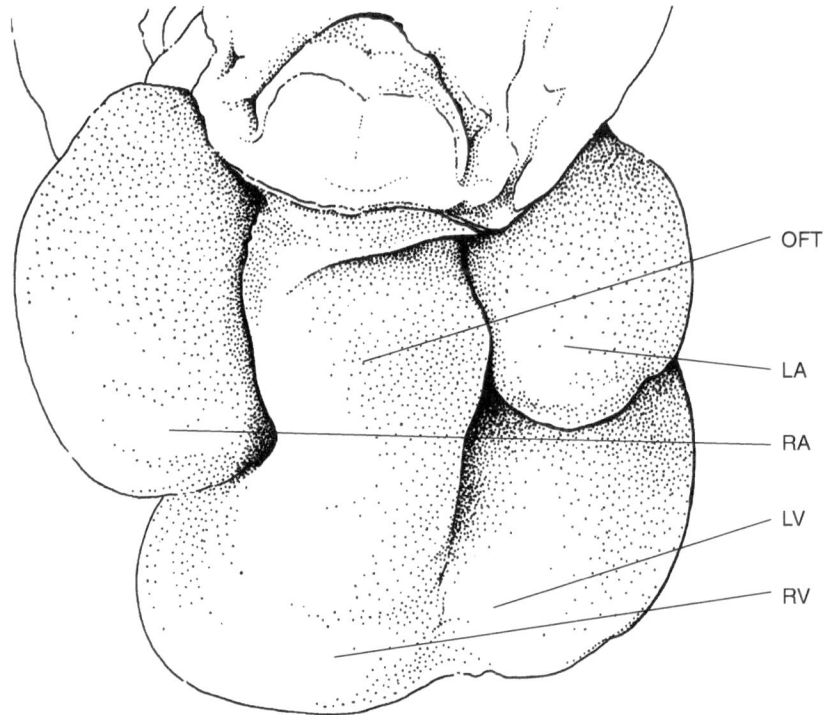

FIGURE 2.21   Complete heart in situ (stage 16), cranial view. The ventral body wall and the pericardium are removed.

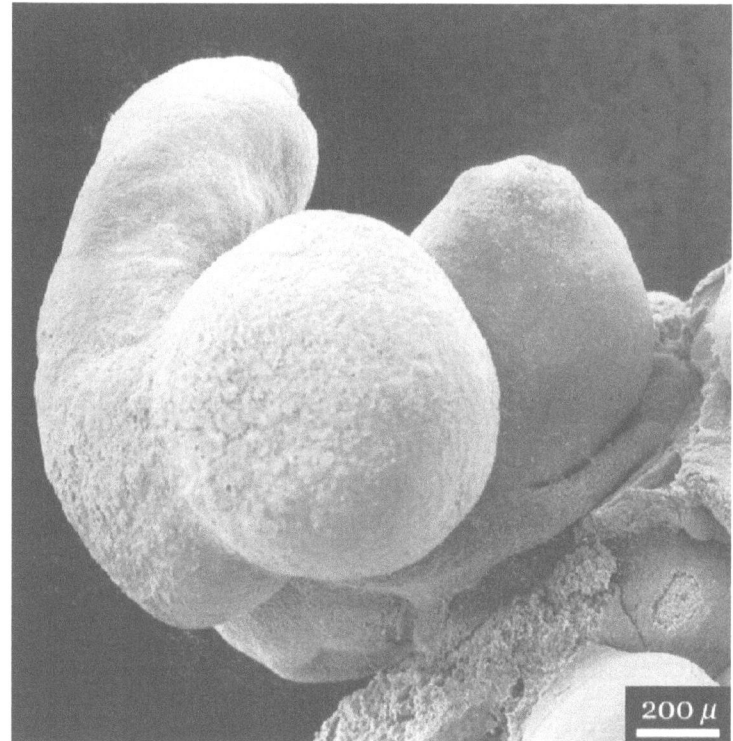

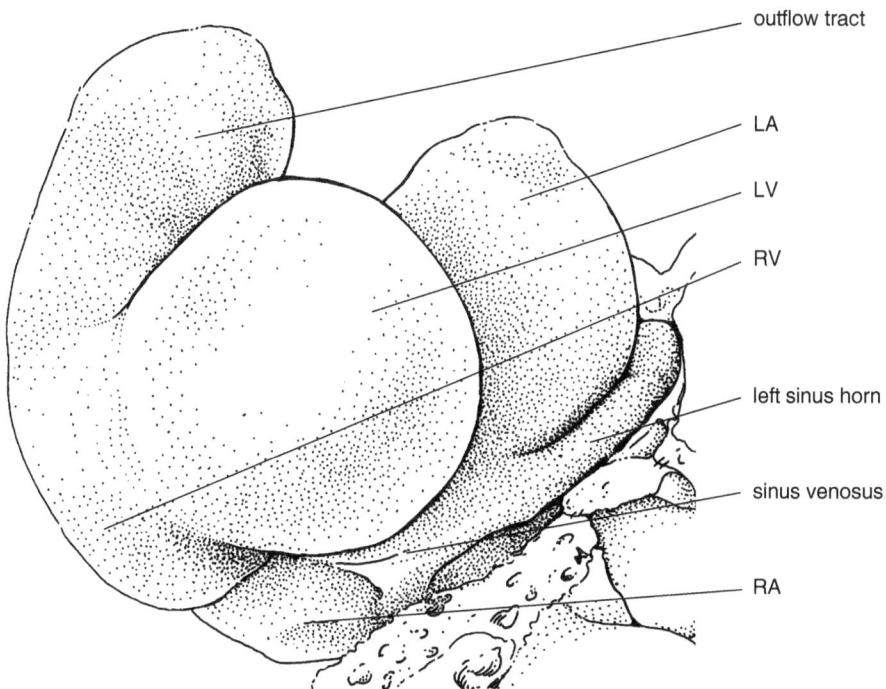

FIGURES 2.22 and 2.23   Complete heart in situ (stage 16), right and left lateral views. The ventral body wall, the pericardium and the distal most part of the outflow tract are removed.

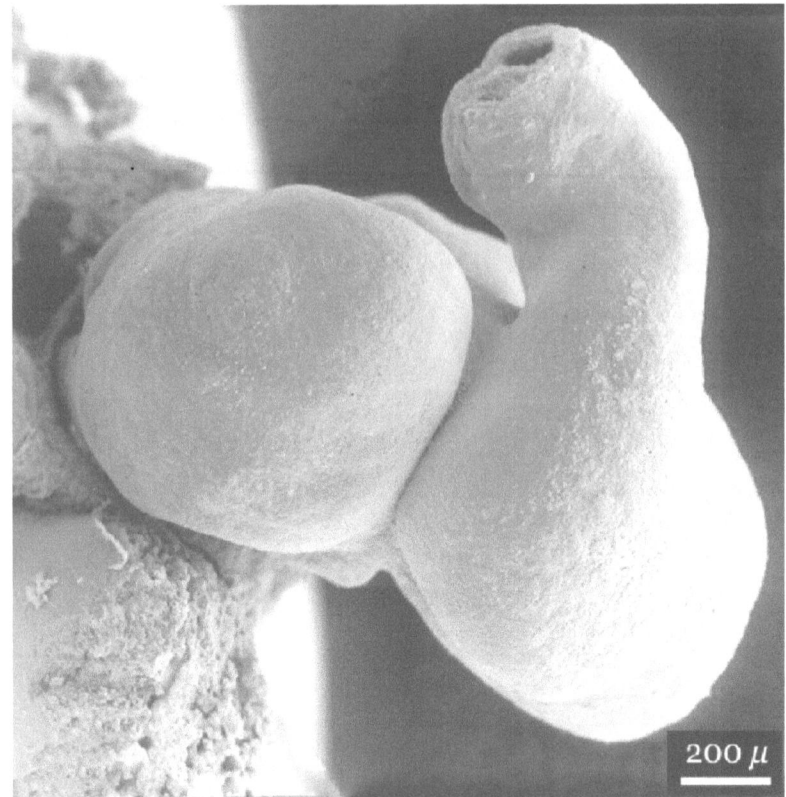

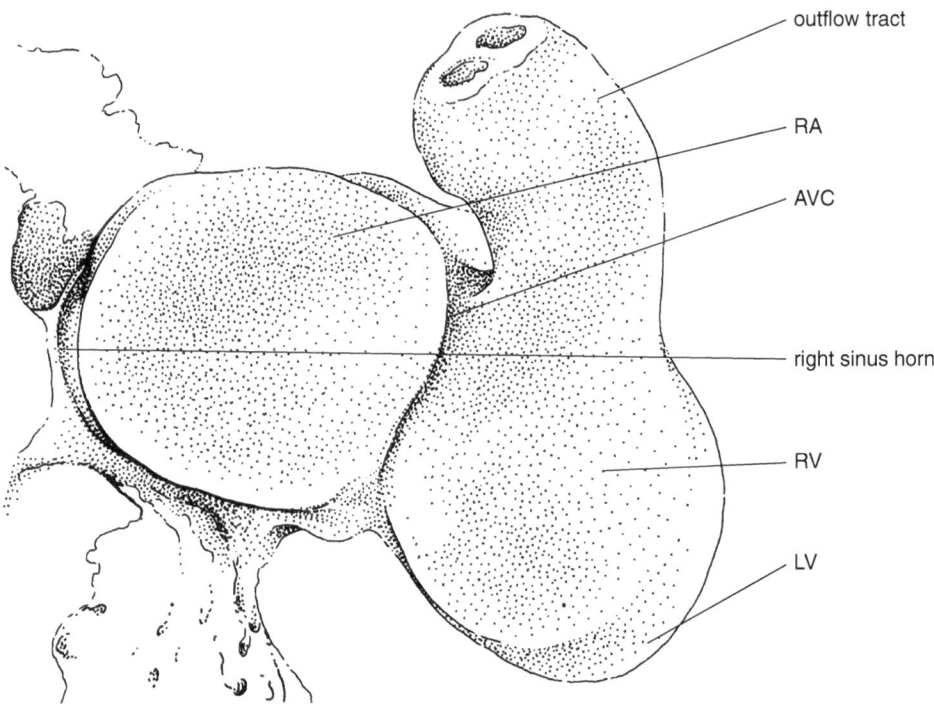

FIGURES 2.22 and 2.23   *Continued*

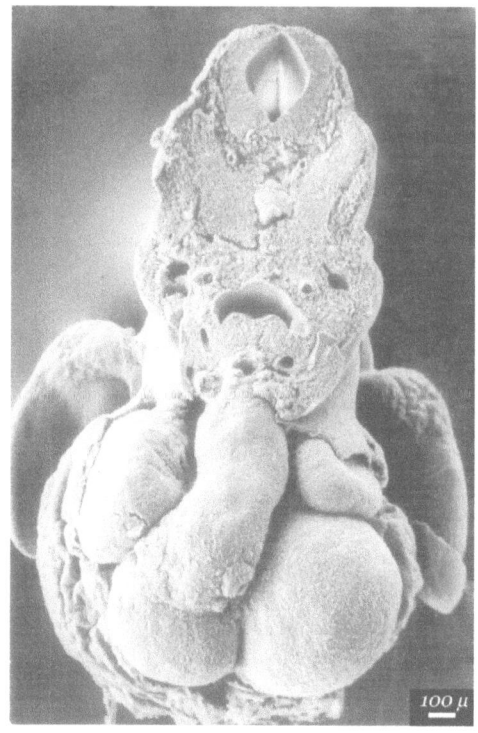

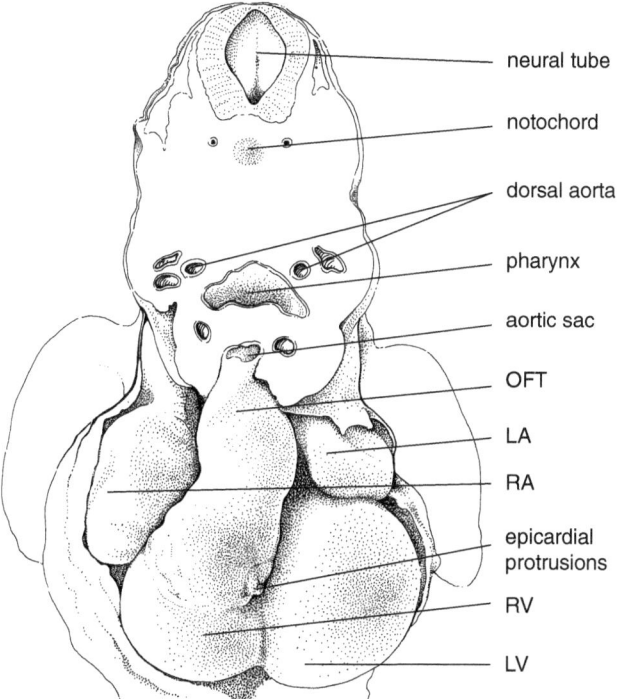

neural tube

notochord

dorsal aorta

pharynx

aortic sac

OFT

LA

RA

epicardial protrusions

RV

LV

FIGURE 2.24   Complete heart in situ (stage 16), cranial view. The ventral body wall and the pericardium are partly removed.

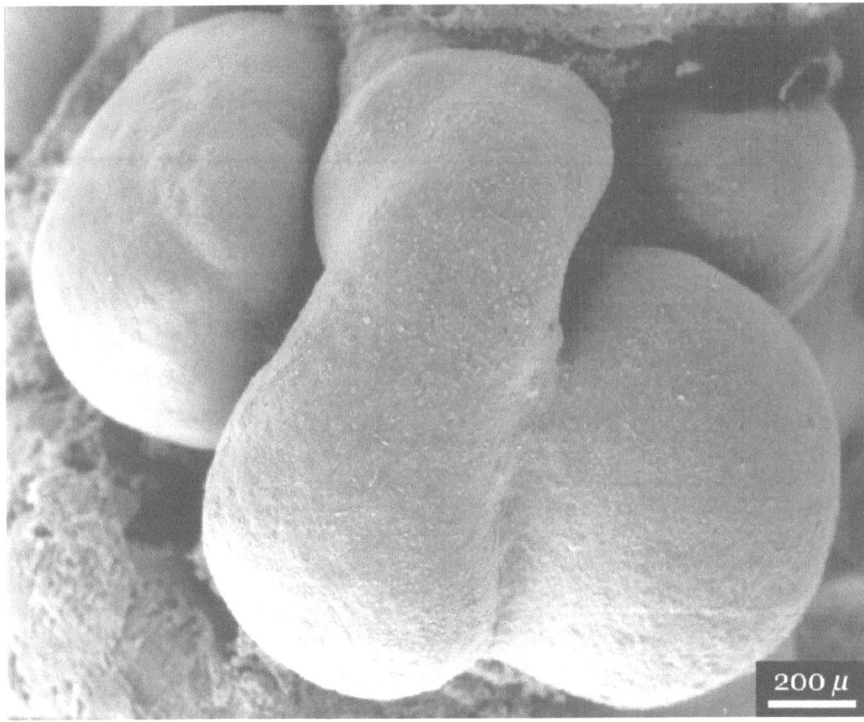

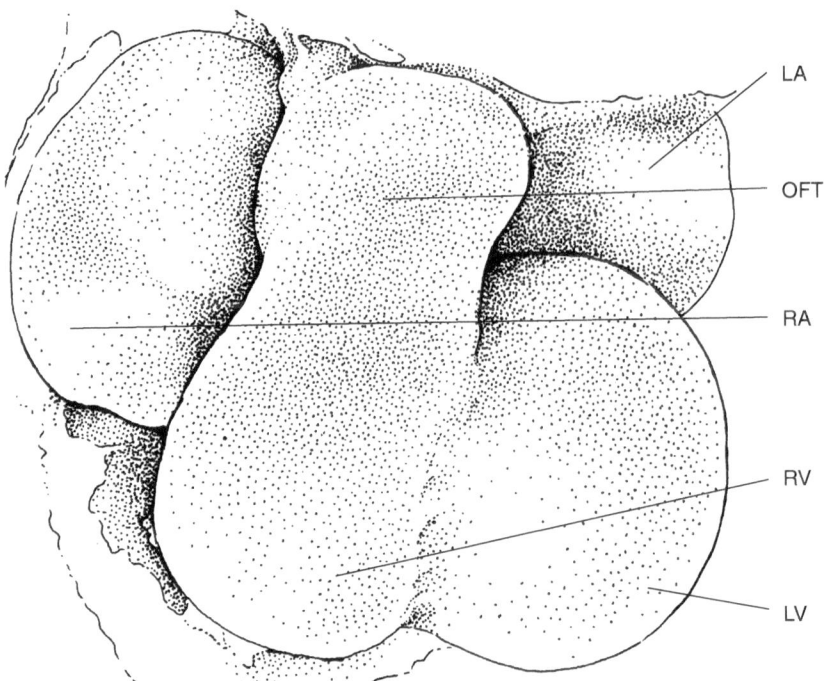

FIGURES 2.25 and 2.26   Complete heart in situ (stage 17), ventral cranial and left lateral view. The ventral body wall and the pericardium are removed. The external visibility of the outflow tract septation becomes more apparent compared to previous stages.

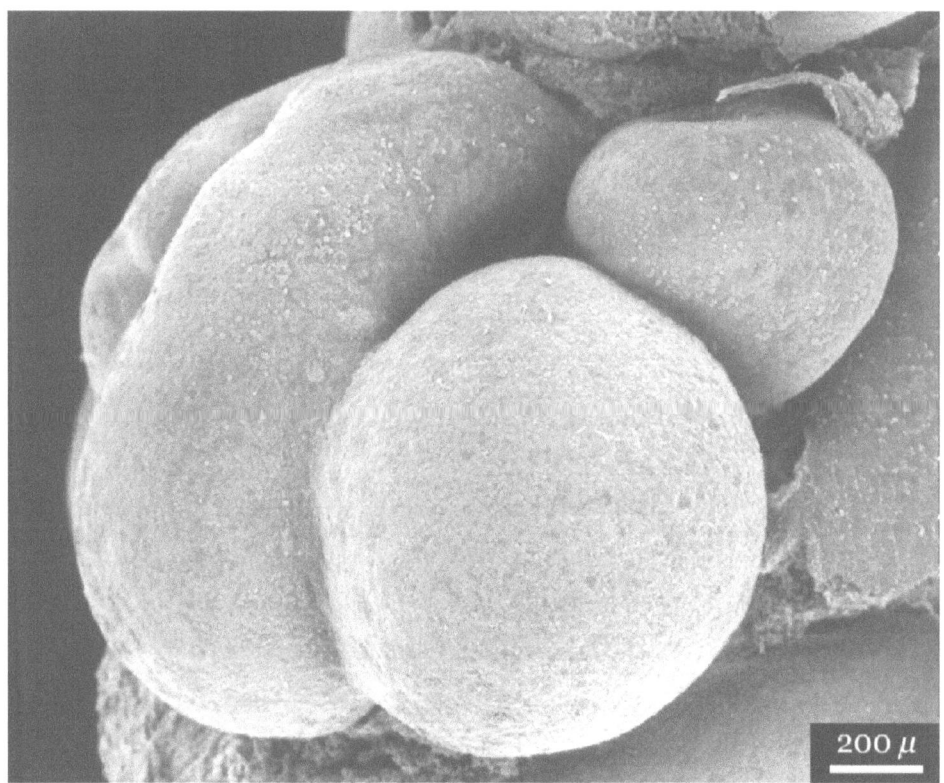

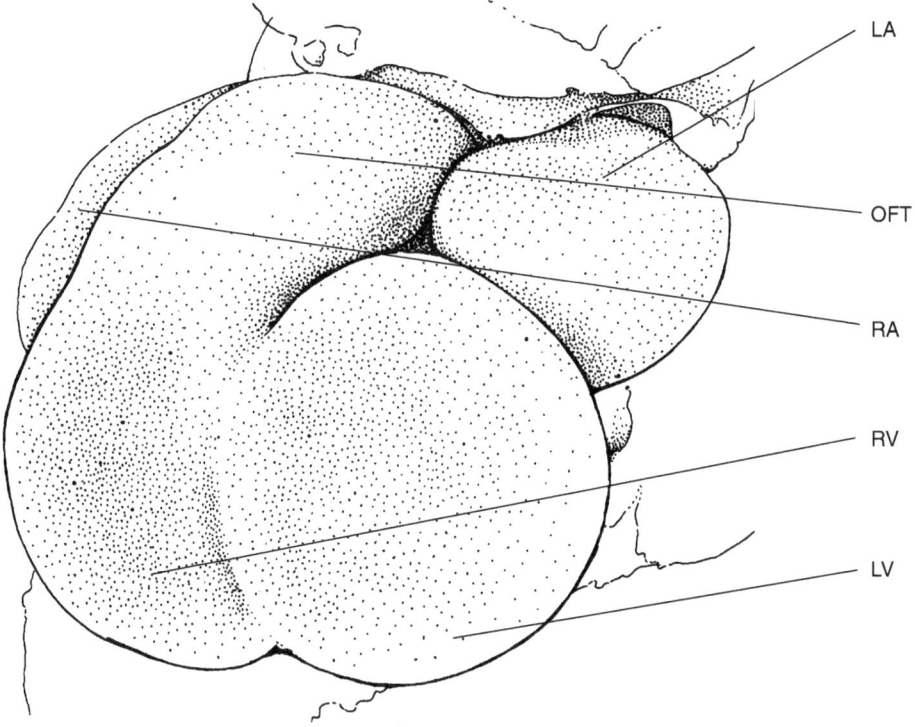

FIGURES 2.25 and 2.26   *Continued*

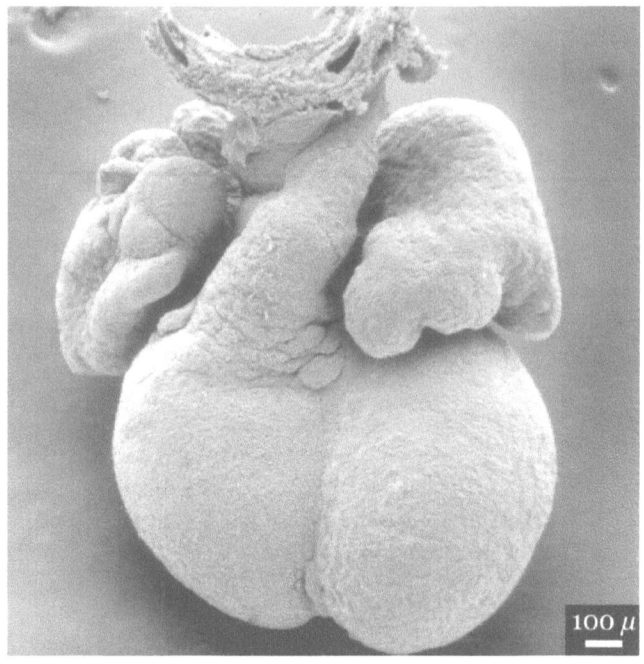

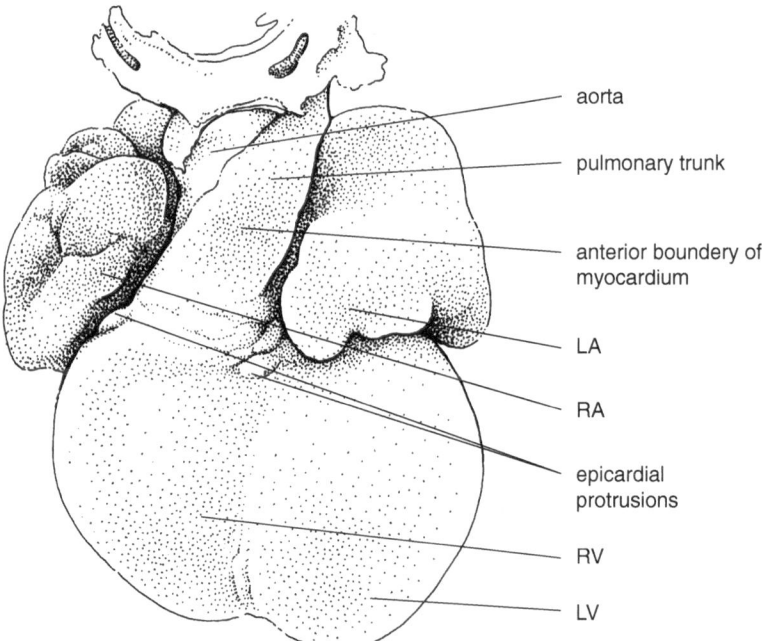

FIGURE 2.27 and 2.28   Complete heart, isolated (stage 17), ventral cranial and caudal views. The heart is fixed in a contracted state. In this state the external visibility of the outflow tract septation is much more pronounced. The right part of the outflow tract shows a narrowing which corresponds to the anterior boundary of the myocardium and the site of the developing semilunar valves of the pulmonary trunk. The contacted state also accentuates the morphology of the auricles.

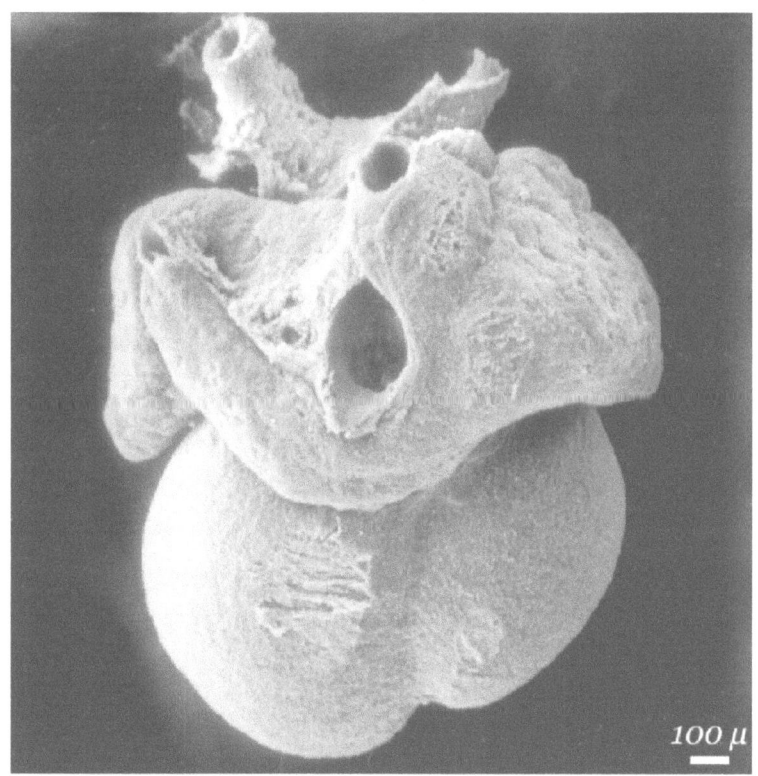

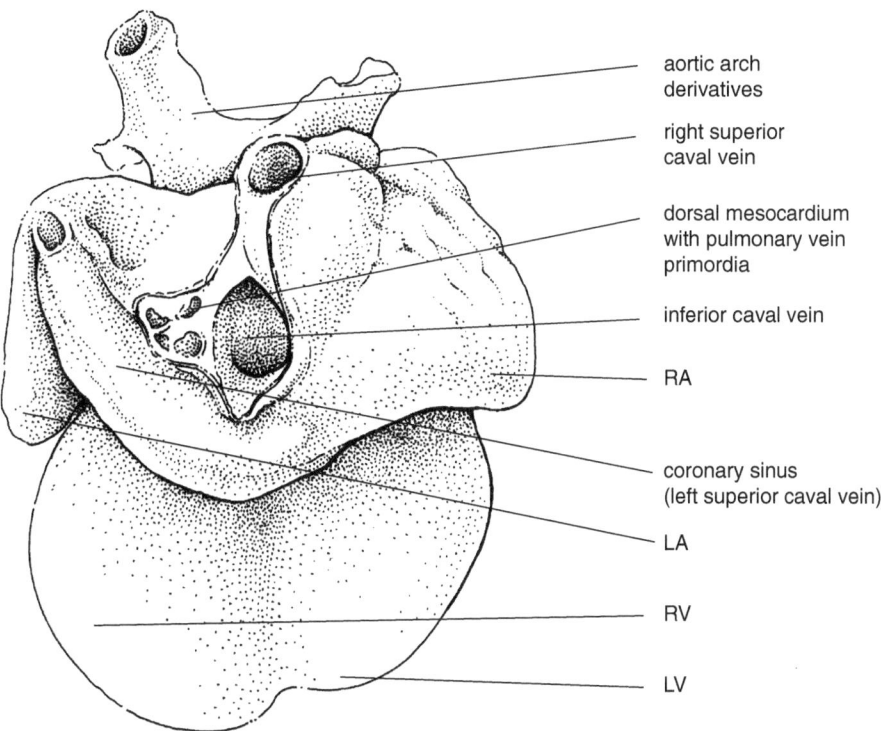

aortic arch
derivatives

right superior
caval vein

dorsal mesocardium
with pulmonary vein
primordia

inferior caval vein

RA

coronary sinus
(left superior caval vein)

LA

RV

LV

FIGURES 2.27 and 2.28   *Continued*

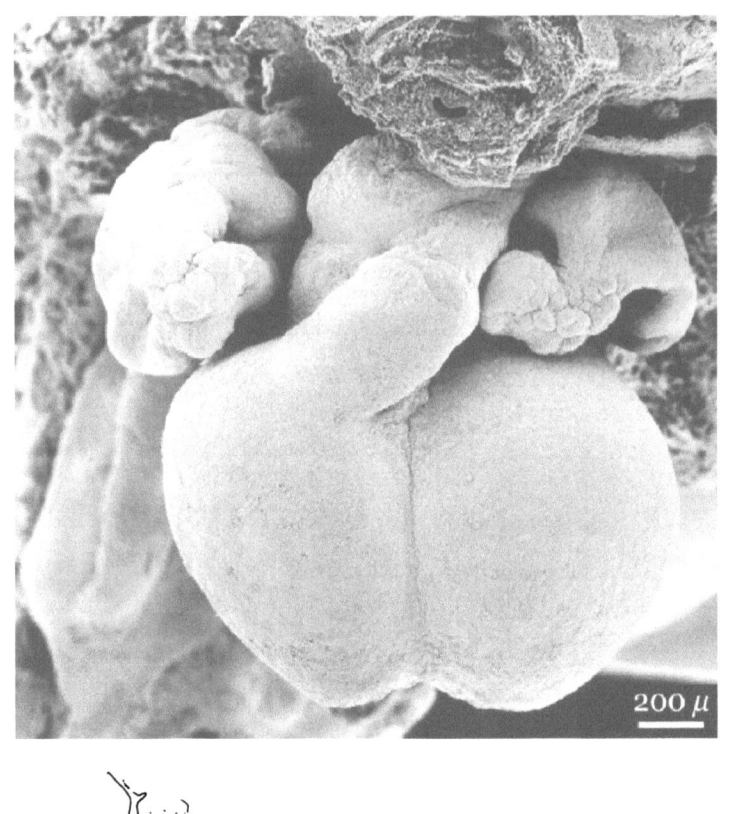

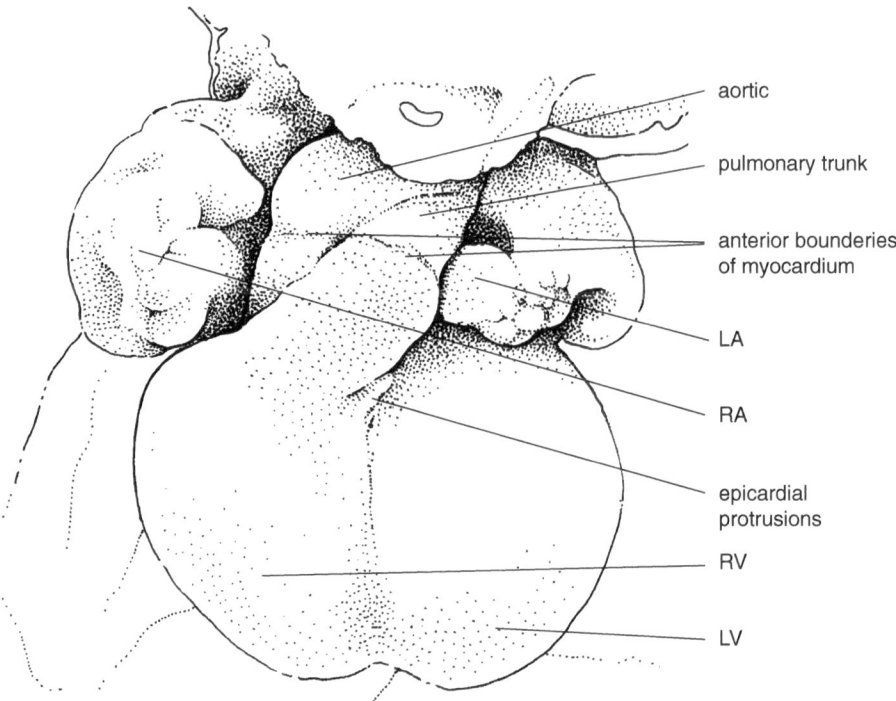

FIGURE 2.29   Complete heart in situ (stage 18), ventral cranial view. The ventral body wall and the pericardium are removed. The heart is fixed in a contracted state. The auricles both show their mature morphological characteristics.

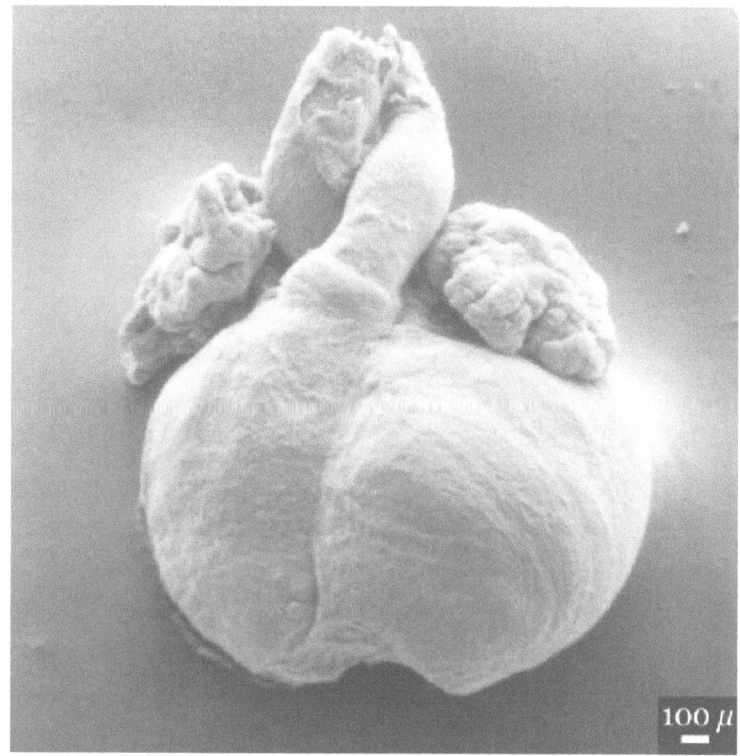

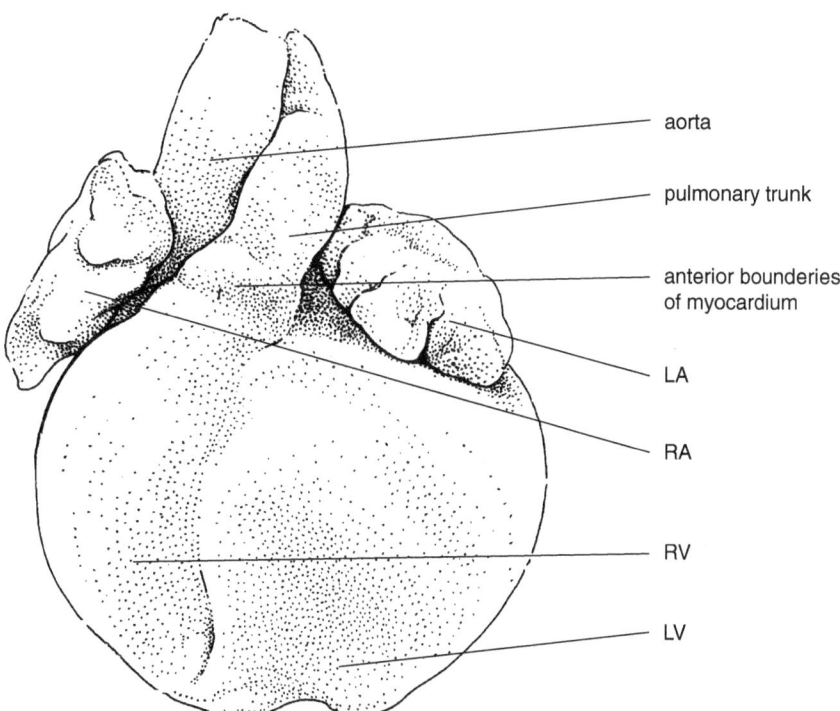

FIGURE 2.30   Complete heart, isolated (stage 19), ventral cranial view. The heart is fixed in a contracted state.

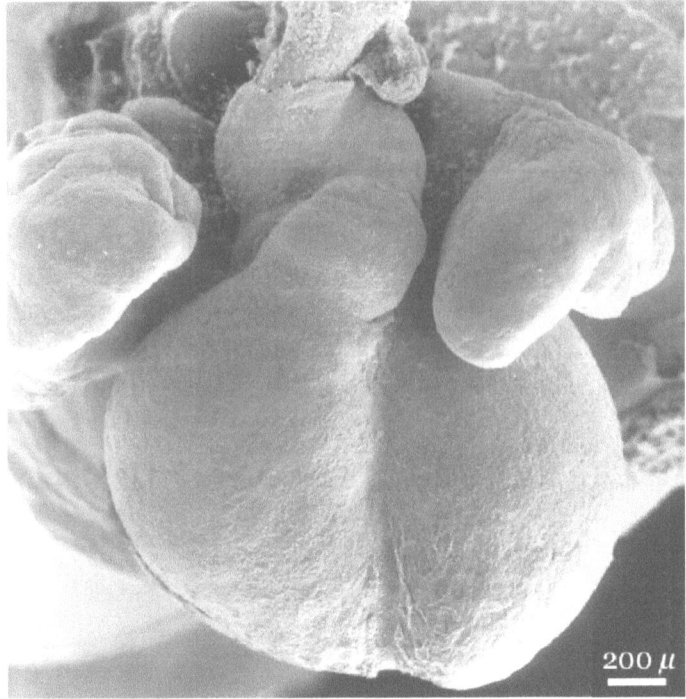

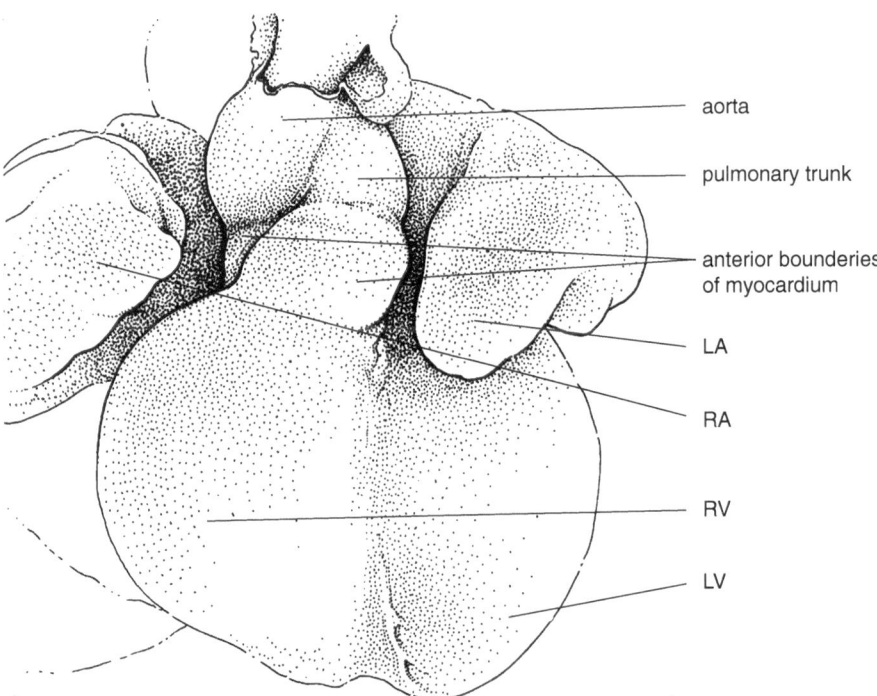

FIGURE 2.31   Complete heart in situ (stage 19), ventral cranial view. The apex of the LV reaches beyond the right ventricular apex. Due to differential growth, the anterior bounderies of the myocardium, and hence the aortic and pulmonary valves, have a more proximal position compared to previous stages.

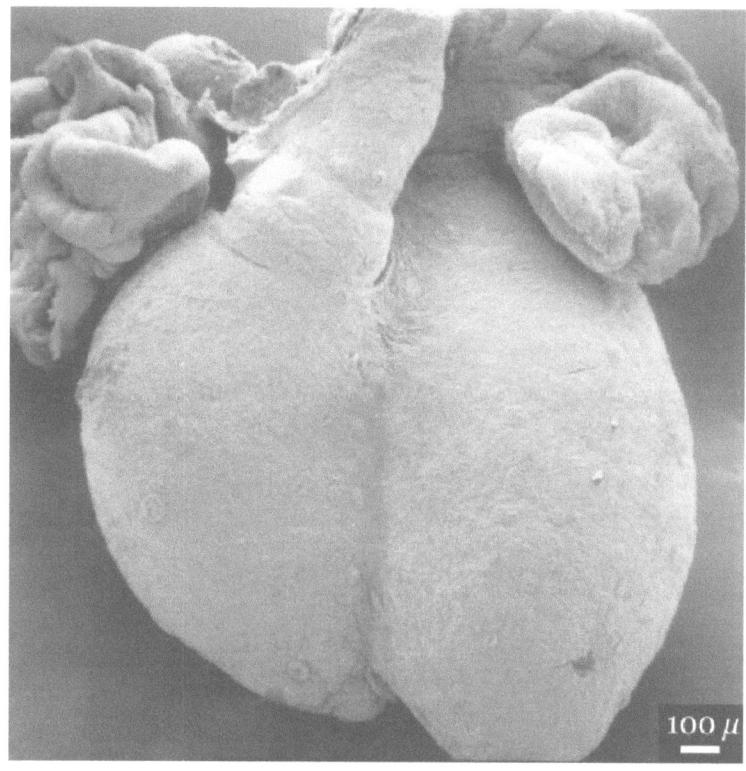

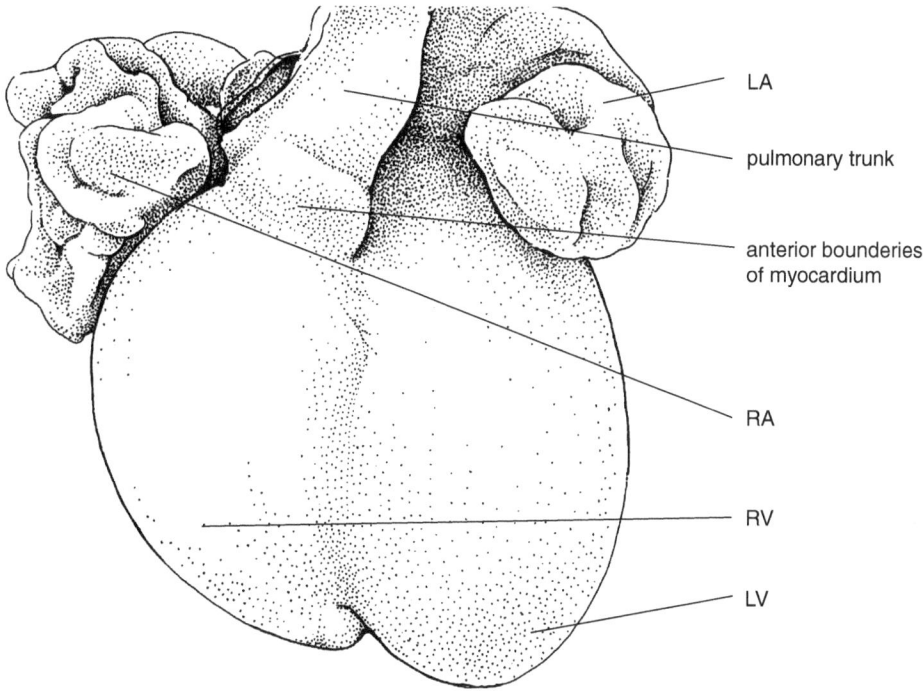

FIGURE 2.32   Complete heart, isolated (stage 20), ventral cranial view. The heart is fixed in a contracted state.

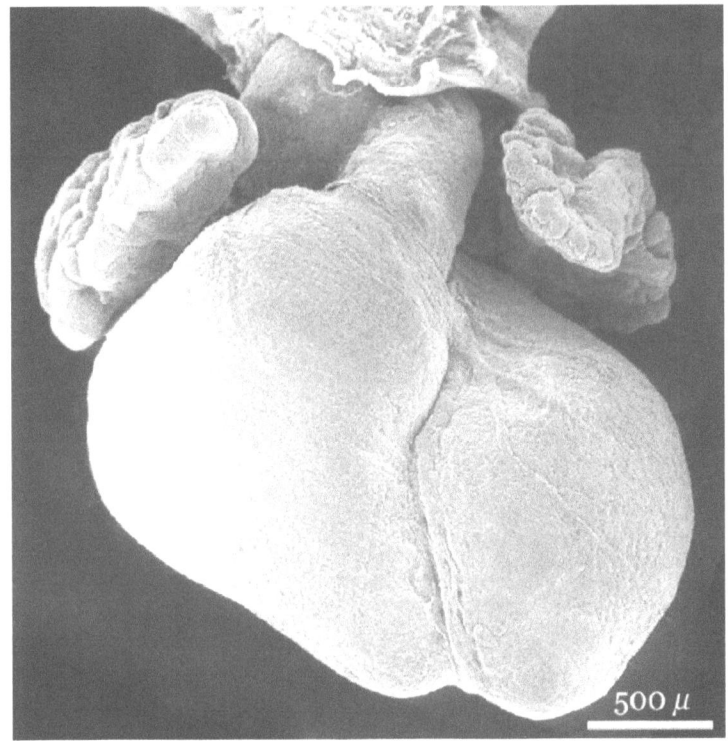

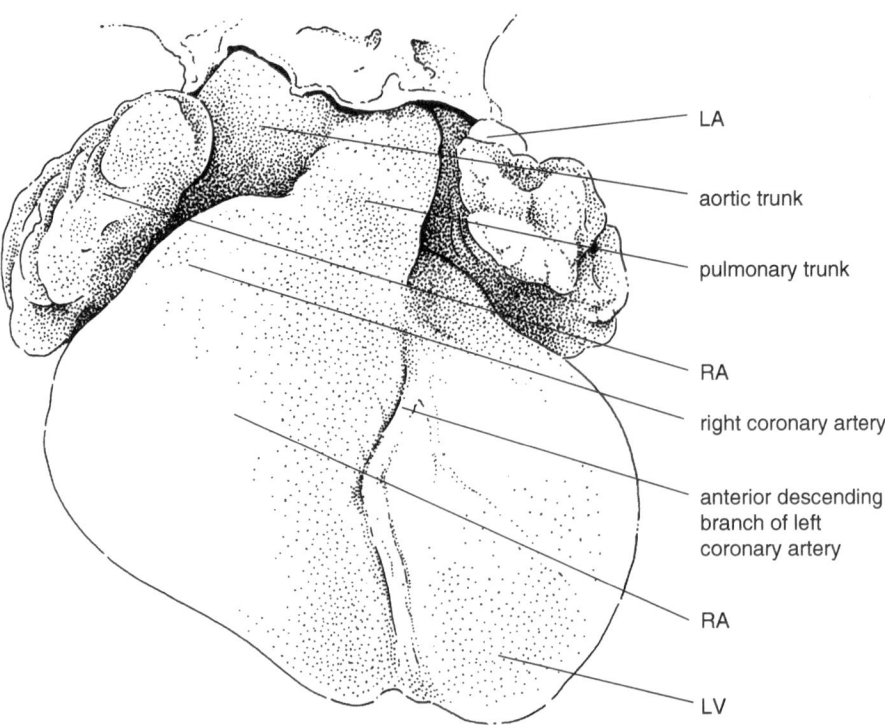

FIGURES 2.33–2.36   Complete heart, isolated (stage 22), ventral, right and left lateral, and caudal view. The contours of the greater coronary arteries are now well distinguishable.

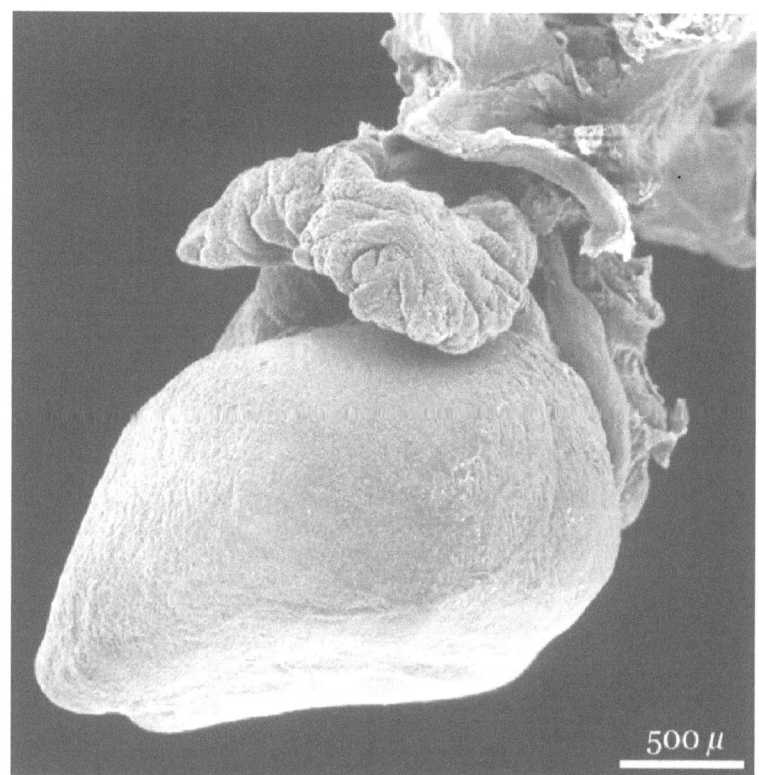

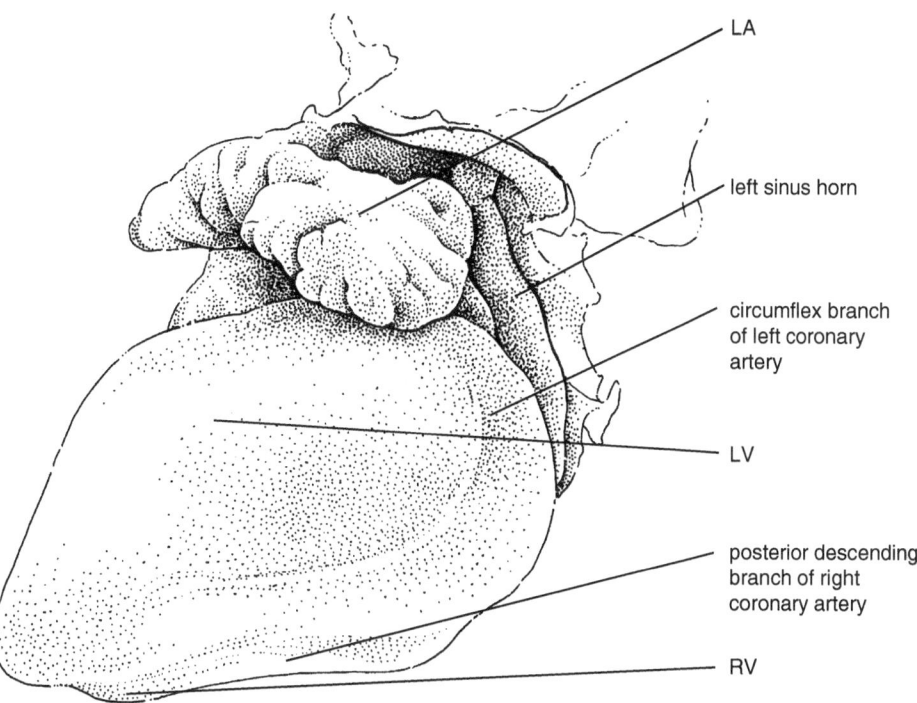

FIGURES 2.33–2.36   *Continued*

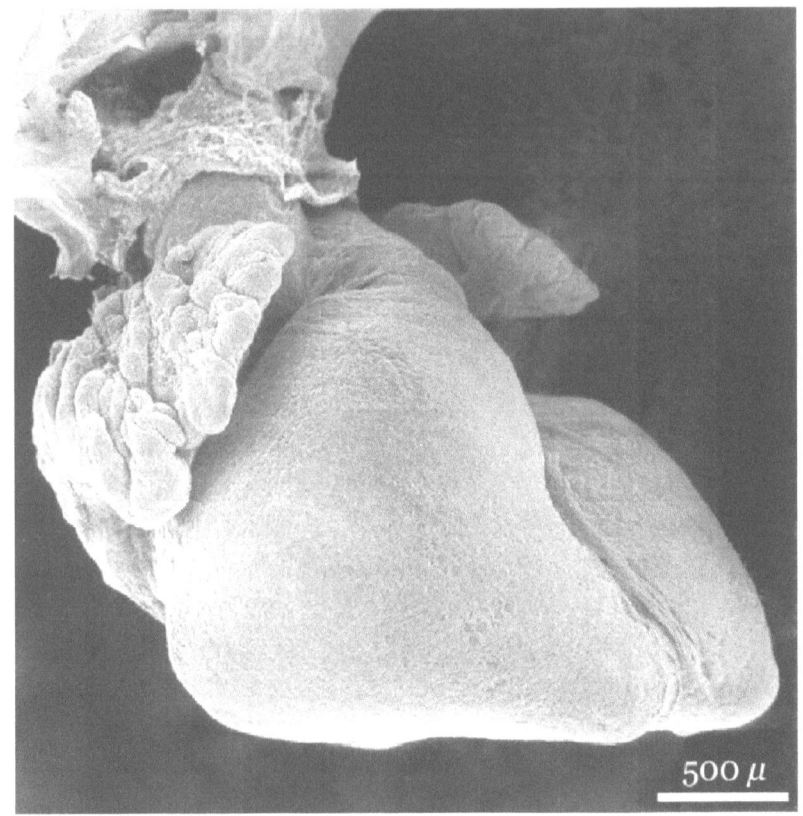

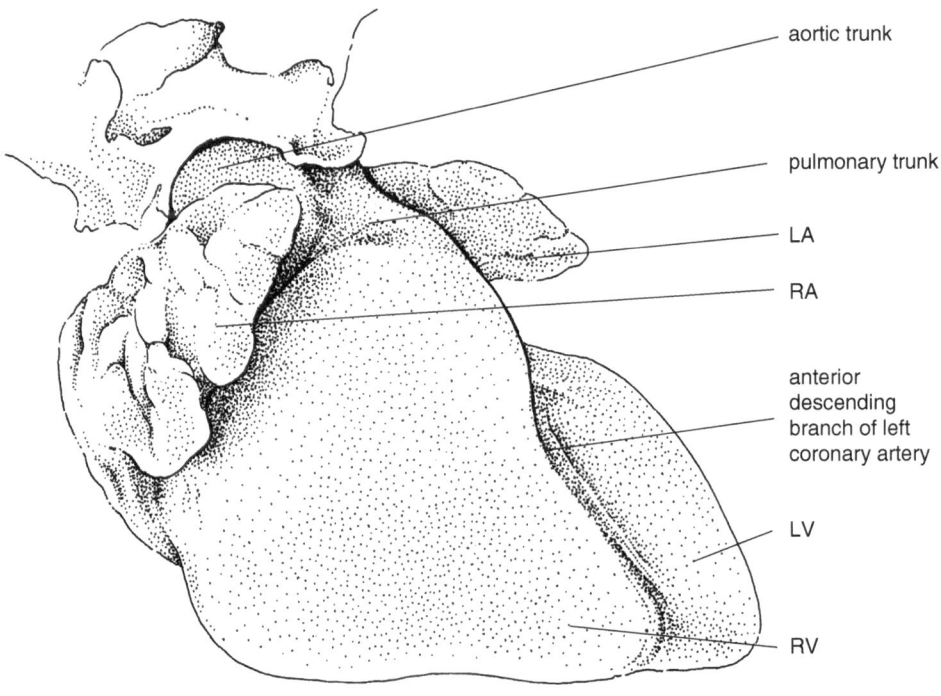

FIGURES 2.33–2.36   *Continued*

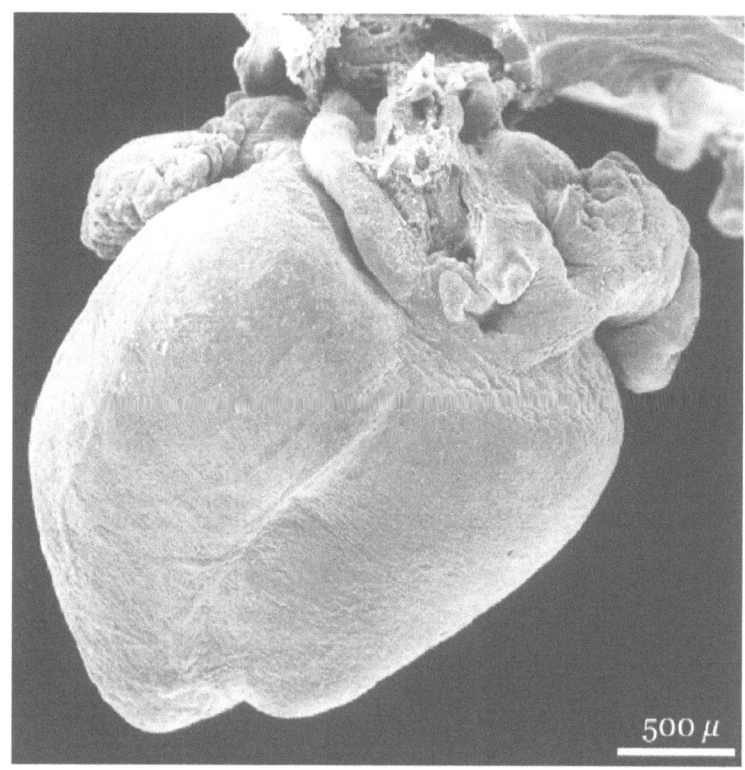

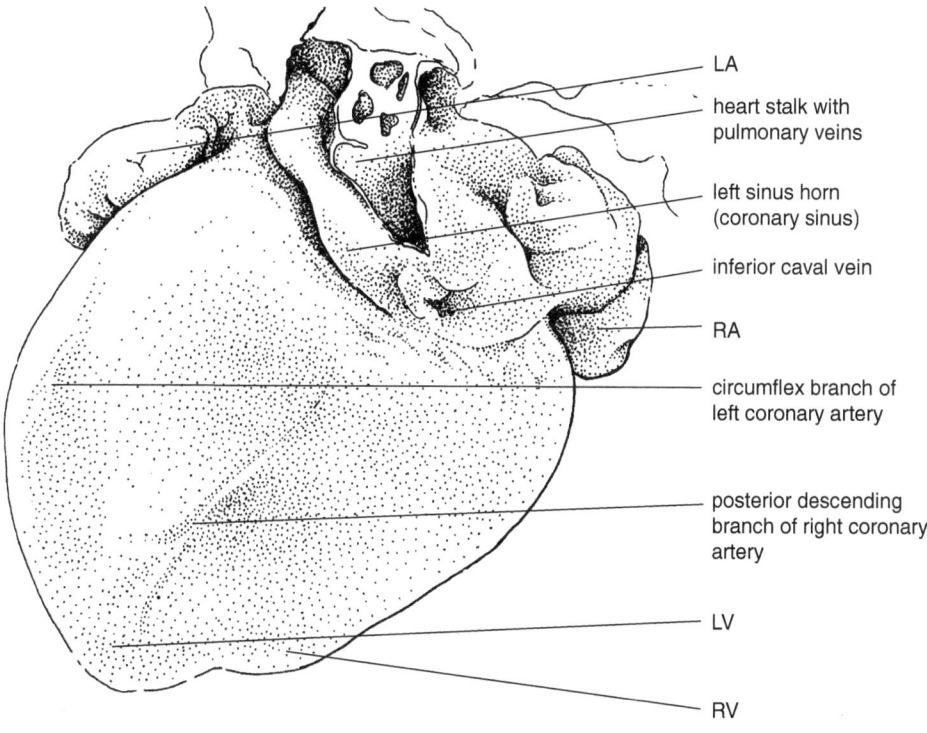

FIGURES 2.33–2.36   *Continued*

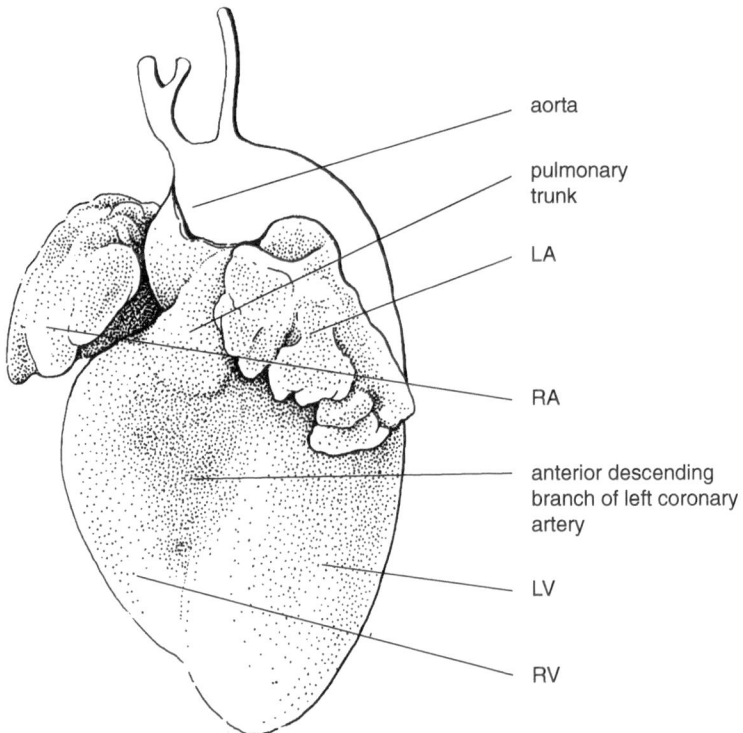

FIGURE 2.37   Complete heart, isolated (stage 23), ventral cranial view.

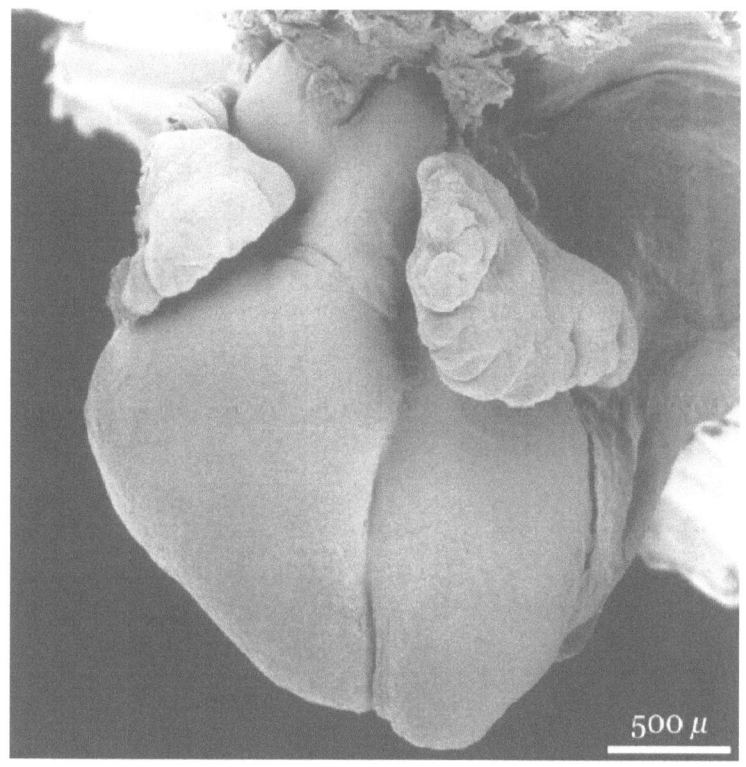

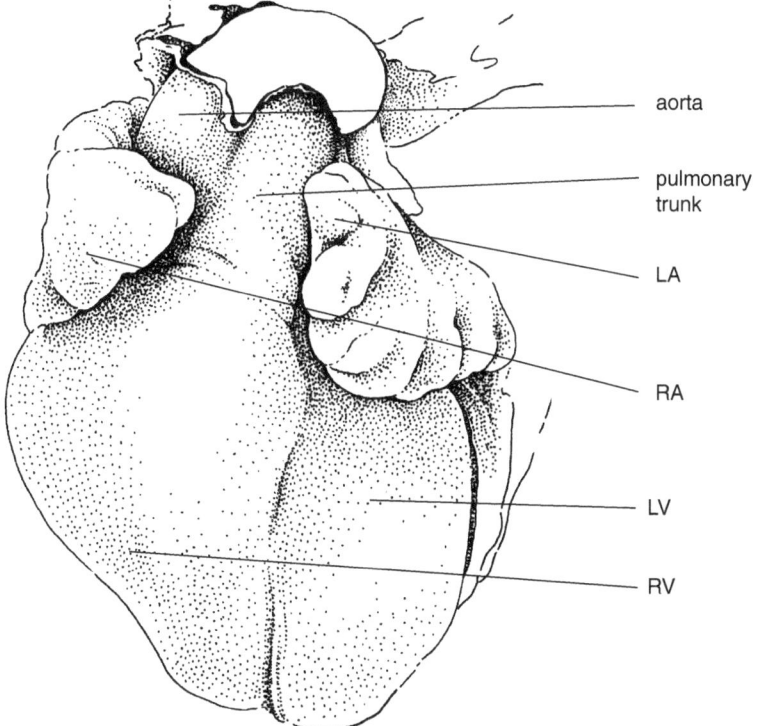

FIGURE 2.38   Complete heart, isolated (9 weeks), ventral cranial view.

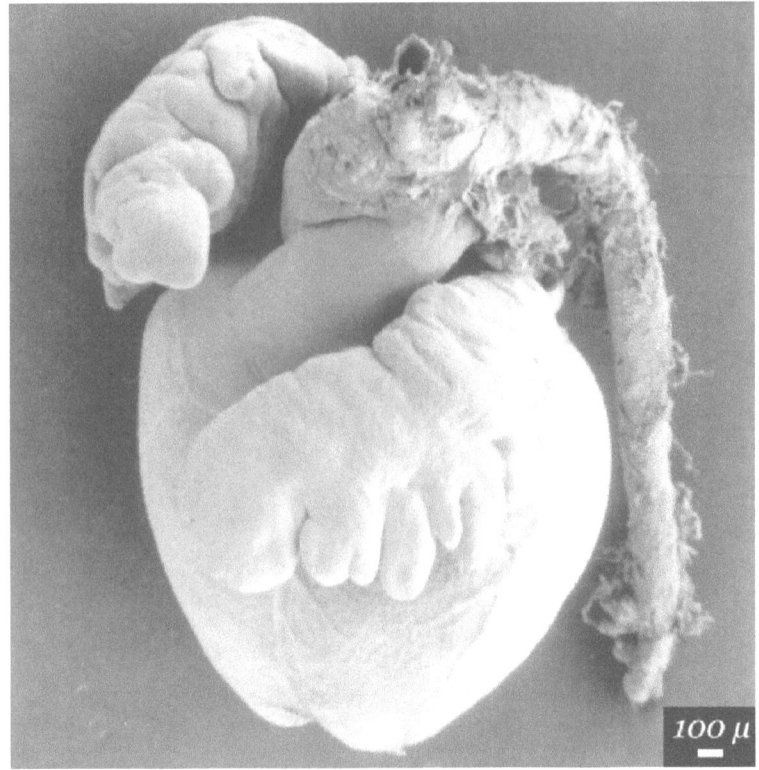

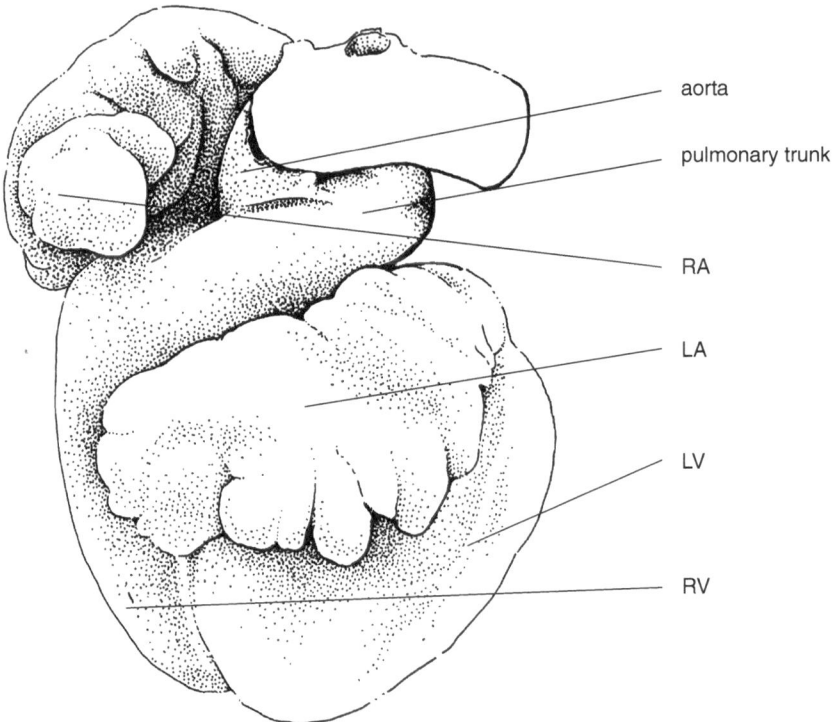

FIGURE 2.39   Complete heart, isolated (10 weeks), left lateral view.

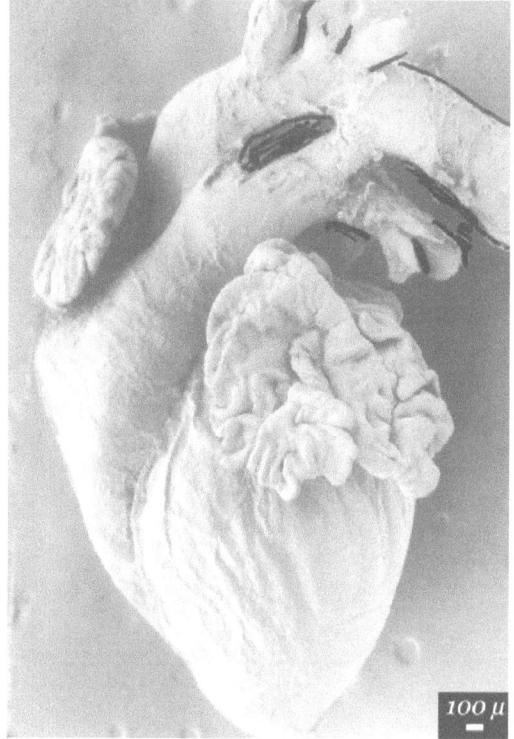

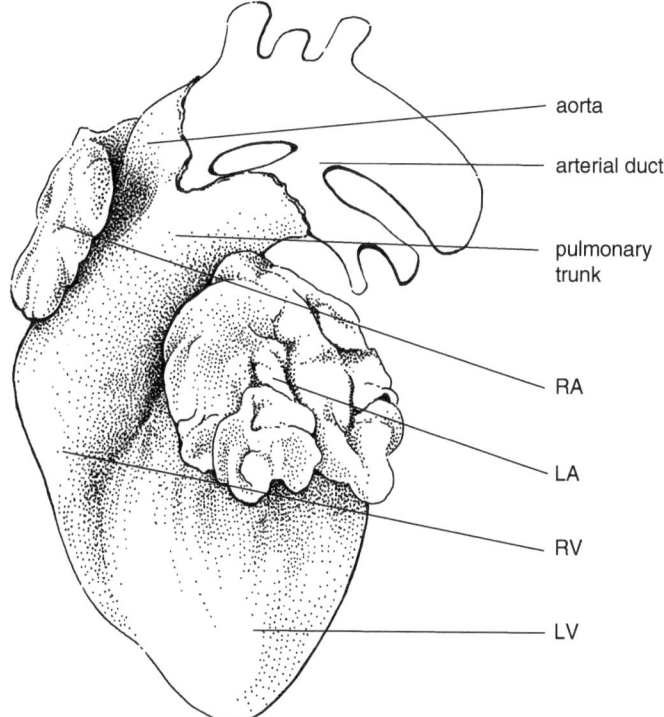

FIGURE 2.40   Complete heart, isolated (11 weeks), ventral cranial view. The heart is fixed in a contracted state.

3

Development and septation of the atria and venous pole

DEVELOPMENT OF THE SINUS VENOSUS AND ITS DERIVATIVES

The posterior most part of the heart tube is commonly known as the sinus venosus which receives the venous blood from the right and left side of the embryo. It consists of two horns connected to the rest of the heart tube via the sinu-atrial foramen [Steding et al., 1990]. These horns receive blood from the vitelline, umbilical and common cardinal veins. Reconstructions of the venous pole of the heart in mouse embryos, based on molecular expression patterns in the surrounding myocardium, have shown that, at least in mice, a sinus venosus *sensu stricto* does not exist at any time in development. Instead, the systemic venous tributaries, i.c. the right and left sinus horns, drain separately and directly into the atria [Soufan et al., 2004]. Whether this situation is comparable to what occurs in human embryos remains to be proven. In this atlas we will therefore conform to the current opinion regarding development of the venous pole in man. In contrast to what is seen in most vertebrate embryos, asymmetry of the venous pole in human embryos, with the left sinus horn being deviated to the right, appears to be present from the beginning onward [Knauth et al., 2002]. When viewed from the luminal side of the heart tube, a bifurcation is seen where the two horns meet [Vernall, 1962; Steding, 1990], like the crotch in a pair of trousers [Webb, 1998]. This structure is called the sinus septum and is situated caudal to the dorsal mesocardium. From stage 12 onwards the superior caval vein is being formed by the right superior cardinal and right common cardinal vein. The proximal portion of the inferior cardinal vein develops from the right omphalomesenteric vein which is intergrated into the (right) hepatic vein. This becomes the most cranial part of the newly formed inferior caval vein. The left sided counterparts steadily regress. At the same time the sinus venosus becomes integrated into the right atrium. The sinus septum, initially a midline structure in the same sagittal plane as the dorsal mesocardium, turns almost 90° to the right. Eventually, the sinus venosus will drain completely to the right atrium, including the left sinus horn, which in humans will become the coronary sinus. In fact, the central part of the sinus venosus is to become the greater part of the mature right atrium. This part remains smooth-walled in contrast to the pectinate musculature of the auricles.

By the end of stage 11, a fold of tissue is formed at the caudal margin of the sinu-atrial foramen, which will become the right sinus valve. The sinus septum separates this valve in two parts that flank the orifices of the right and left sinus horns. Later on, these parts develop into the Eustachian and Thebesian valves that flank the orifices of the inferior caval vein and the coronary sinus, respectively. At the junction of these valves a fibrous structure is formed, called the tendon of Todaro, which, as observed in mouse embryos, runs through the sinus septum and terminates at the site where the primary interatrial septum will fuse with the atrioventricular cushions [Webb et al., 1998b]. Although both sinus valves are generally considered to result from incorporation of the sinus horns into the atrium, it has been suggested that, in contrast to the right sinus valve, the left sinus valve, which is formed at the cranial margin of the sinu-atrial foramen, is not formed by folding but by ingrow of a myocardial protrusion [Wessels et al., 2000]. In their superior most aspect the right and left venous valves fuse to form the spurious septum, that flanks the inlet of the future superior caval vein, will eventually be incorporated into the terminal crest, which separates the auricle from the rest of the right atrium. The remainder of the left venous valve fuses with the atrial septum by the end of the embryonic period.

DEVELOPMENT OF THE PULMONARY VEINS

The smooth-walled part of the mature left atrium develops from the myocardium surrounding the pulmonary veins. The ongoing discussion about the origin of this myocardium, whether derived from the sinus venosus [e.g. De Ruiter et al., 1995] or from the left atrium [e.g. Bliss & Hutchins, 1994], appears to be largely a semantic problem [Webb, 1998], given the fact that in the early embryonic heart there are no well-recognizable demarcations between the two compartments, i.c. the sinus septum and the dorsal mesocardium. However, it should be realized that the dorsal mesocardium, which encloses the primordium of the pulmonary veins, is always cranial to the sinus septum and connects the atrial compartment, rather than the sinus venosus, with the body wall, which it remains to do so throughout development [Webb et al., 1998]. Therefore, the atrial compartment should be considered as the site of pulmonary venous origin. Moreover, from the outset onward, both the sinus venosus and the pulmonary venous primordium are surrounded by myocardium with different molecular phenotypes, as has been demonstrated in mouse embryos [Soufan et al., 2004]. When seen from the luminal side, the area of the atrium connected to the dorsal mesocardium initially appears as a horse shoe-shaped elevation of the myocardium, the legs of which are called the right and left pulmonary ridges. The right pulmonary ridge, also called vestibular spine, is covered with a cap of epithelially lined mesenchymal tissue and plays a role in atrial septation (see below). In their dorsocranial aspect the pulmonary ridges are continuous with the primary interatrial septum [Webb et al., 1998], which just like the sinus septum and the dorsal mesocardium, is initially a midline structure. The pulmonary ridges surround a dimple, dubbed the pulmonary pit [Webb et al., 1998], which will become the portal to the pulmonary veins. These veins lumenize within the mesenchyme of the dorsal mesocardium and the developing lung buds and are initially part of the vascular plexus around the foregut that also gives rise to bronchial and pharyngeal arch vessels [De Ruiter et al., 1993; Rammos et al., 1990]. This process involves canalization of endothelial strands [De Ruiter et al., 1995; Webb et al., 1998; Wessels et al., 2000] rather than budding of veins from the left atrial wall, as proposed in the past [Neil, 1956; Los, 1958]. The first indications of pulmonary vein development are usually found at stage 12 or 13 but more than one pulmonary vein is not found consistently until stage 20 [Bliss & Hutchins, 1995].

DEVELOPMENT AND SEPTATION OF THE ATRIA

Septation of the early inter atrial compartment commences with the appearance of the primary atrial septum, the first indication of which is found at stage 12. When seen from the lumenal side of the primary atrial compartment a myocardial protrusion, called the primary interatrial septum appears in the midline of the dorsocranial wall (Figure 3-A). The dorsal rim of the primary interatrial septum is in continuity with the tissue that surrounds the pulmonary pit, which at this stage is also a midline structure. This tissue forms the right and left pulmonary ridges. The primary interatrial septum grows into the direction of the atrioventricular transition, thereby reducing the size of the space between the free edge of the primary interatrial septum and the fusing atrioventricular cushions. This space is dubbed the primary interatrial foramen. The leading edge of the primary interatrial septum is covered with a cap of epithelially lined mesenchymal tissue. In its ventral and dorsal aspects, it is continuous with respectively the superior and inferior endocardial cushions in the atrioventricular canal. When these three structures grow towards an imaginary center point, the atrioventricular cushions will meet and the primary interatrial foramen will diminish and subsequently close by the end of stage 16 [Webb et al., 1998b]. It is still a matter of debate whether or not atrial septation requires extracardiac mesenchymal contributions. Prior to the closure of the primary interatrial foramen, during stage 15, perforations appear in the dorsocranial part of the primary interatrial septum, which run together to form a single large opening: the secondary interatrial foramen. At a later stage (from stage 17 on), the ventral cranial atrial wall in between the primary interatrial septum and the left venous valve starts to fold inward to form the secondary interatrial septum (Figure 3-B, C). This process commences around stage 17 but remains rather insignificant until stage 21 [Anderson et al., 2002]. Since this structure is a fold rather than a separately growing protrusion, it has been debated whether it should be called a septum [Anderson et al., 1999].

Besides contributions of the auricles, the sinus venosus and the pulmonary primordium, a fourth tissue source participates in the morphogenesis of the atria: the atrioventricular canal. In the early stages of cardiac development this part of the heart tube is a slow-conducting myocardial continuity between the atria and the

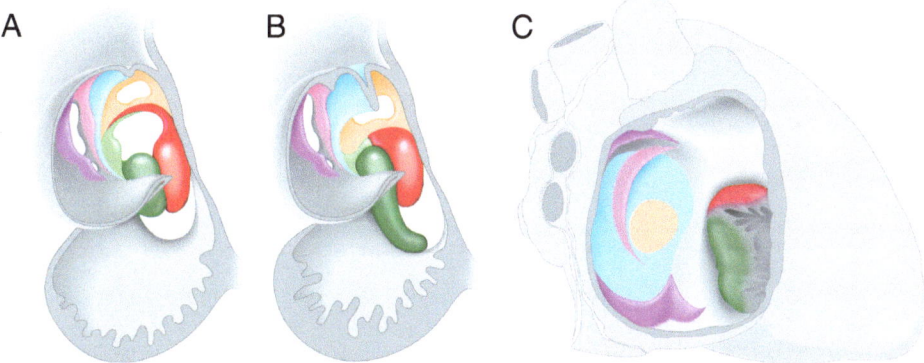

FIGURES 3 A–C   Structures involved in atrial septation (right lateral views), including the superior endocardial cushion (red), inferior endocardial cushion (dark green), vestibular spine (light green), primary interatrial septum (ochre), secondary interatrial septum (light blue), right venous valve (lilac), and left venous valve (pink).

ventricles [Anderson et al., 1978; Arguello et al., 1986; Wessels et al., 1991; De Jong et al., 1992]. Later on the myocardium of the atria becomes physically insulated from the ventricles by fibrous tissue, except for the area where the atrioventricular node and bundle will reside. Atrioventricular insulation at least partially involves proliferation of extra-cardiac mesenchyme into the atrioventricular sulcus which, however, is not achieved by active in growth. Rather than that, the proliferating extra-cardiac mesenchyme is enclosed by the thickening and bulging of the free walls of the ventricles [Wessels et al., 1996]. Although the insulation process is already initiated during stages 14 and 15, the first interruptions in atrioventricular myocardial contuinity are not found prior to stage 20, when the extra-cardiac mesenchyme fuses with endocardial cushion tissue [Wessels et al., 1996]. This is first noted in the anterior section of the right atrioventricular junction and it is not before the end of the 3rd month of gestation that atrioventricular insulation is completed [Wessels et al., 1996], except for the region where the atrioventricular bundle passes. Immunohistochemistry has revealed that the interruption itself takes place at the ventricular margin of the atrioventricular canal, suggesting that either the complete myocardial wall of the atrioventricular canal is incorporated in the forming mature atria [Wessels et al., 1996], or that the myocardium of the atrioventricular canal disappears by apoptosis. The four tissue sources of the embryonic inflow tract can be differentiated from each other on the basis of their specific expression pattern of developmental genes [Franco et al., 2000; Soufan et al., 2004]. Moreover, the expression pattern of laterality genes such as Pitx2 shows that each of these tissue sources has distinct left and right components. This is obvious for the right and left embryonic atria (auricles), the right and left sinus horns (caval veins and coronary sinus) and the atrioventricular canal (left and right atrial vestibuli). Together with the pulmonary primordium, the interatrial septa (see below) are part of the left component of a distinct transcriptional domain which has been dubbed "mediastinal myocardium", the right component of which comprises a small area of the right atrium in between the secondary interatrial septum and the left venous valve [Franco et al., 2000; Soufan et al., 2004].

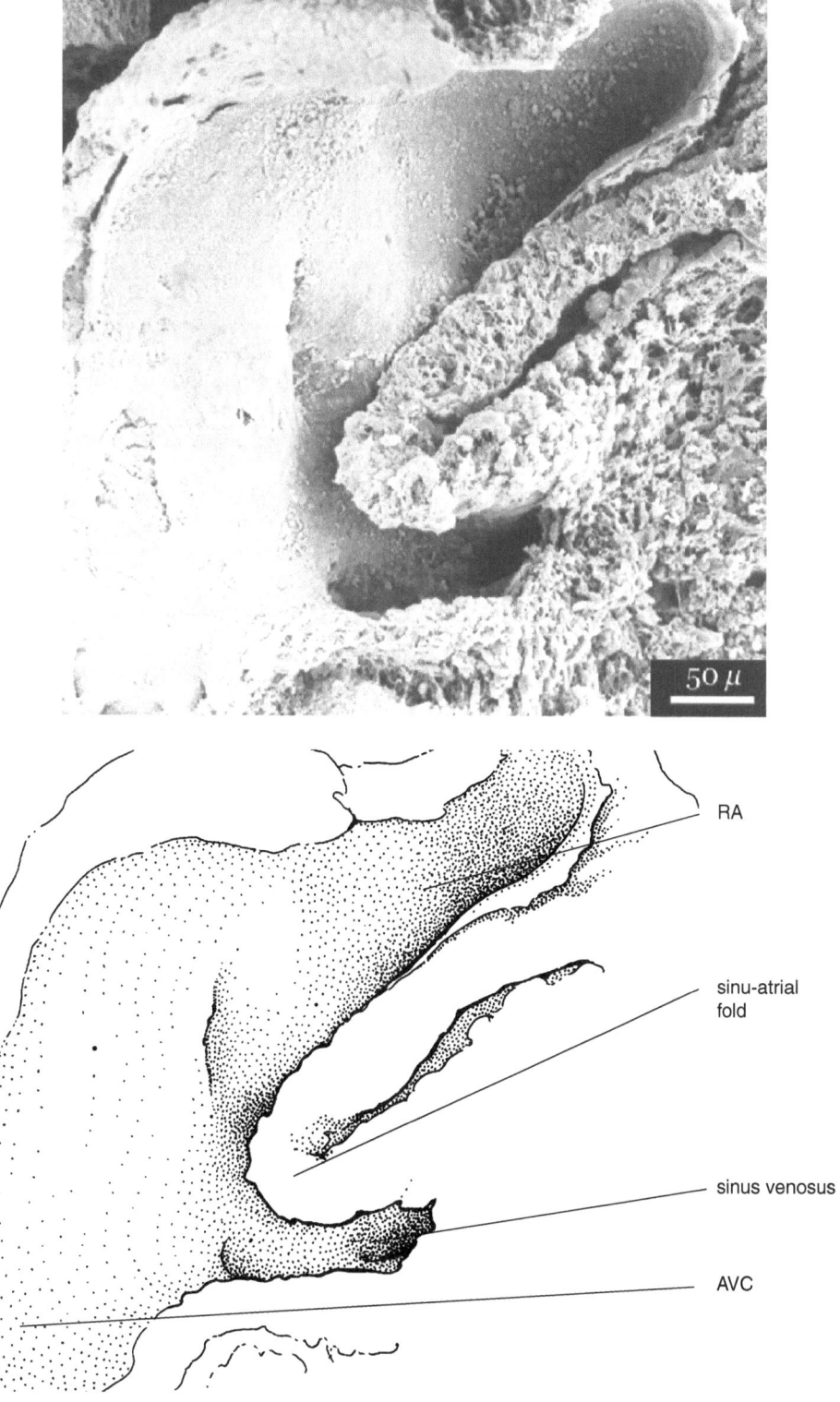

FIGURE 3.1   RA and sinus venosus (stage 11), left medial view.

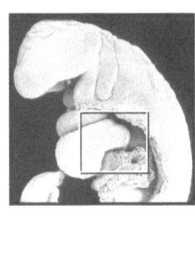
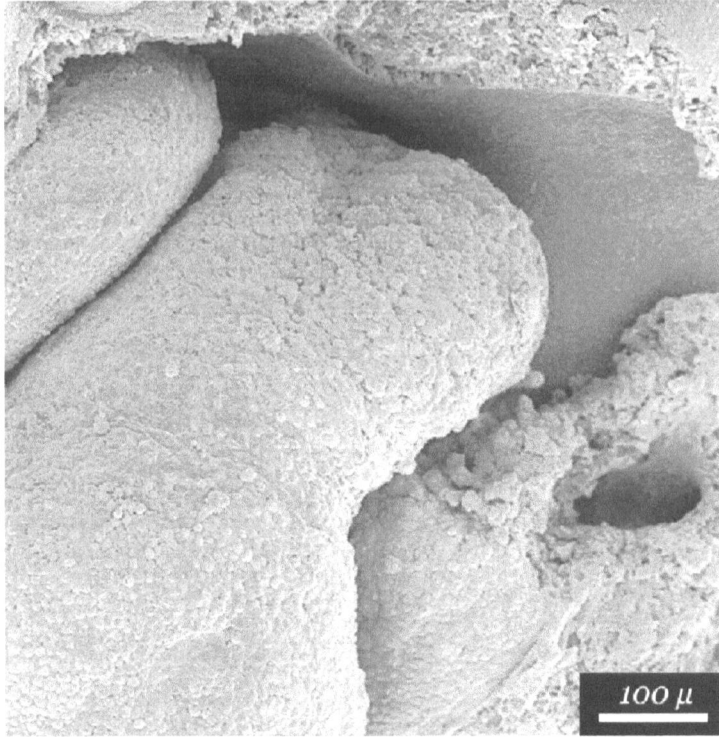
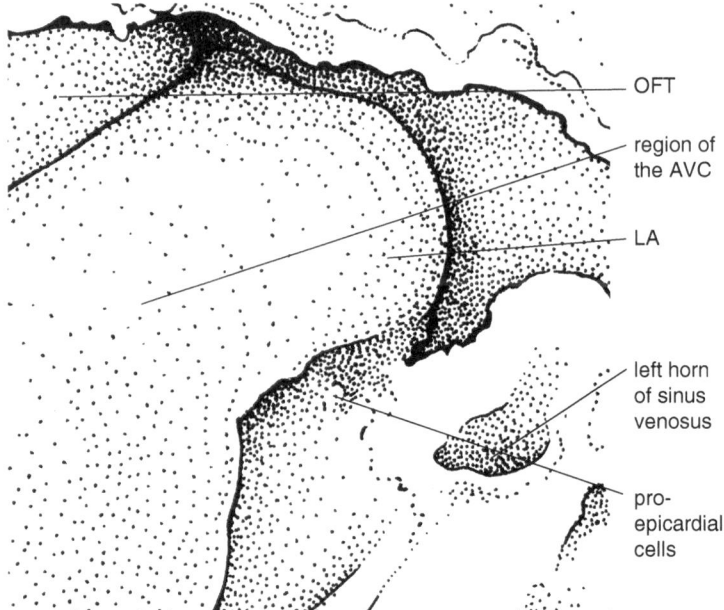

FIGURE 3.2   Complete heart (stage 12), detailed left lateral view.

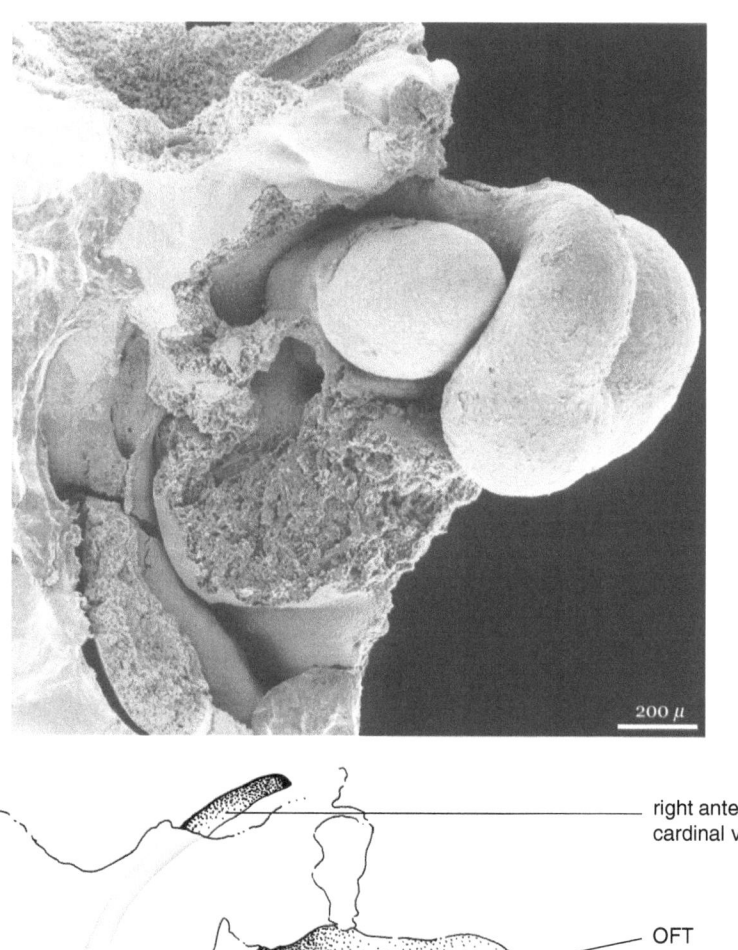

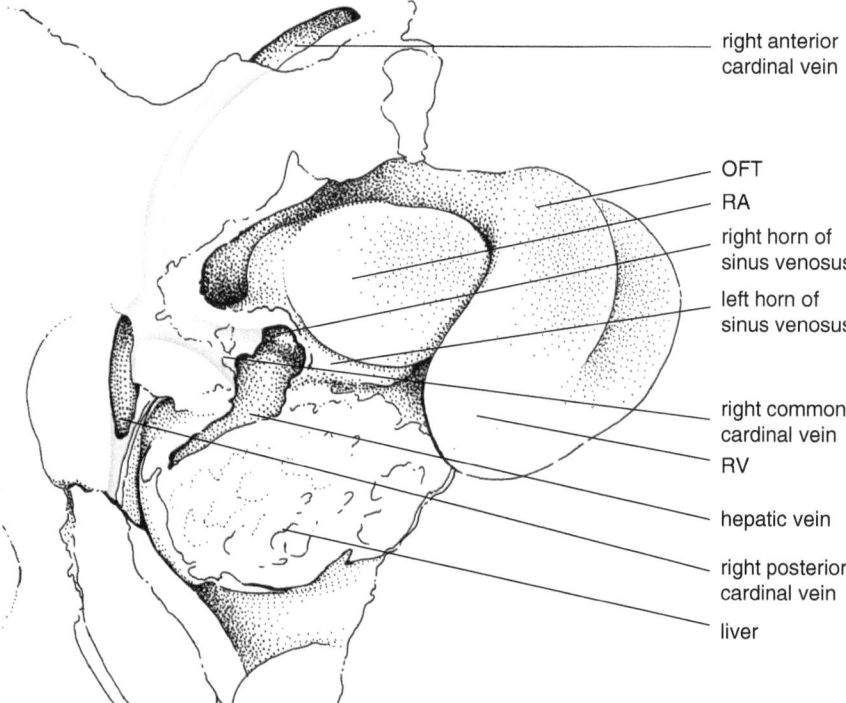

right anterior
cardinal vein

OFT

RA

right horn of
sinus venosus

left horn of
sinus venosus

right common
cardinal vein

RV

hepatic vein

right posterior
cardinal vein

liver

FIGURE 3.3   Complete heart in situ (stage 13), right lateral view. The ventral body wall and the pericardium are removed. The right lateral body wall is dissected to expose the tributes to the sinus venosus.

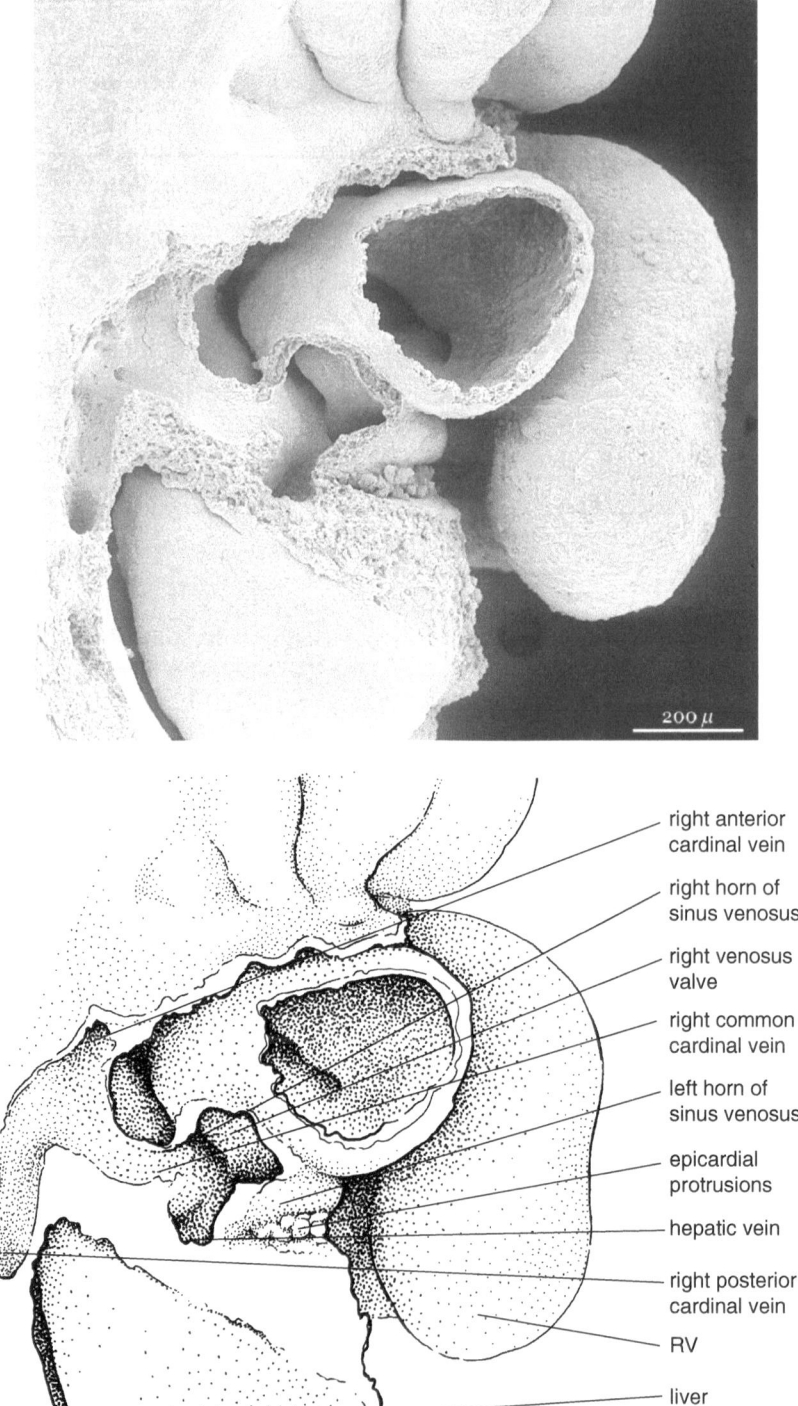

FIGURE 3.4   RA and sinus venosus (stage 14), right lateral view. The lateral body wall and the pericardium are removed.

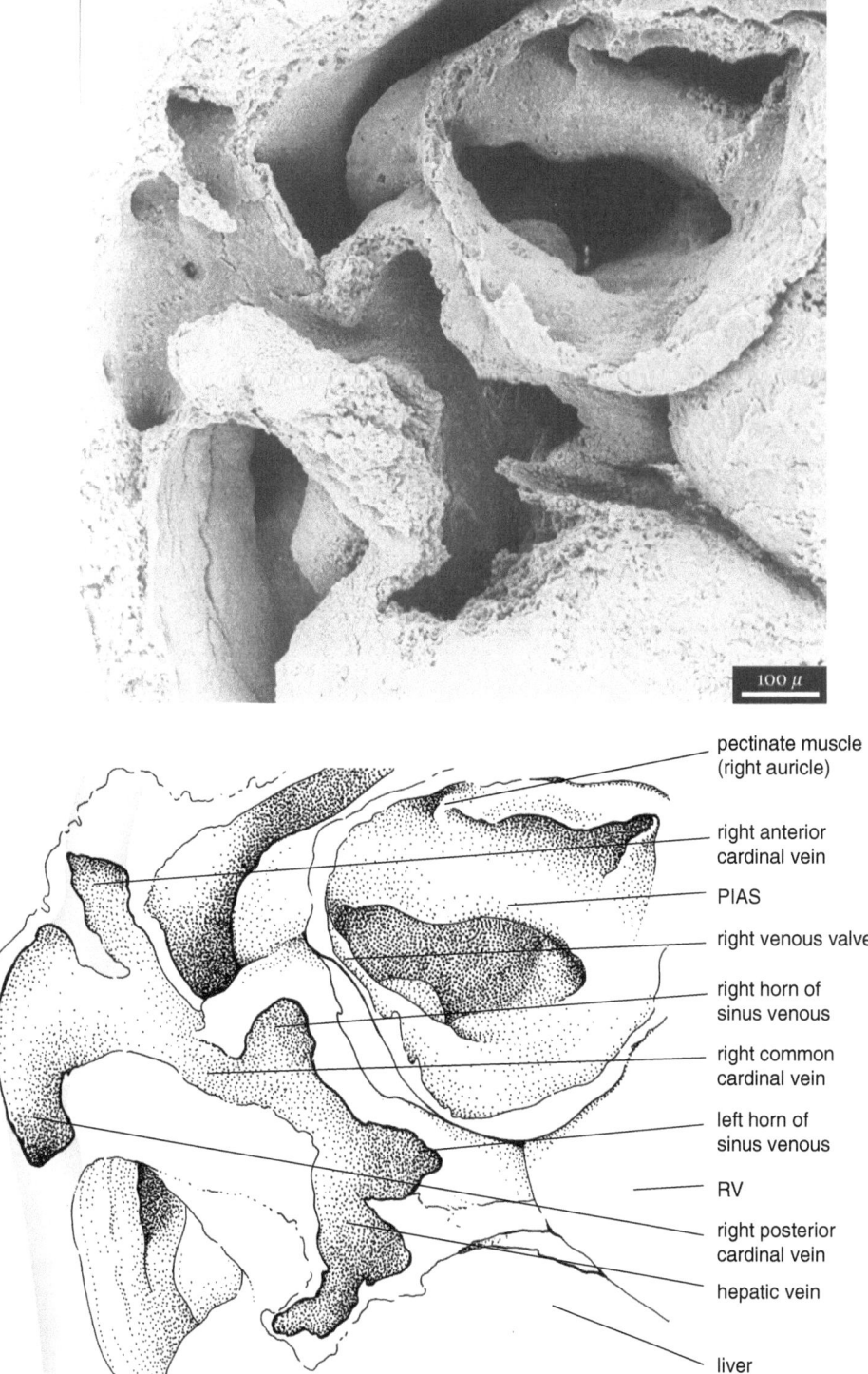

FIGURE 3.5   RA and sinus venosus (stage 14), right lateral view. The lateral body wall and the pericardium are removed.

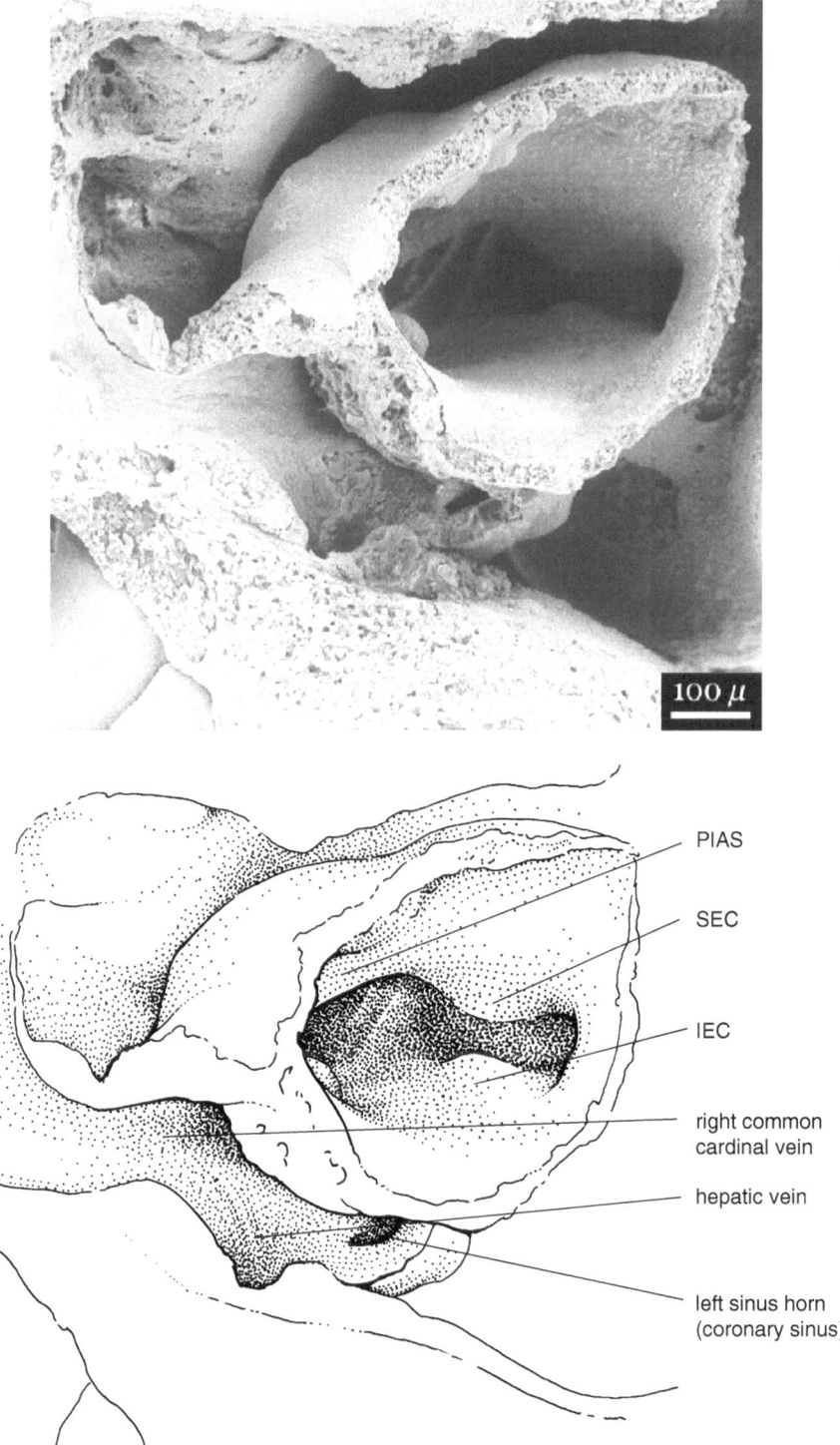

FIGURE 3.6   RA and sinus venosus (stage 14), right lateral view. The ventral apect of the free edge of the primary interatrial septum becomes connected with the superior endocardial cushion.

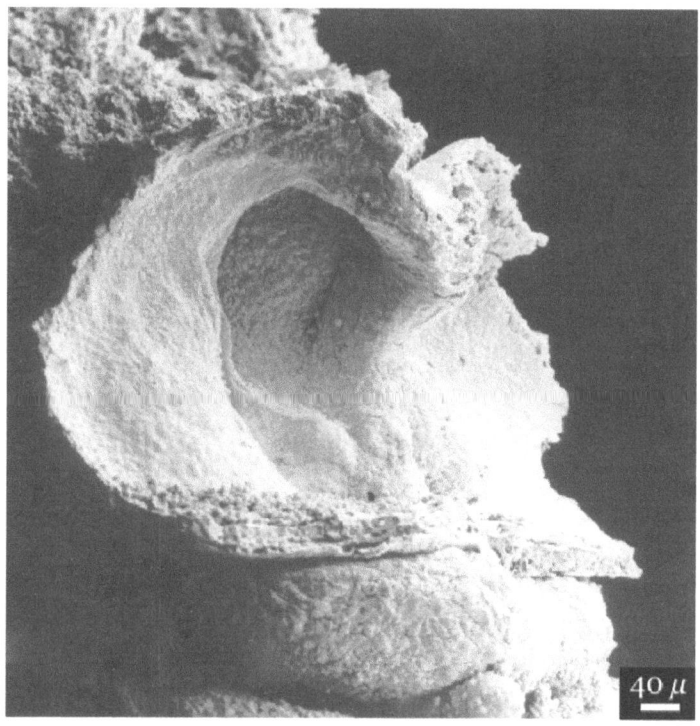

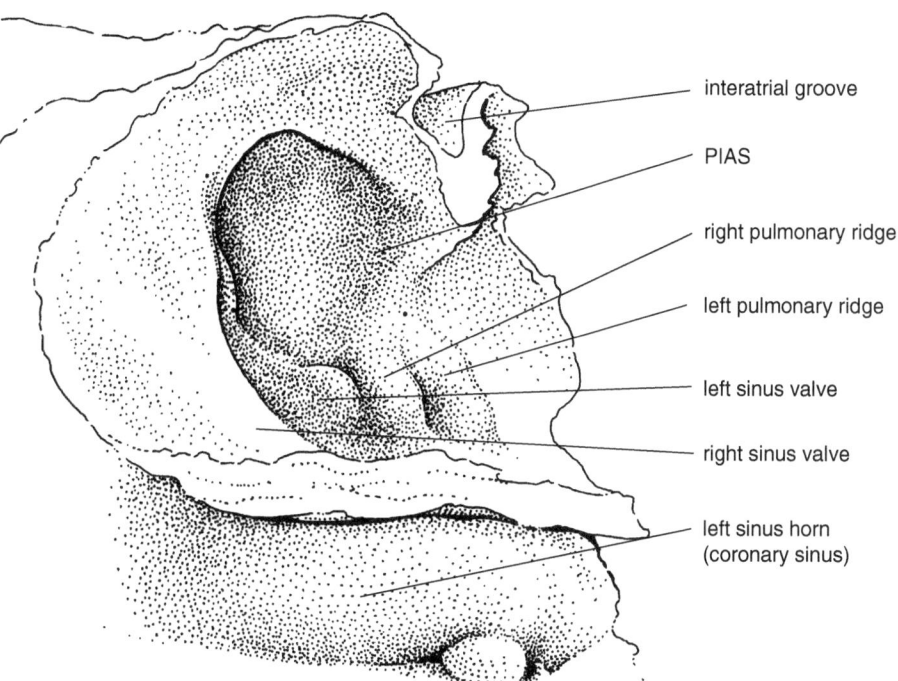

interatrial groove

PIAS

right pulmonary ridge

left pulmonary ridge

left sinus valve

right sinus valve

left sinus horn
(coronary sinus)

FIGURES 3.7-3.9   RA and LA and left sinus horn (stage 14), right lateral, ventral, and left lateral views. The ventral and lateral walls are removed. The primary interatrial septum, originating from the dorsal cranial wall, grows in ventral caudal direction. Its dorsal rim is in continuity with the cranial ends of the right and left pulmonary ridge.

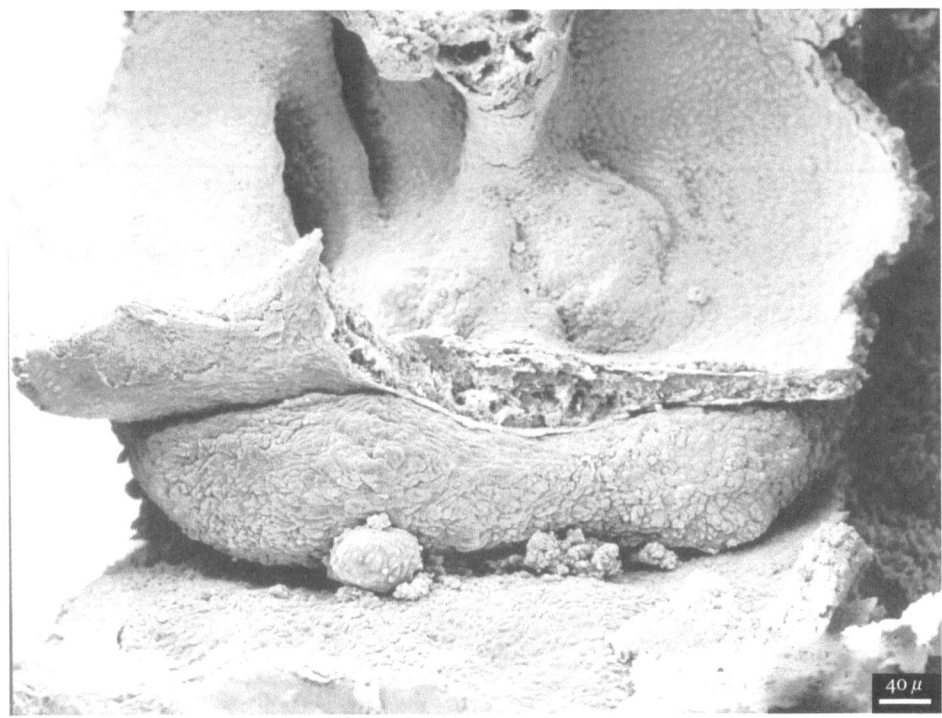

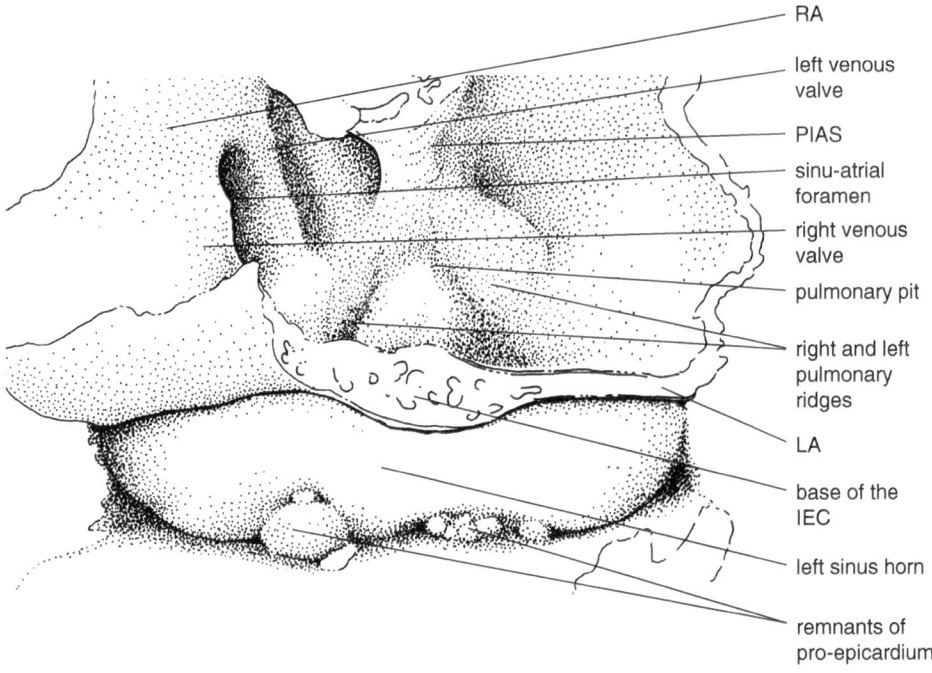

RA

left venous
valve

PIAS

sinu-atrial
foramen

right venous
valve

pulmonary pit

right and left
pulmonary
ridges

LA

base of the
IEC

left sinus horn

remnants of
pro-epicardium

FIGURES 3.7–3.9   *Continued*

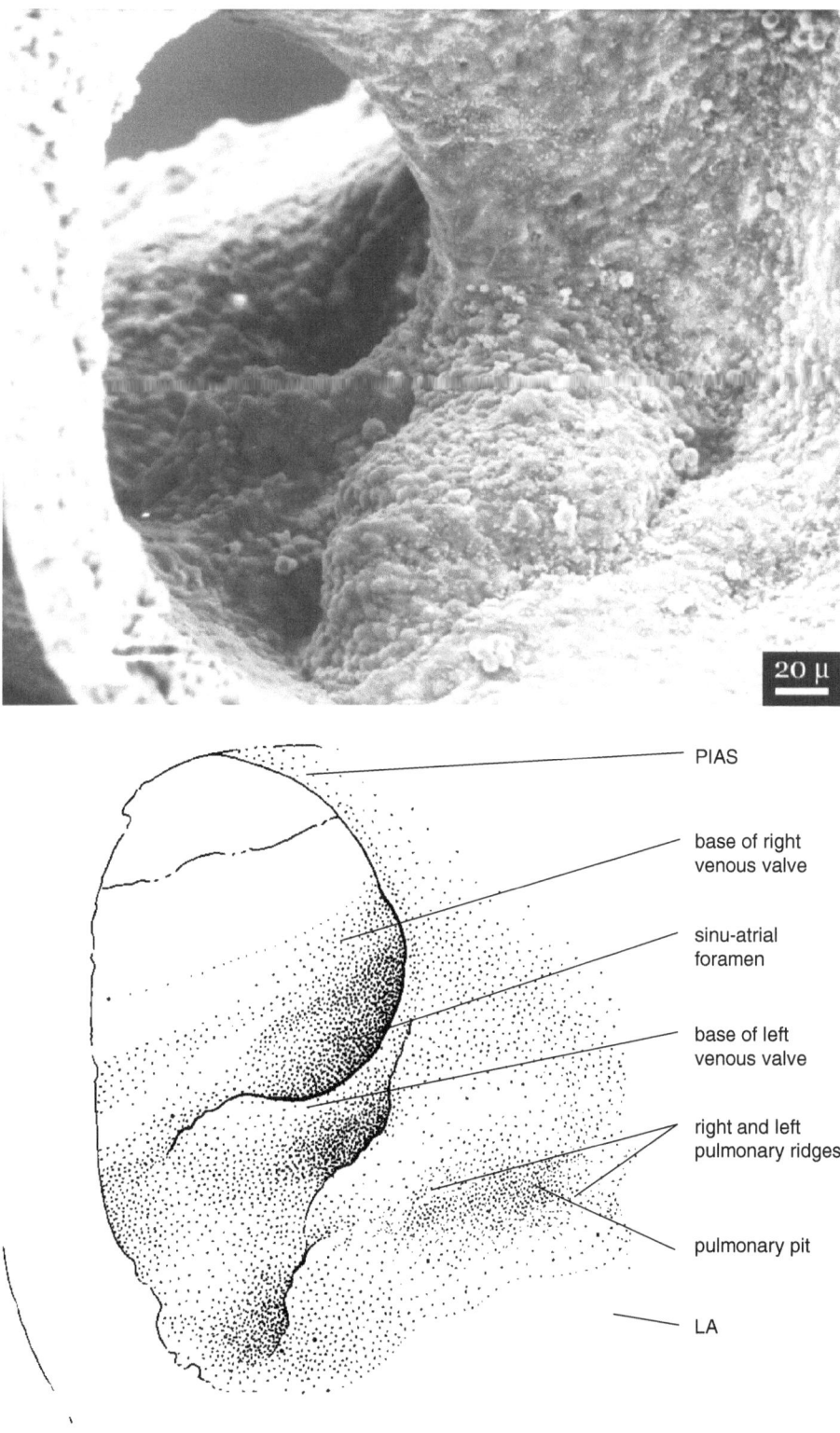

FIGURES 3.7-3.9   *Continued*

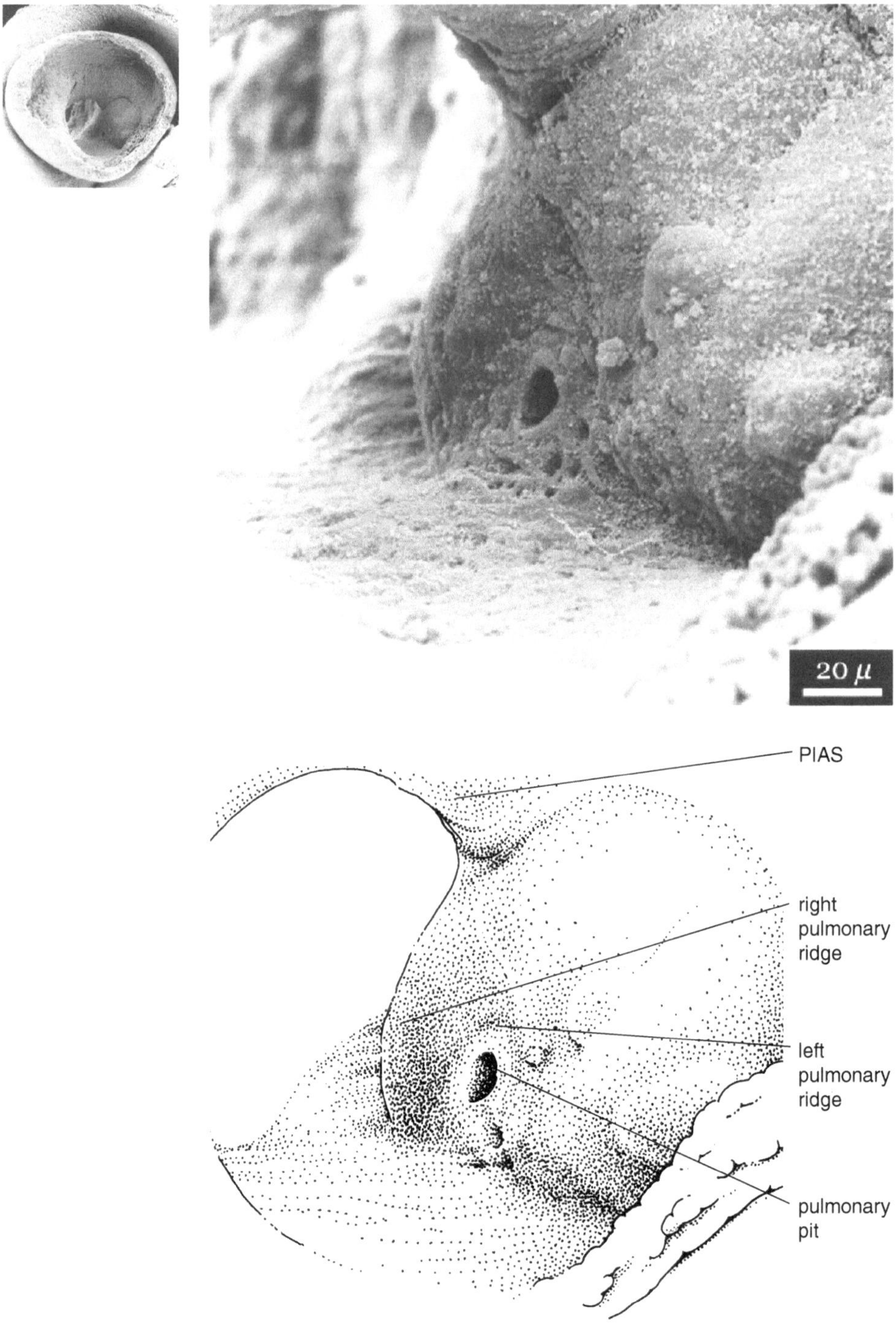

FIGURE 3.10   LA (stage 14), lateral view. The lateral wall is removed. In between the right and left pulmonary ridges a dimple is present, the pulmonary pit, with a single opening of the developing pulmonary veins.

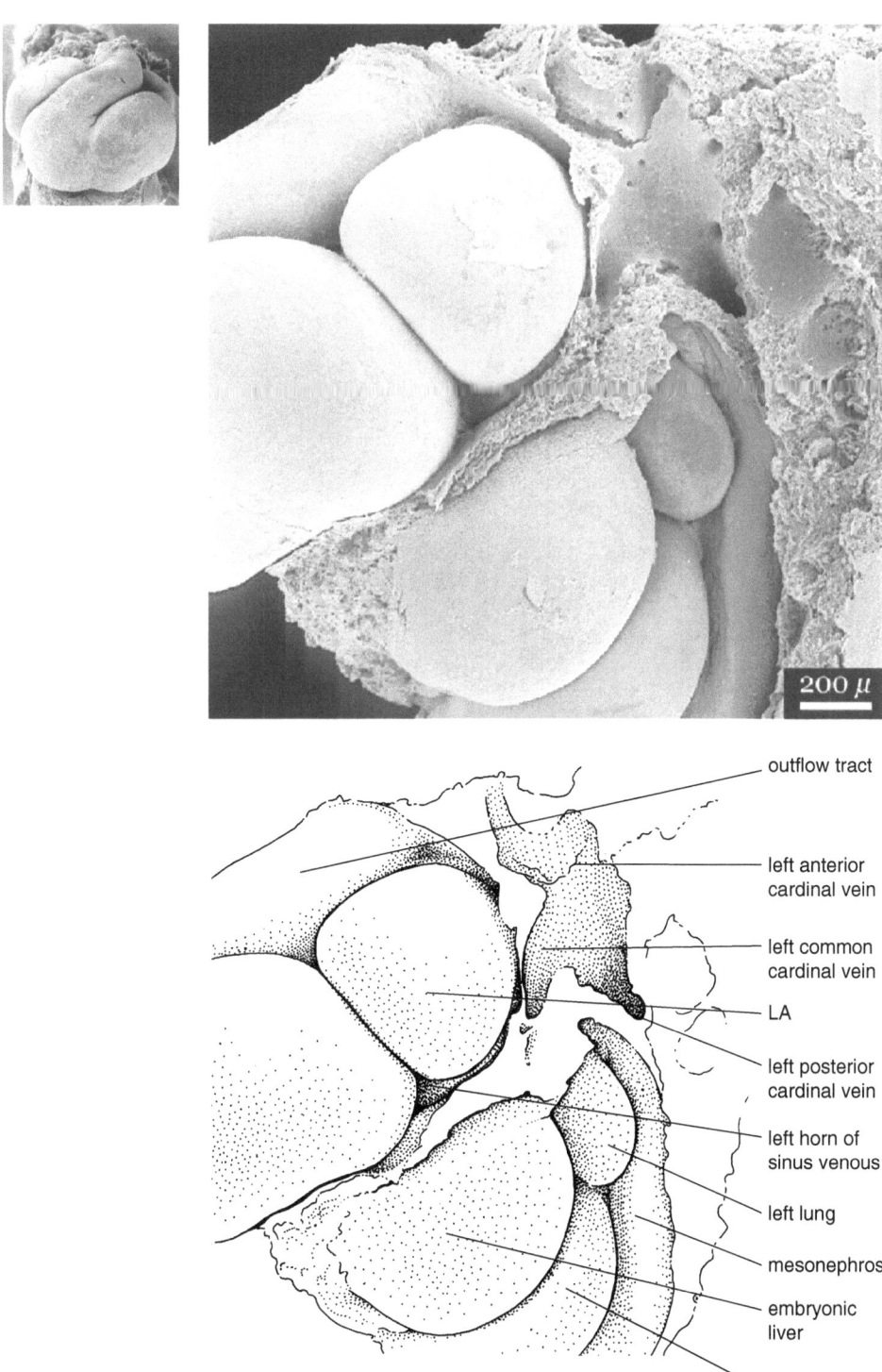

FIGURE 3.11   LA and sinus venosus (stage 15), left lateral view. The lateral body wall and the pericardium are removed.

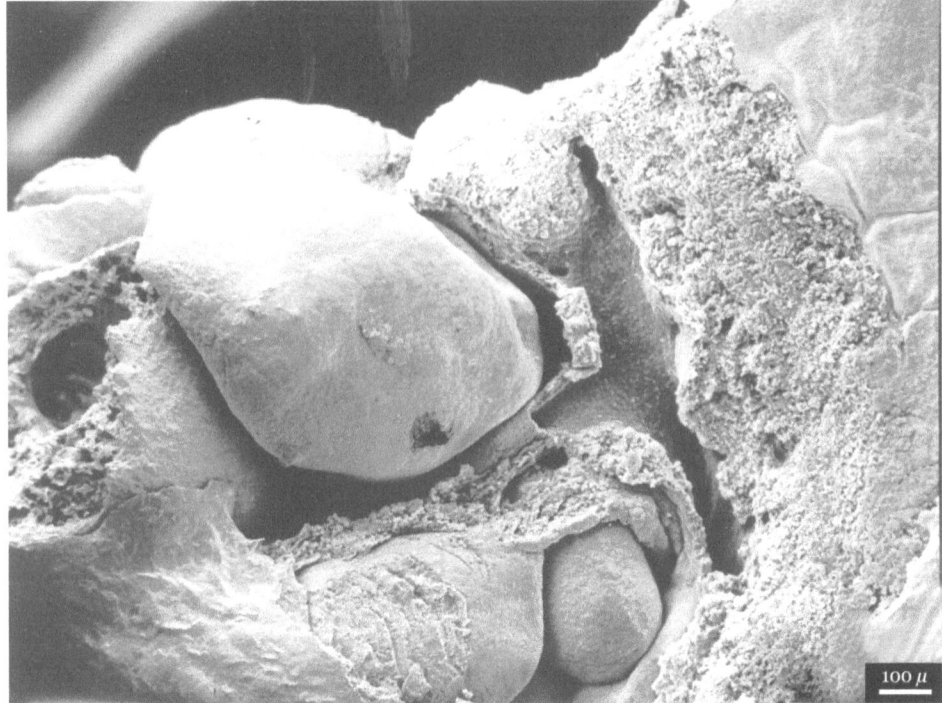

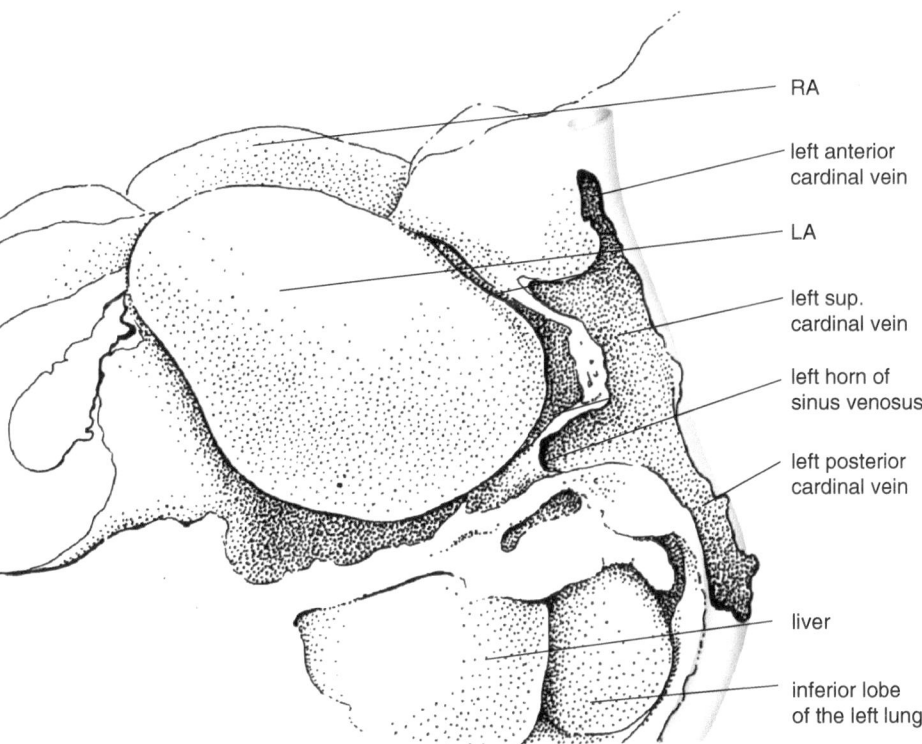

FIGURE 3.12   LA and sinus venosus (stage 15), left lateral view. The lateral body wall and the pericardium are removed.

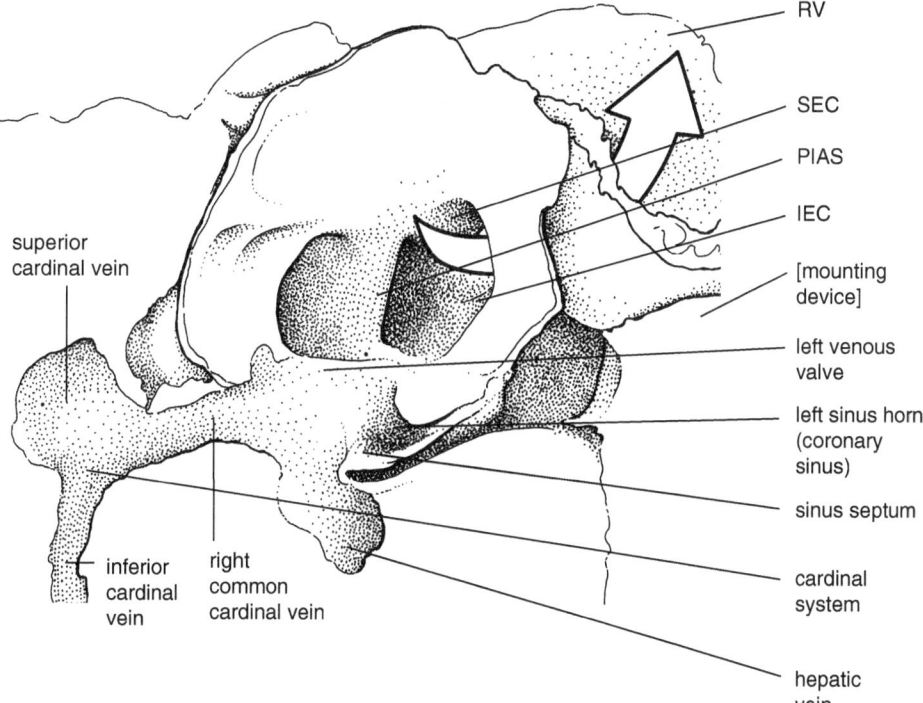

FIGURE 3.13   Sinus venosus, RA and RV (stage 15), right lateral view. The lateral wall is removed. The free edge of the primary interatrial septum is approximating the atrioventricular transition, thereby reducing the size of the primary interatrial foramen.

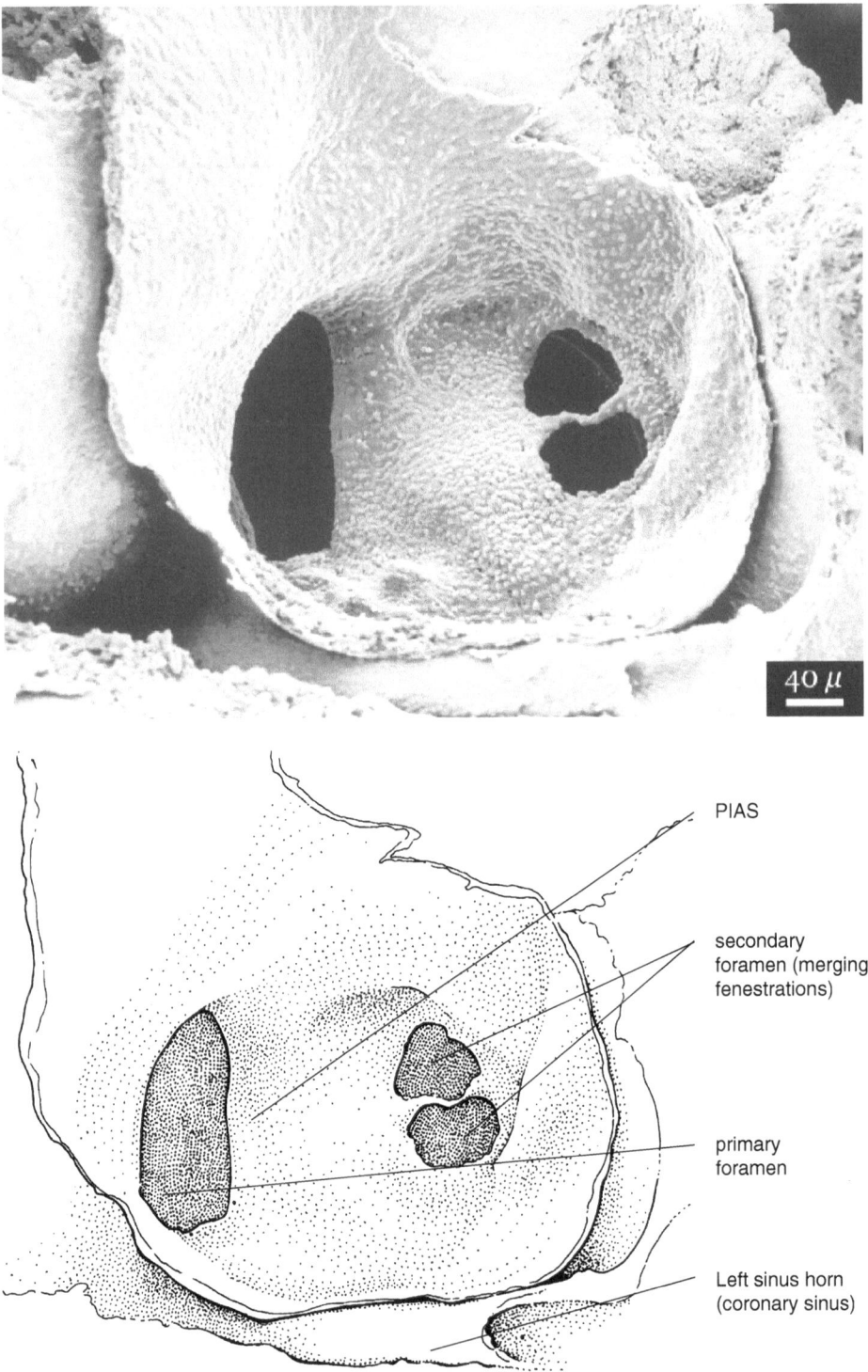

FIGURE 3.14   LA (stage 15), left lateral view. The lateral wall is removed. Fenestrations are present in the cranial part of the primary interatrial septum, that will merge to form the secundary foramen.

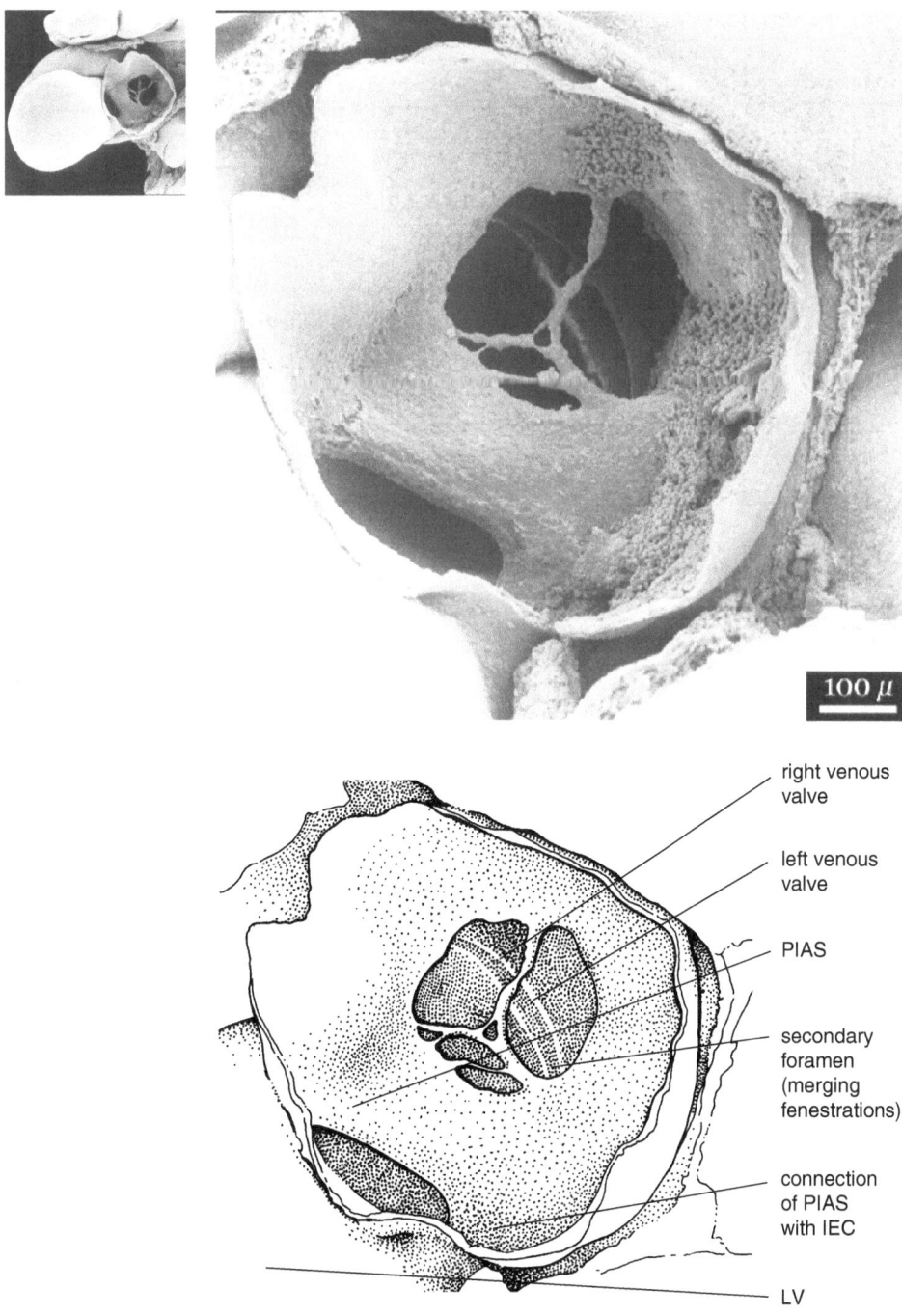

FIGURE 3.15   Complete heart in situ (stage 15), left lateral view. The lateral wall of the LA is removed. The primary interatrial septum is fusing with the atrioventricular cushions and the fenestrations have almost completely run together to form the secundary foramen.

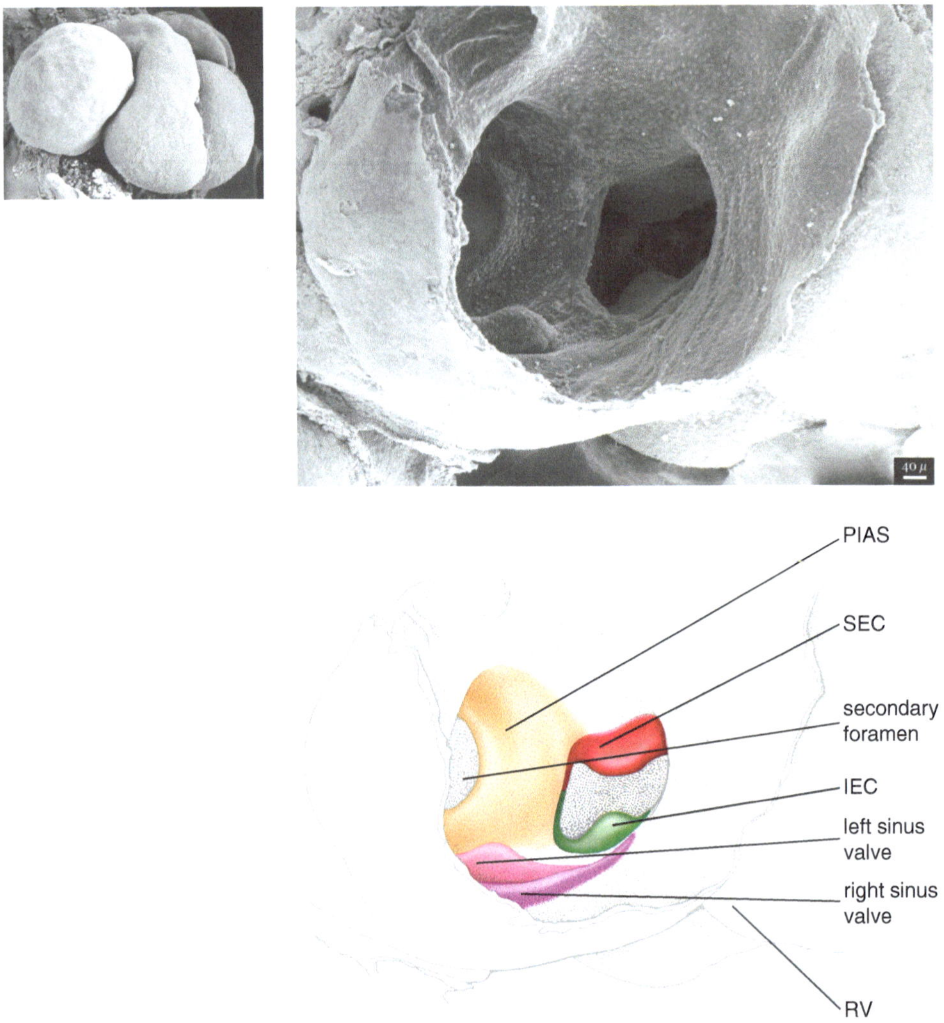

PIAS

SEC

secondary
foramen

IEC

left sinus
valve

right sinus
valve

RV

FIGURE 3.16   RA (stage 16), right lateral view. The lateral wall is removed. Colors indicate the superior endocardial cushion (red), inferior endocardial cushion (dark green), primary interatrial septum (ochre), right venous valve (lilac), and left venous valve (pink).

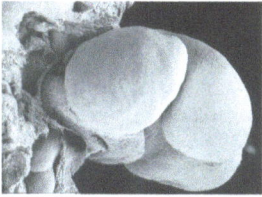
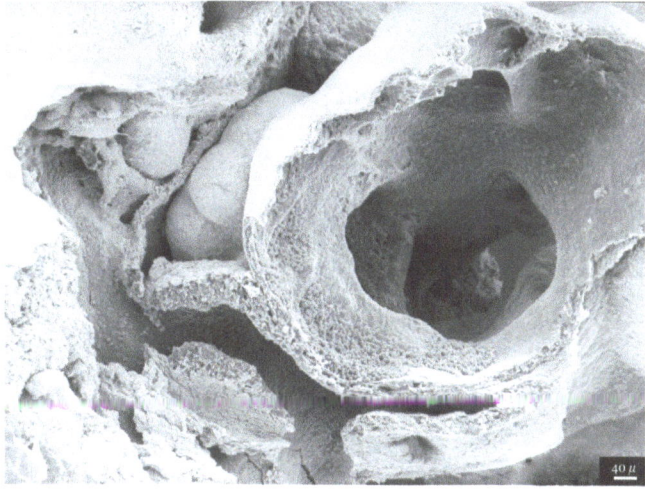

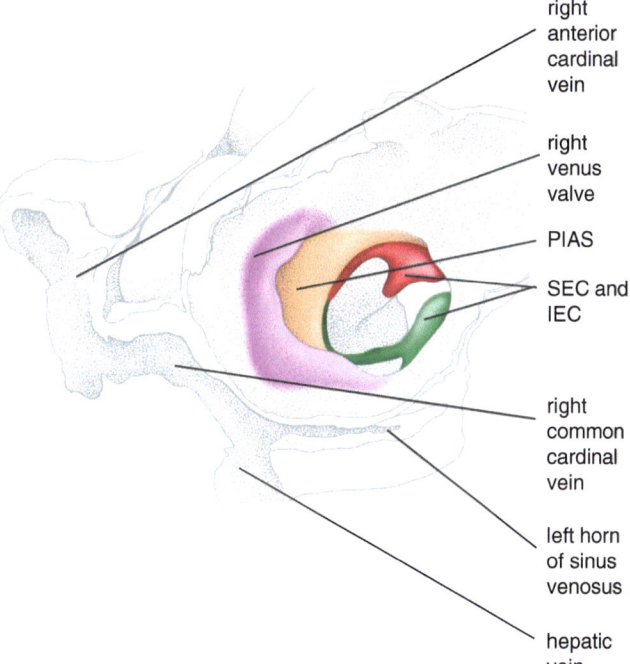

right
anterior
cardinal
vein

right
venus
valve

PIAS

SEC and
IEC

right
common
cardinal
vein

left horn
of sinus
venosus

hepatic
vein

FIGURE 3.17   Sinus venosus and RA (stage 16), right lateral view. The lateral wall is removed. Colors indicate the superior endocardial cushion (red), inferior endocardial cushion (dark green), primary interatrial septum (ochre), and right venous valve (lilac).

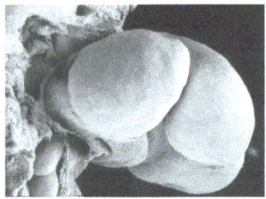
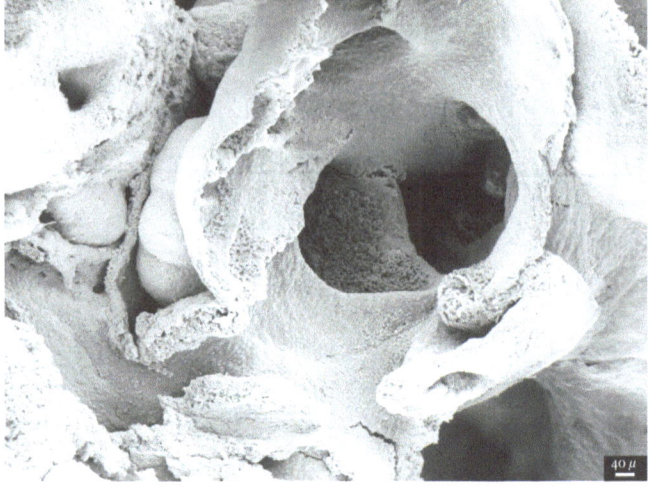
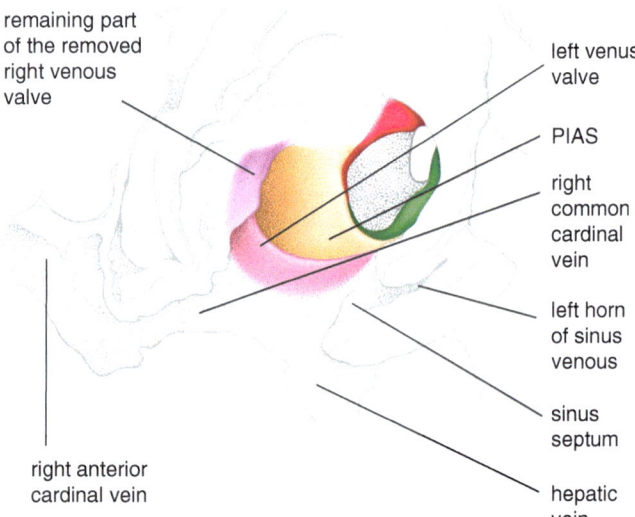

FIGURE 3.18   Sinus venosus and RA (stage 16), right lateral view. The lateral wall and right venous valve are removed. Colors indicate the superior endocardial cushion (red), inferior endocardial cushion (dark green), primary interatrial septum (ochre), right venous valve (lilac), and left venous valve (pink).

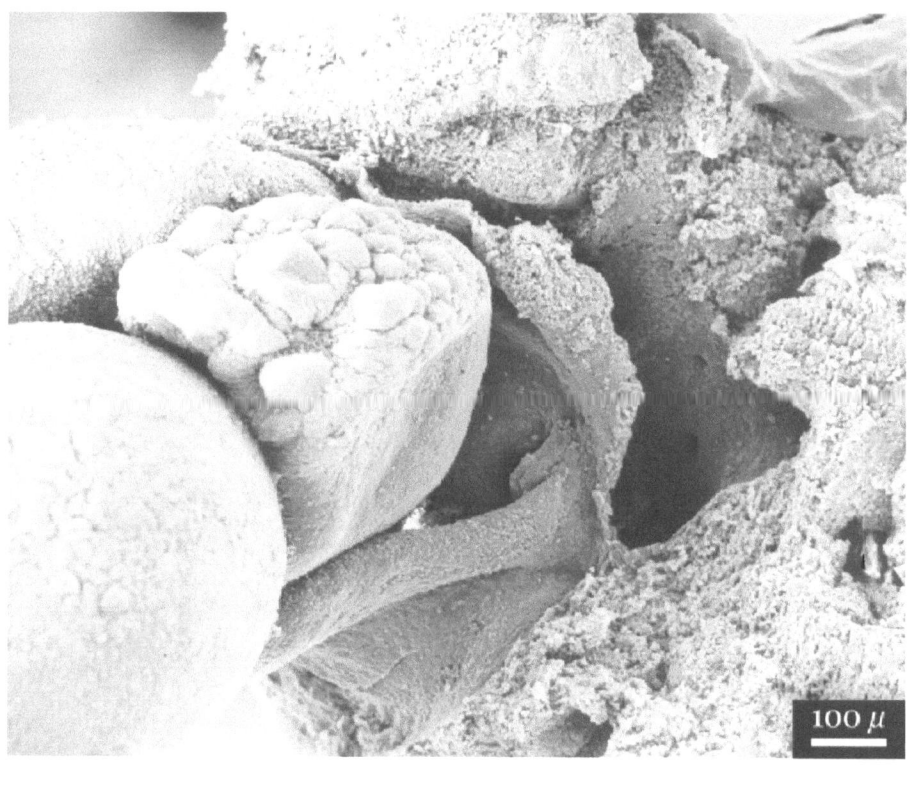

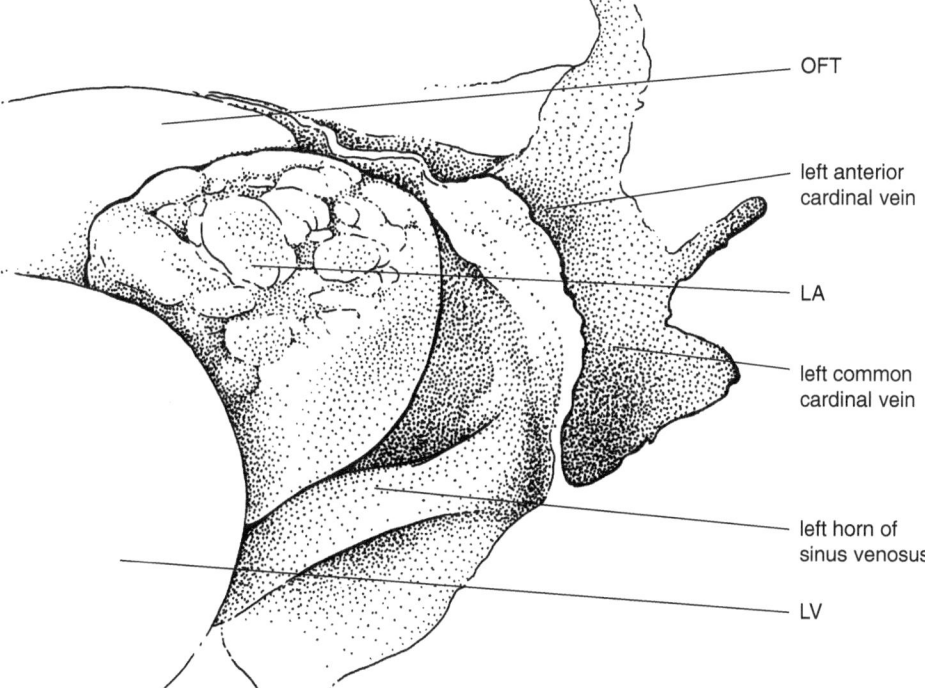

FIGURE 3.19   Sinus venosus and LA (stage 16), left lateral view. The lateral wall is partly removed.

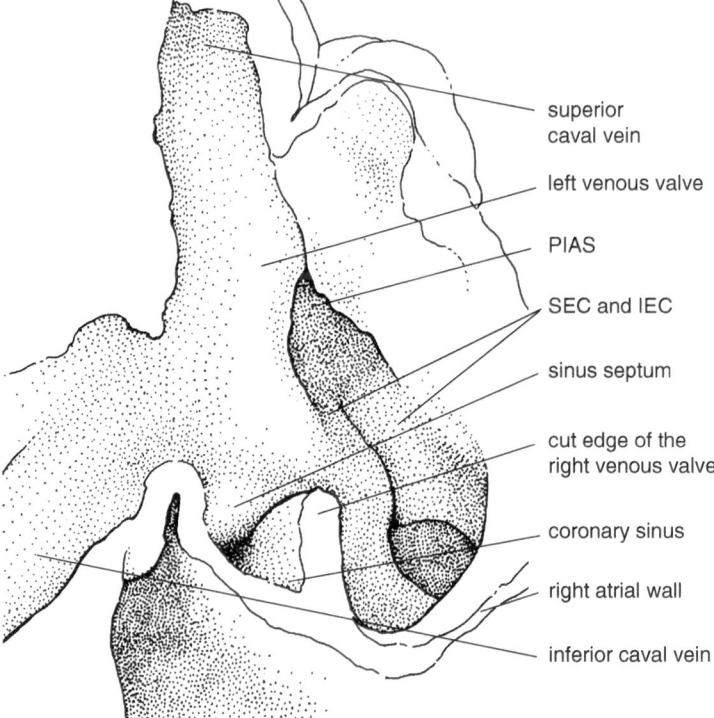

superior
caval vein

left venous valve

PIAS

SEC and IEC

sinus septum

cut edge of the
right venous valve

coronary sinus

right atrial wall

inferior caval vein

FIGURE 3.20   Sinus venosus and RA (stage 17), right lateral view.
The lateral wall and right venous valve are removed.

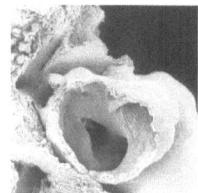
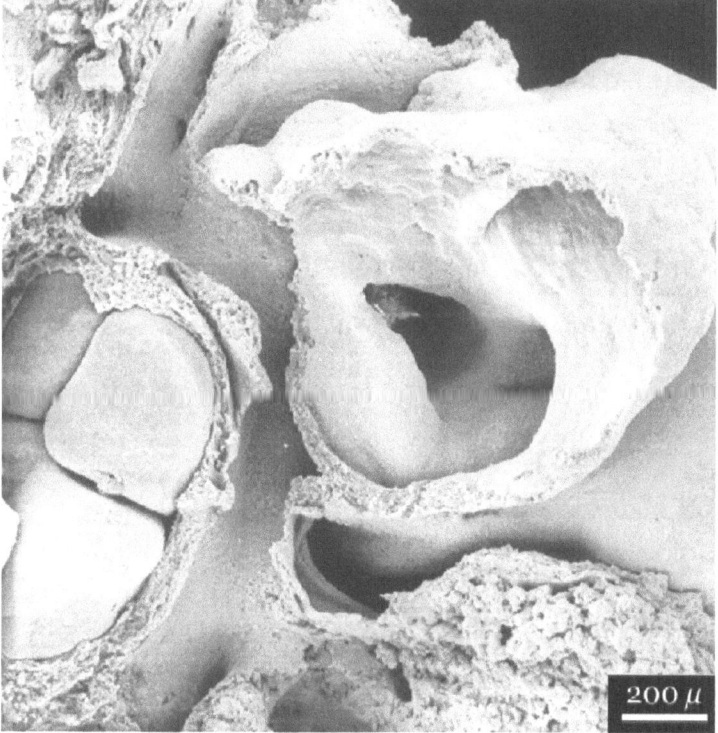

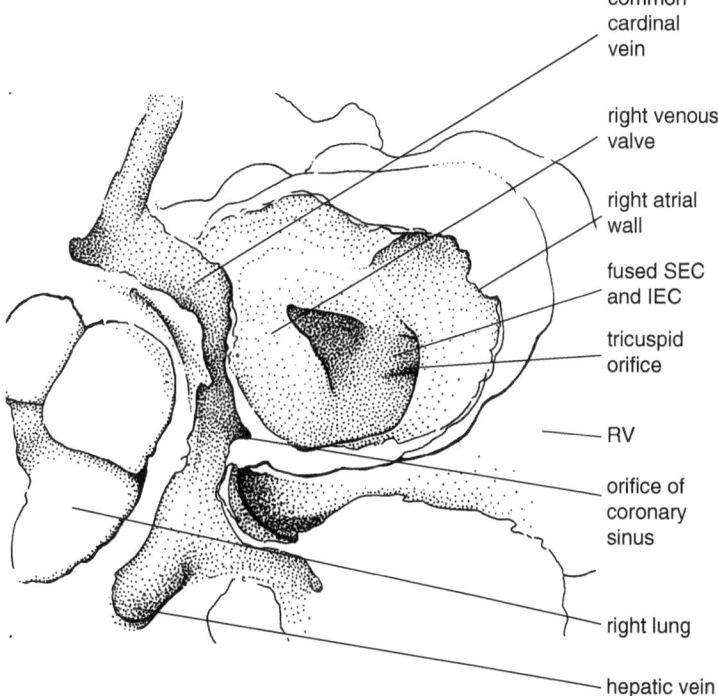

common
cardinal
vein

right venous
valve

right atrial
wall

fused SEC
and IEC

tricuspid
orifice

RV

orifice of
coronary
sinus

right lung

hepatic vein

FIGURE 3.21   Sinus venosus and RA (stage 17), right lateral view. The lateral wall is removed.

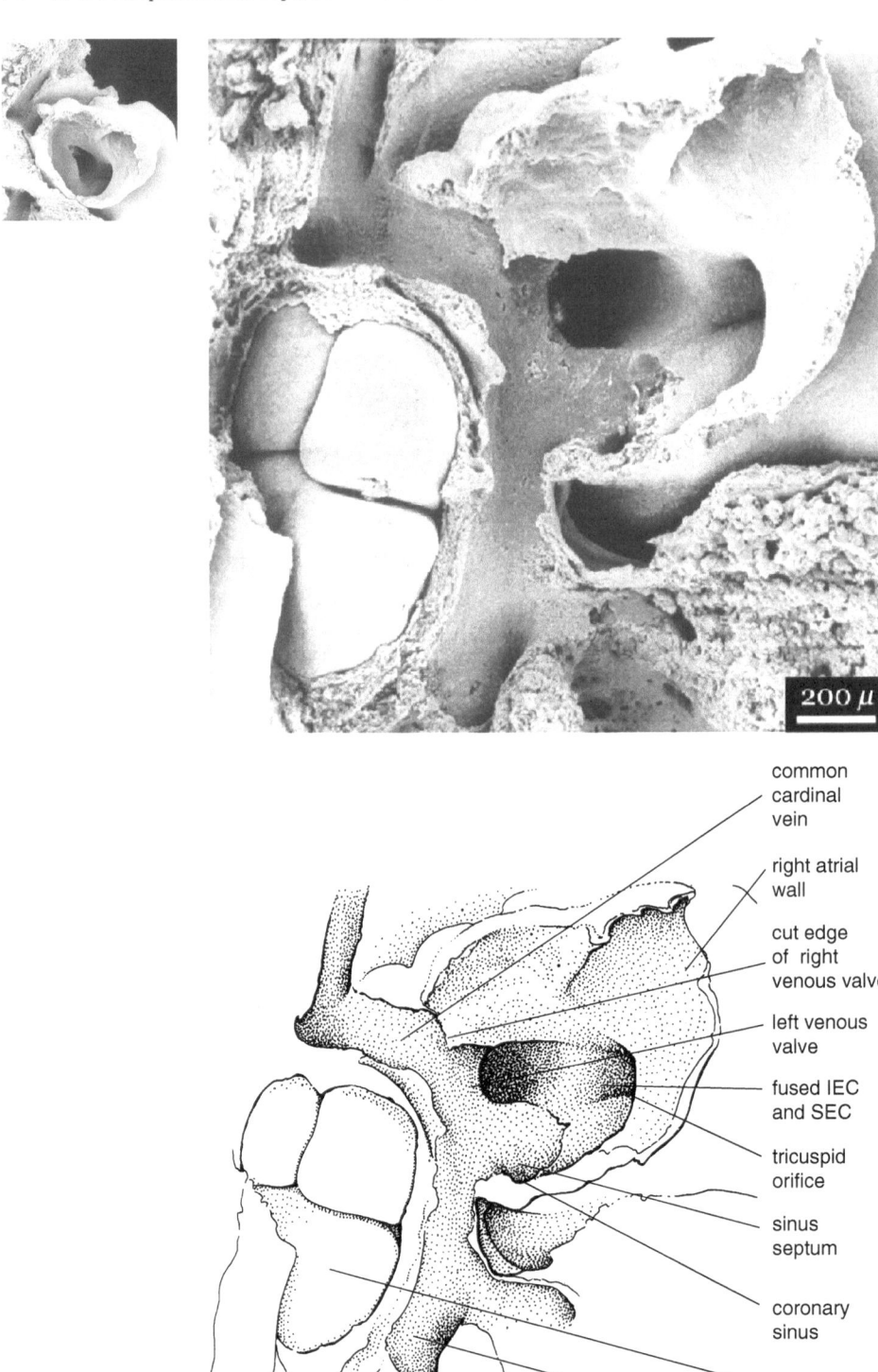

FIGURE 3.22   Sinus venosus and RA (stage 17), right lateral view. The lateral wall and right venous valve are removed.

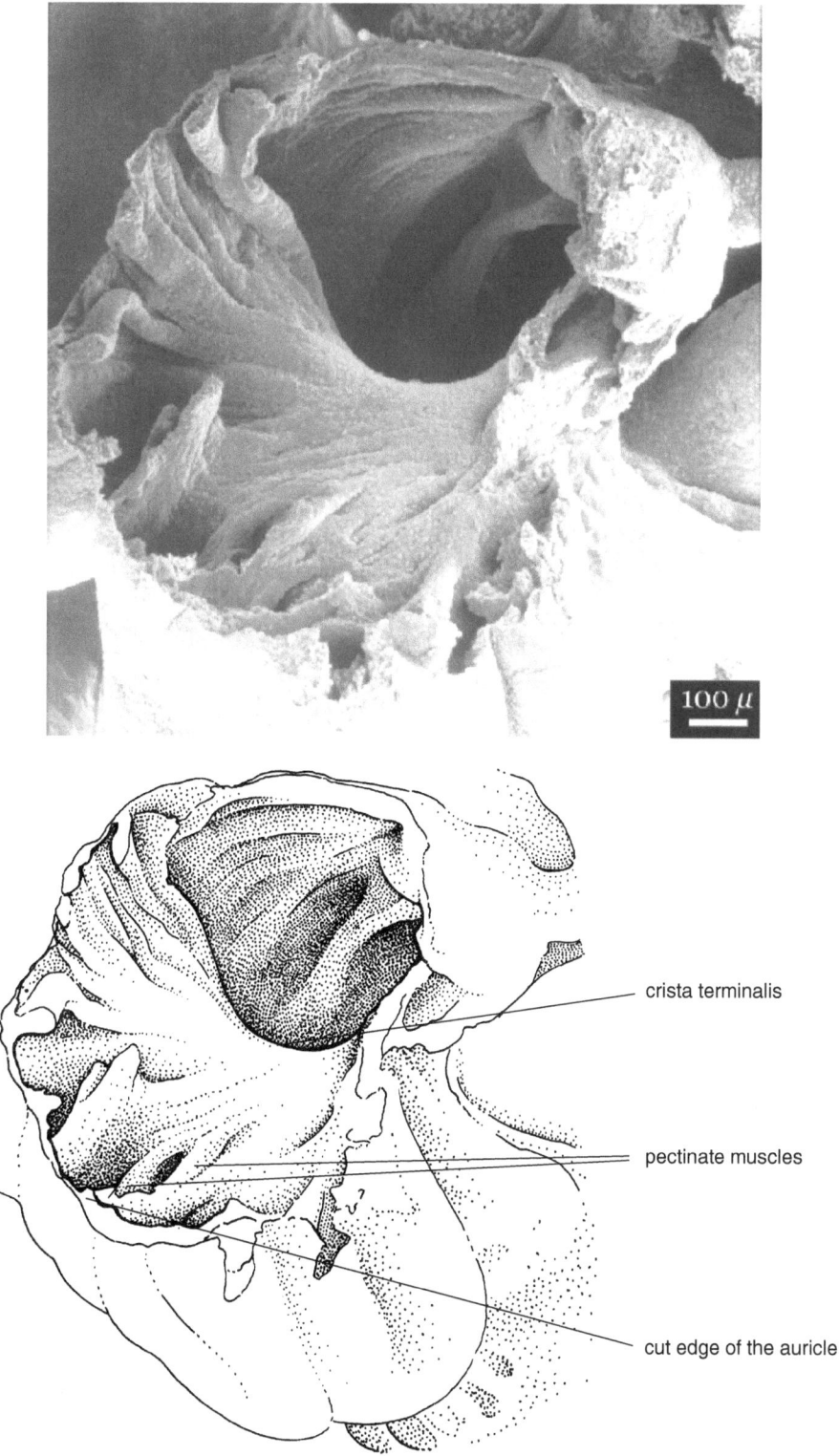

100 μ

crista terminalis

pectinate muscles

cut edge of the auricle

FIGURE 3.23   Opened right auricle (stage 17), right lateral view.

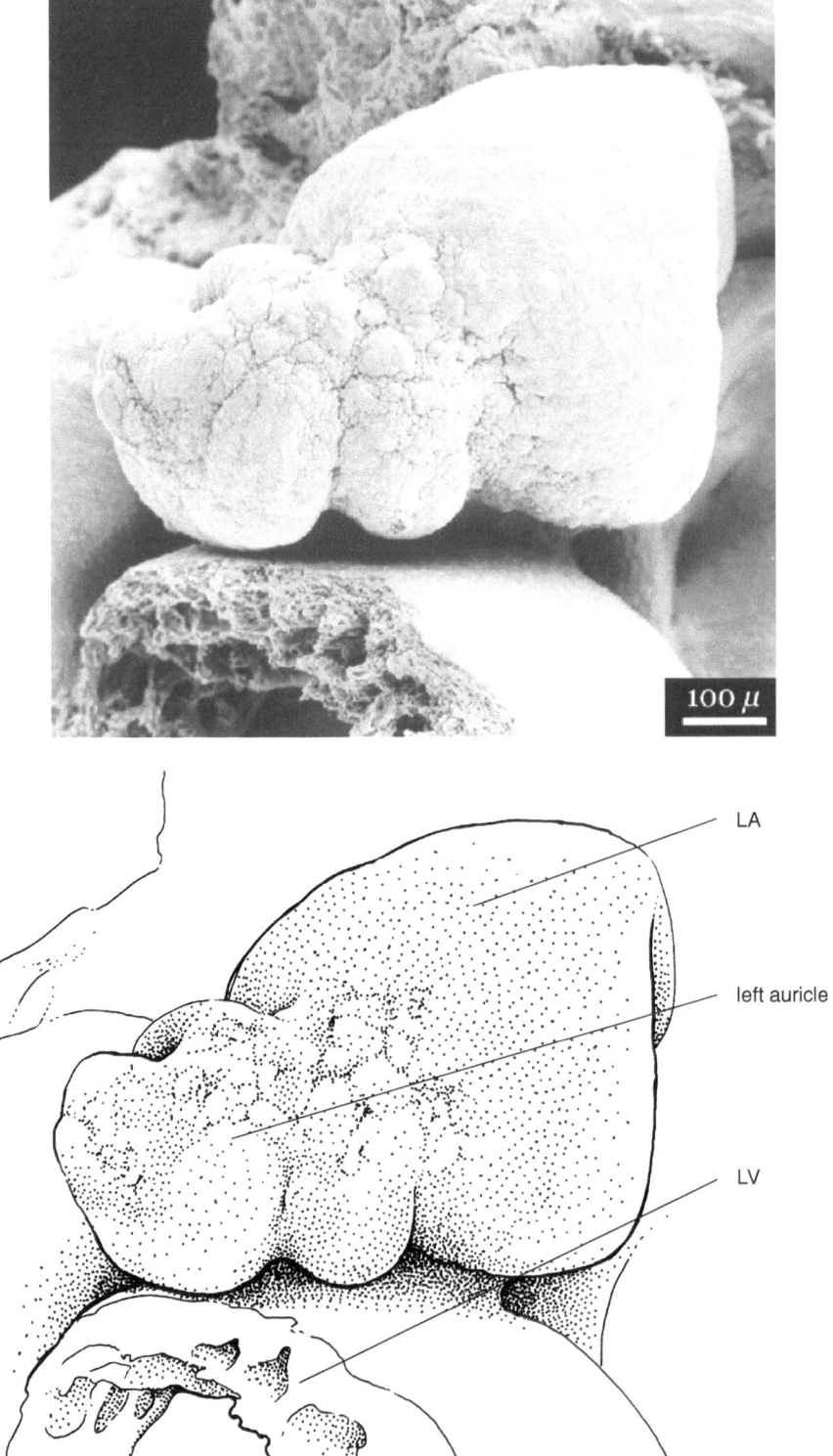

FIGURE 3.24   Left auricle (stage 17), left lateral view.

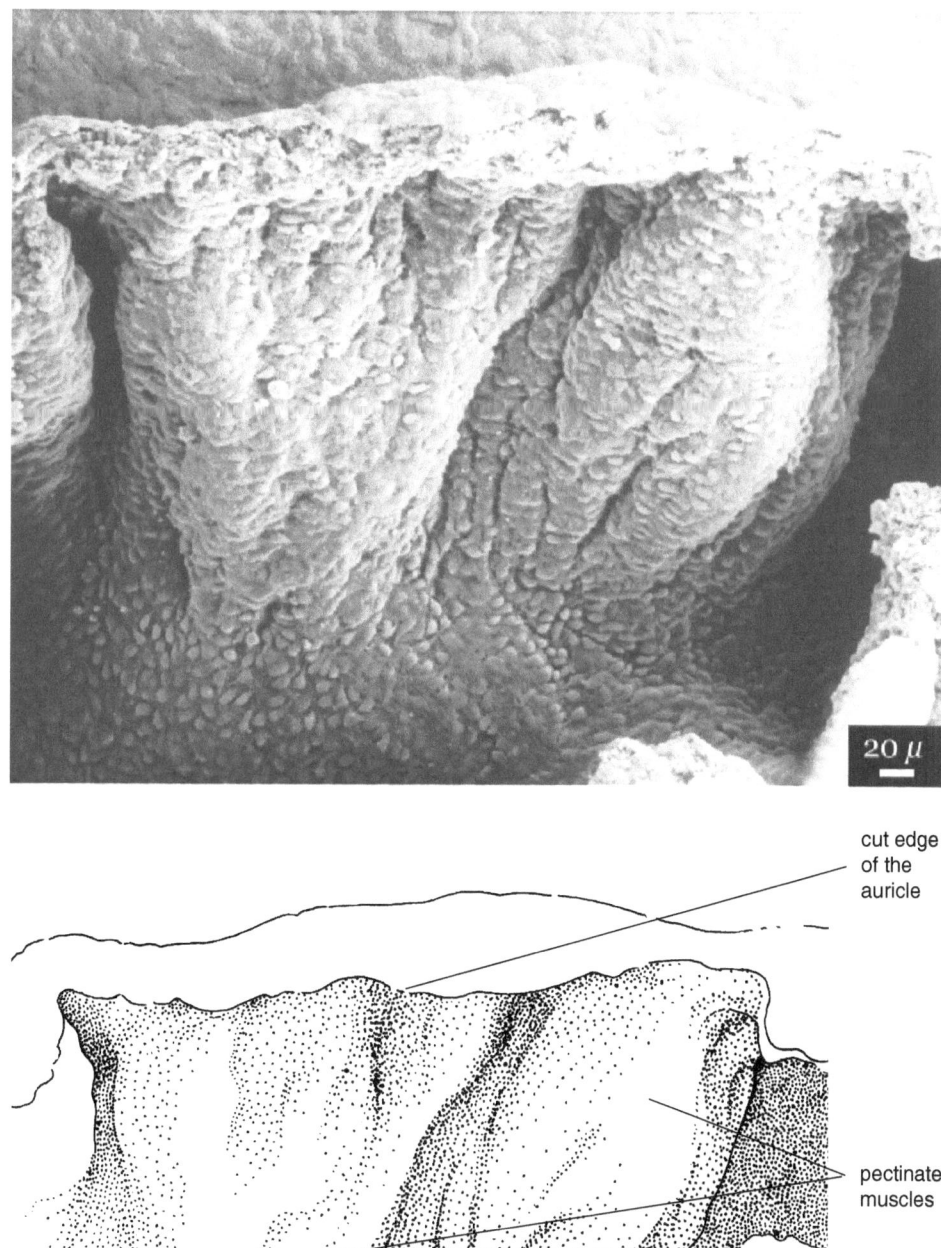

cut edge
of the
auricle

pectinate
muscles

FIGURE 3.25   Opened left auricle (stage 17), left lateral view.

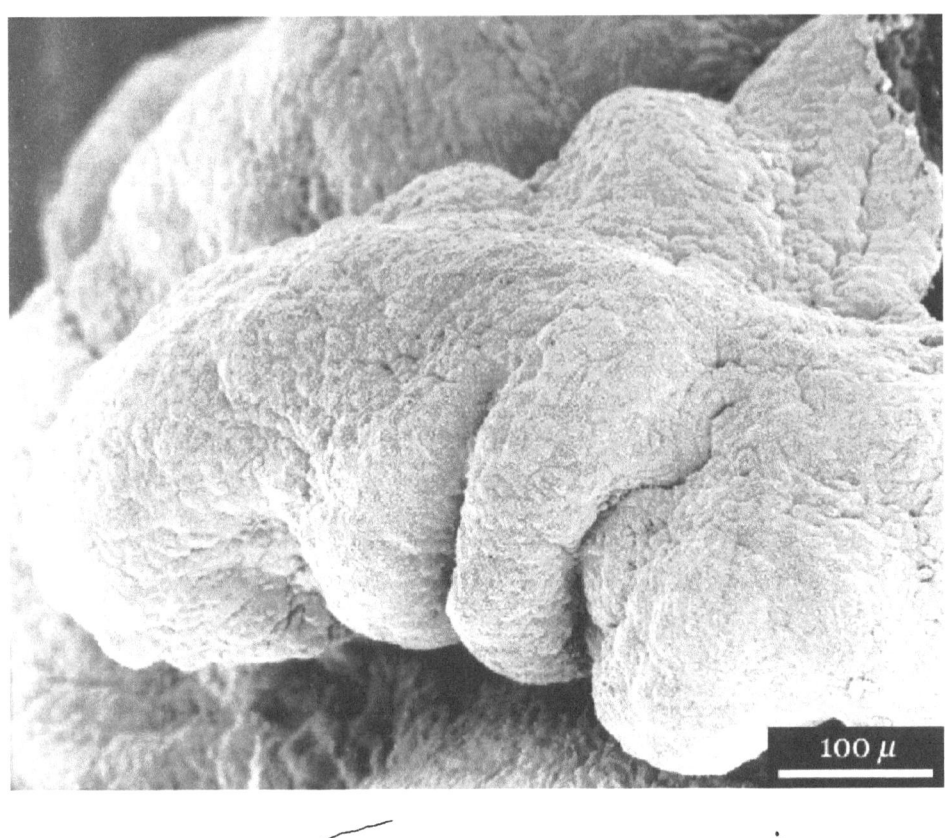

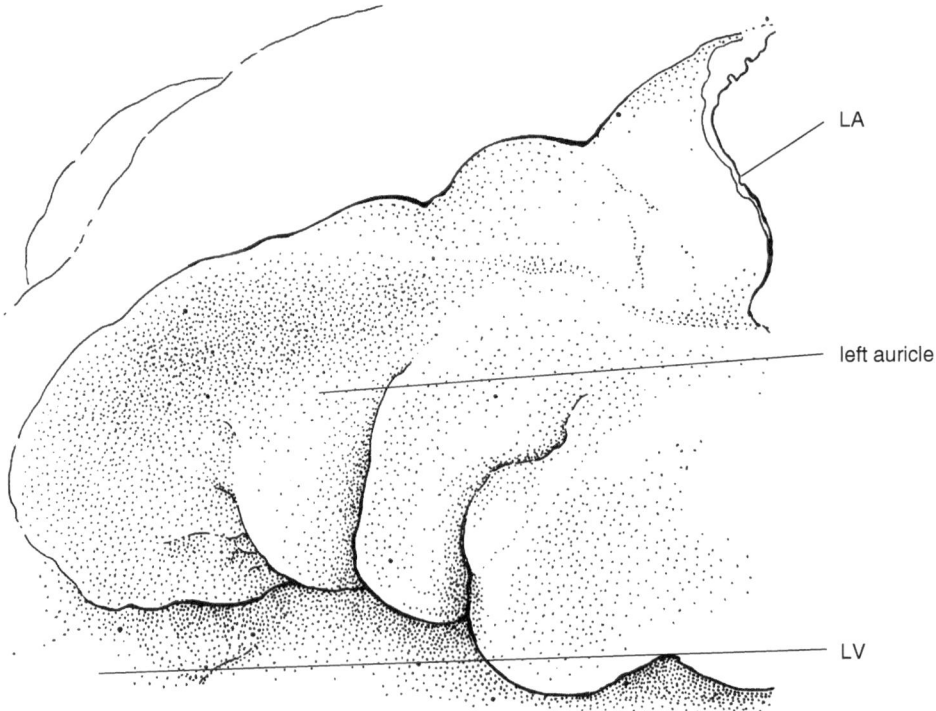

FIGURE 3.26   Left auricle (stage 18), left lateral view.

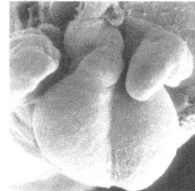

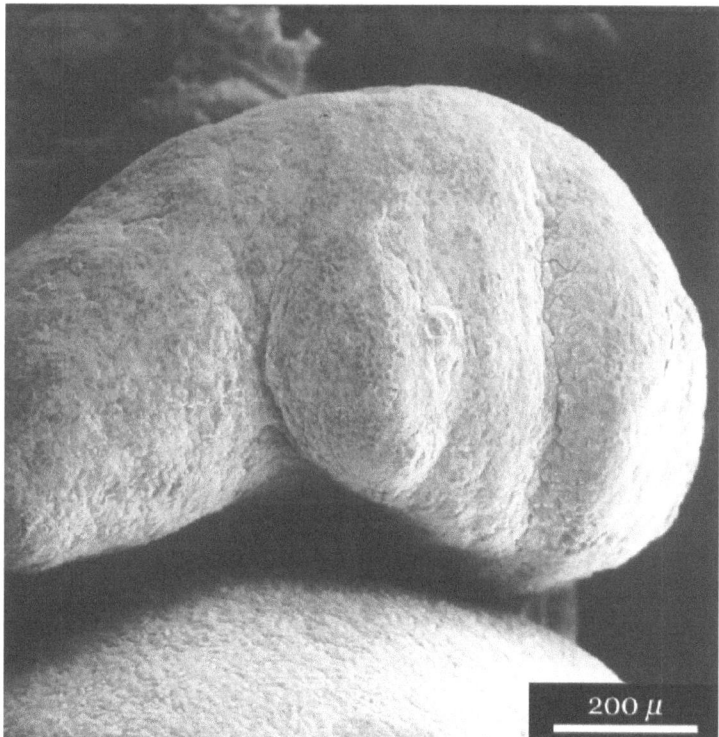

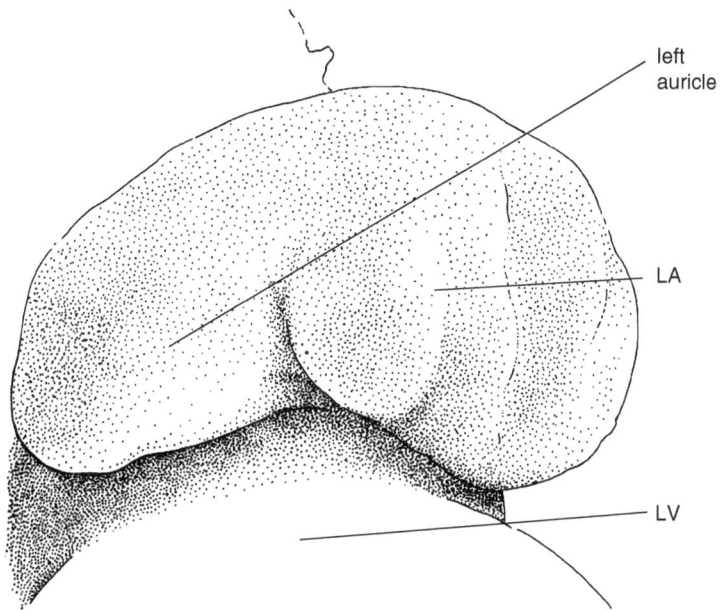

FIGURE 3.27   Left auricle (stage 19), ventral view.

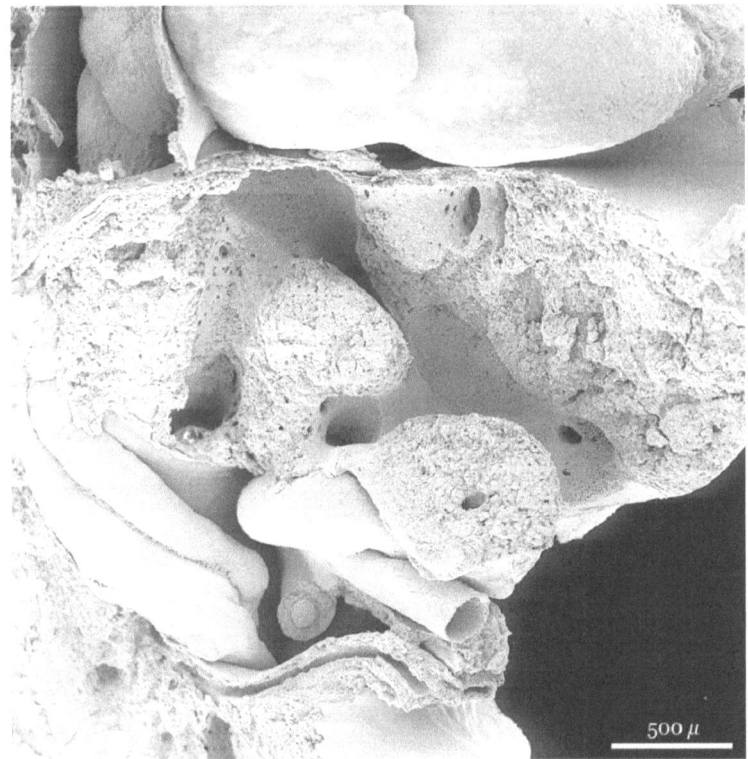

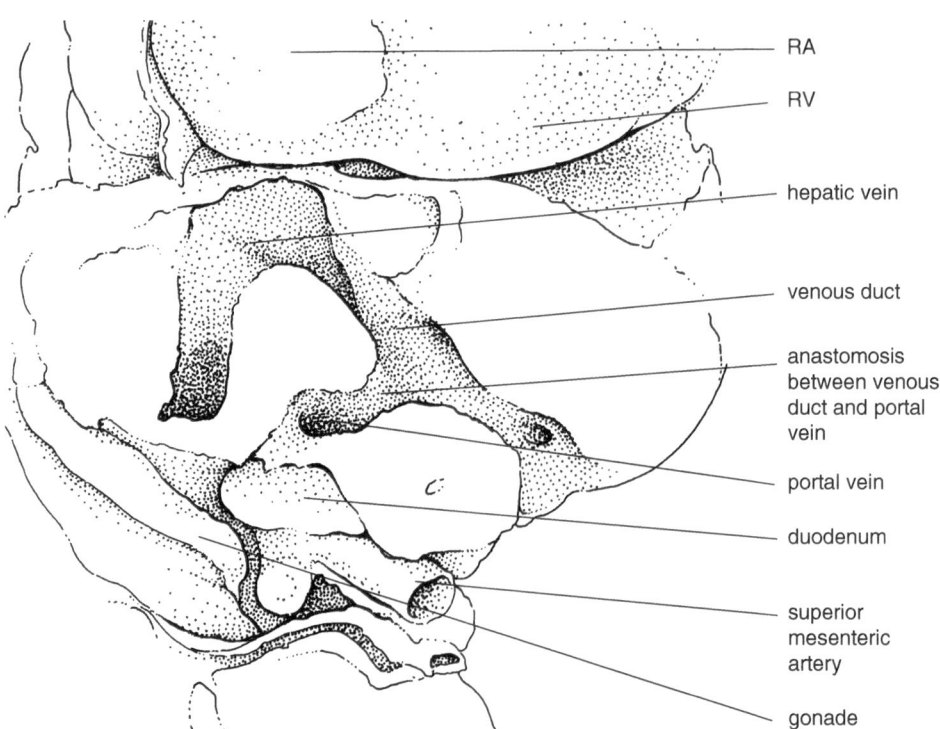

FIGURE 3.28   Dissected liver (stage 19), ventral view.

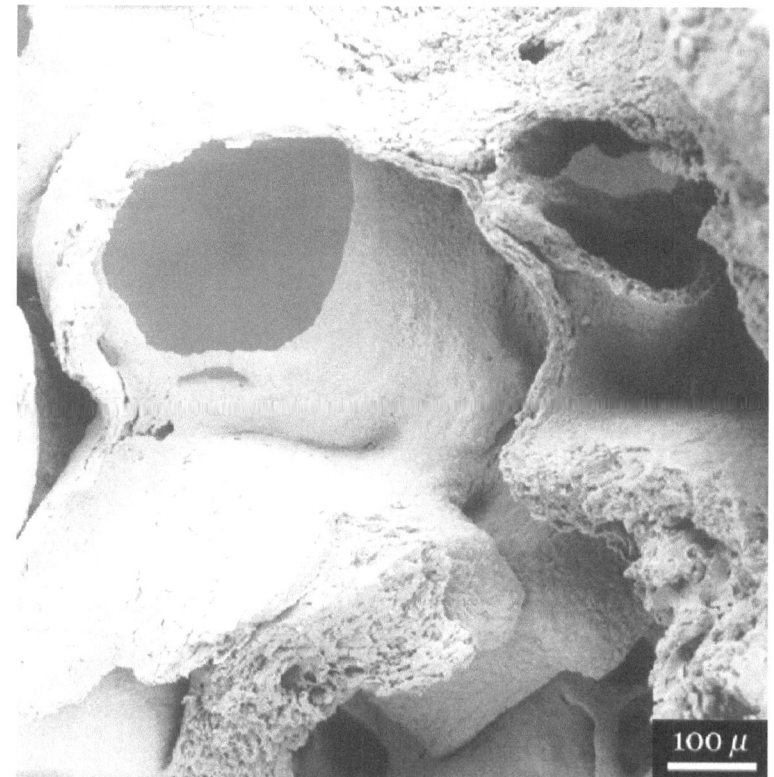

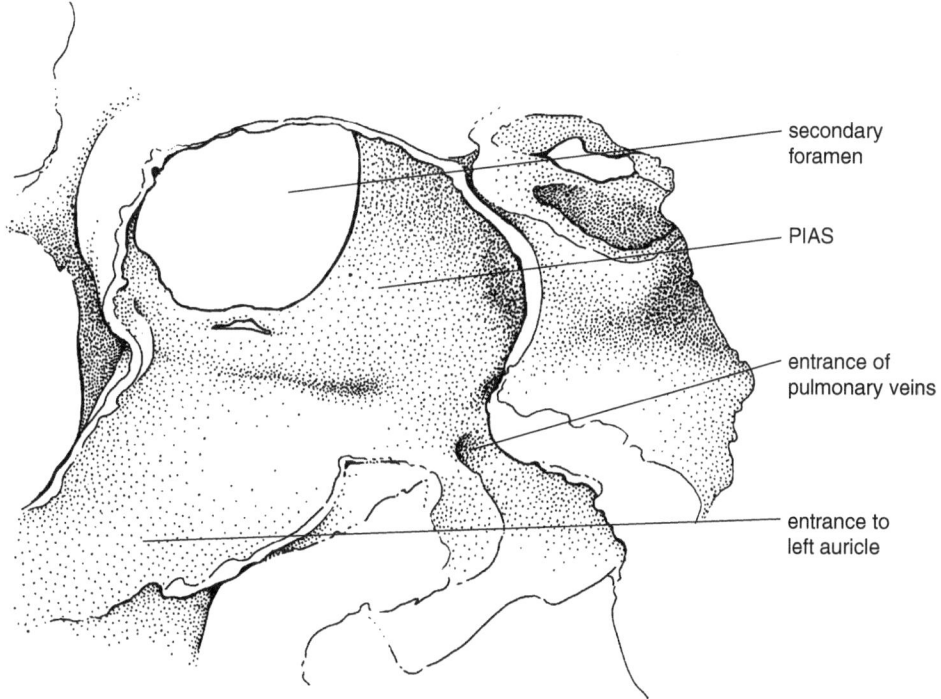

FIGURE 3.29   LA (stage 19), left lateral view. The lateral wall is removed.

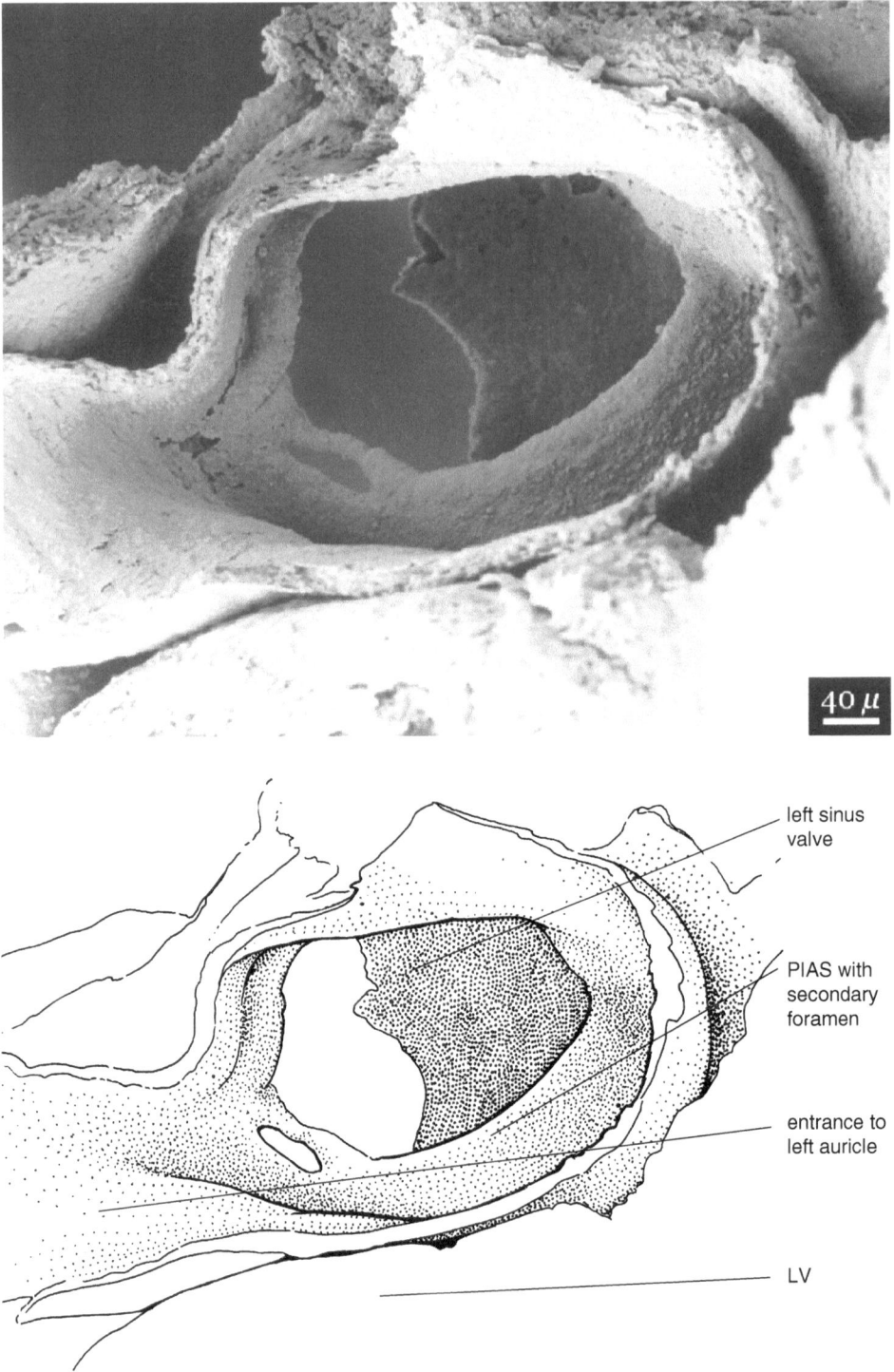

FIGURE 3.30   LA (stage 19), left lateral view. The lateral wall is removed.

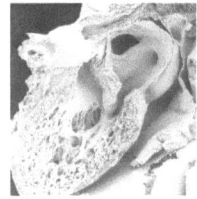

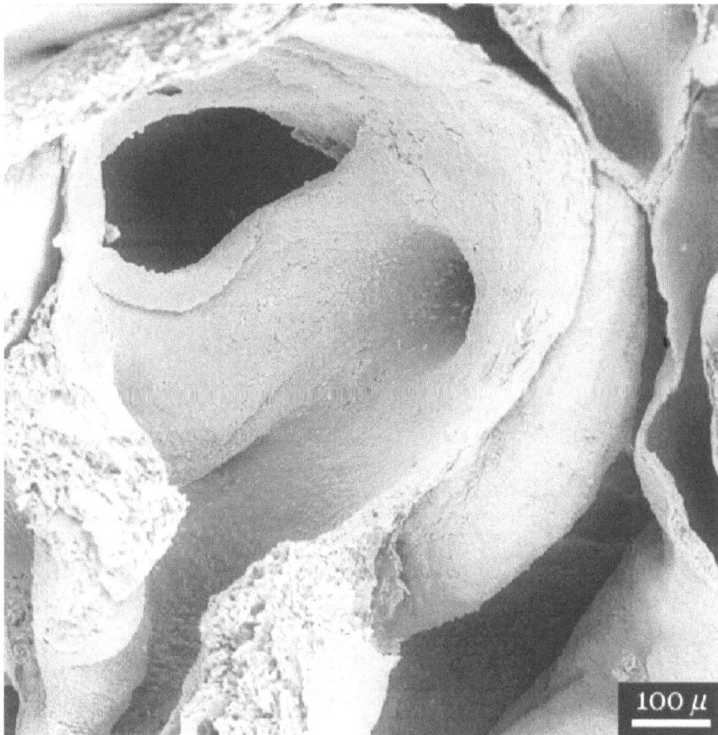

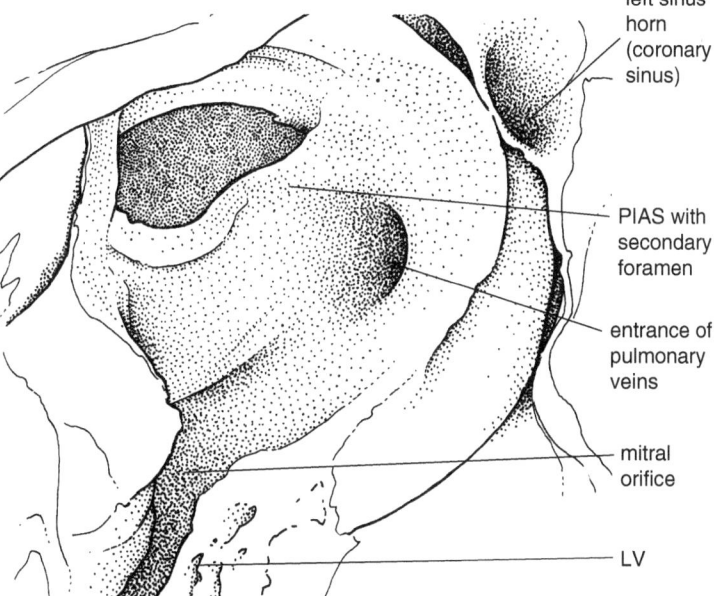

FIGURE 3.31   LA (stage 20), left lateral view. The lateral wall is removed.

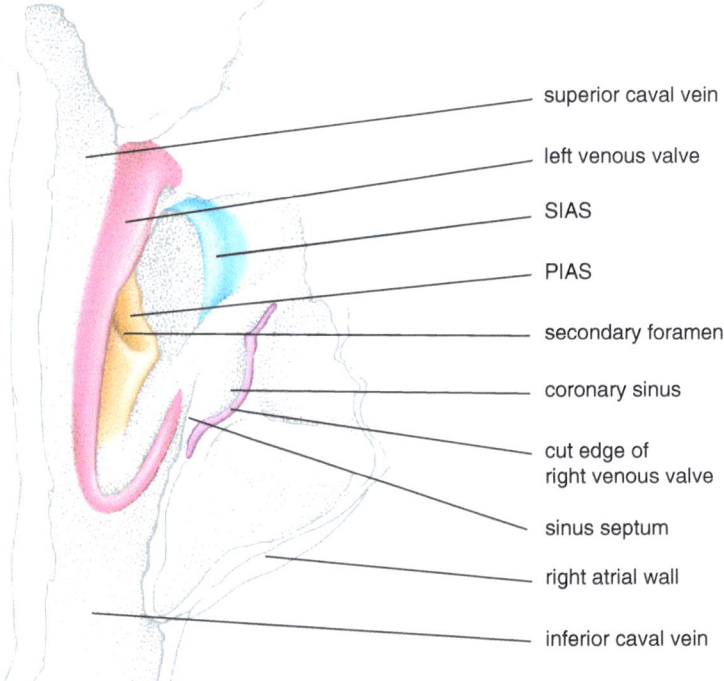

superior caval vein

left venous valve

SIAS

PIAS

secondary foramen

coronary sinus

cut edge of
right venous valve

sinus septum

right atrial wall

inferior caval vein

FIGURE 3.32   Sinus venosus and RA (stage 22), right lateral view. The lateral wall and right venous valve are removed. Colors indicate the primary interatrial septum (ochre), secondary interatrial septum (light blue), right venous valve (lilac), and left venous valve (pink).

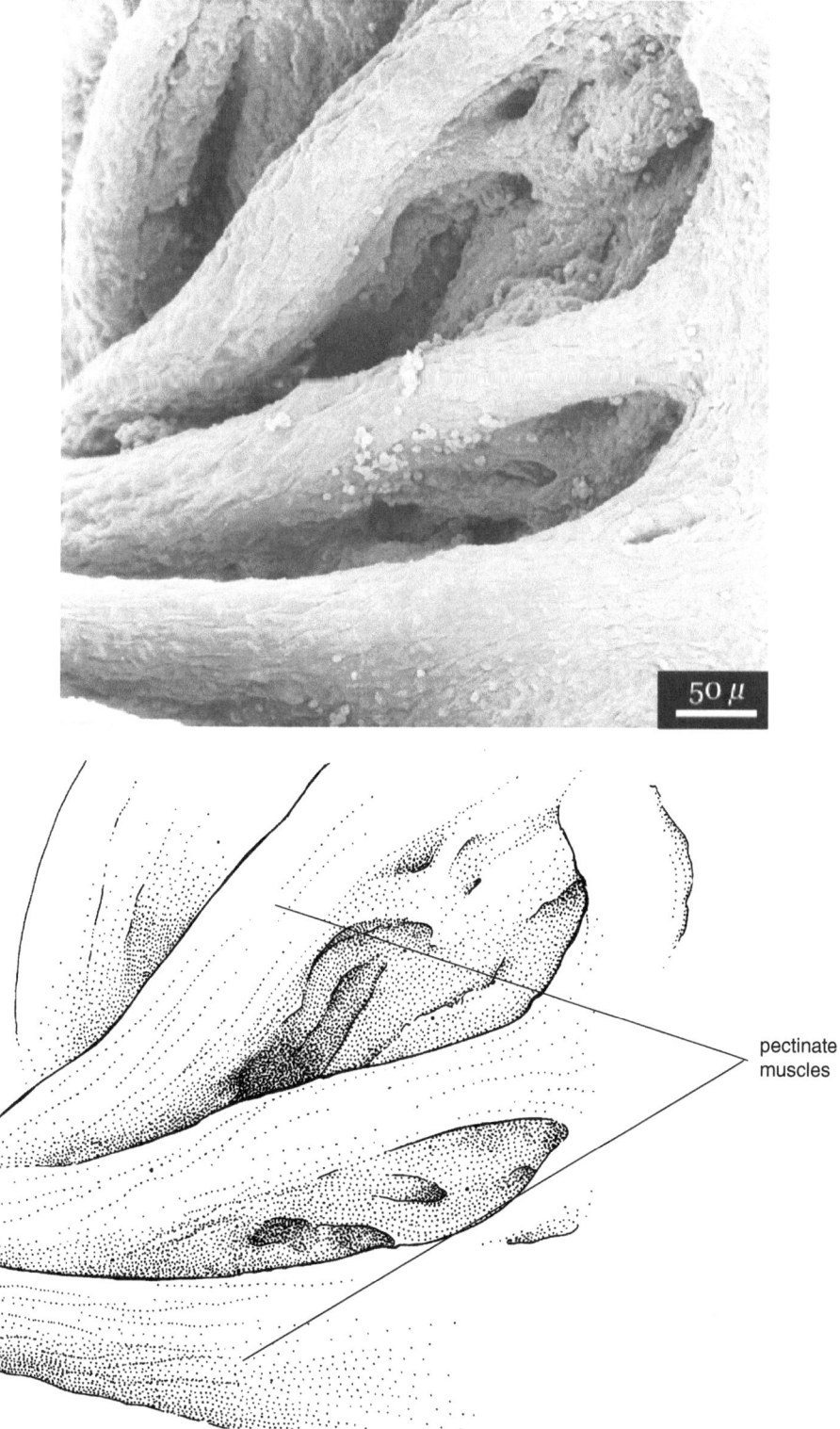

FIGURE 3.33   Opened left auricle (stage 23), left lateral view.

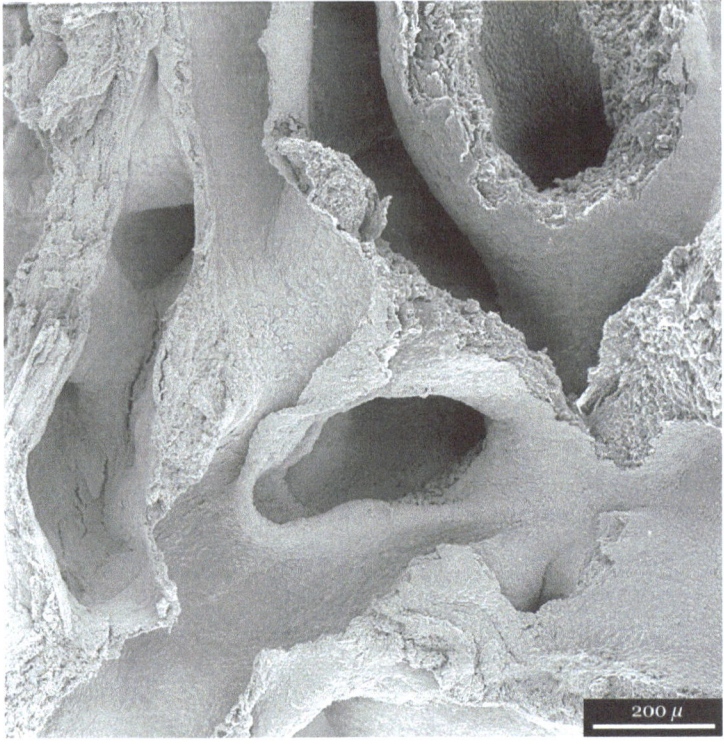

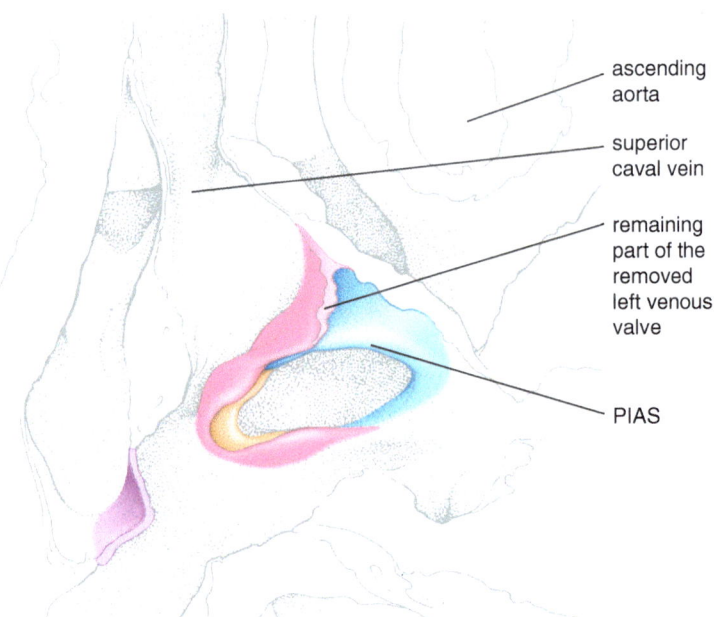

ascending
aorta

superior
caval vein

remaining
part of the
removed
left venous
valve

PIAS

FIGURE 3.34   Sinus venosus and RA (9 weeks), right lateral view. The lateral wall and right venous valve are removed. Colors indicate the primary interatrial septum (ochre), secondary interatrial septum (light blue), right venous valve (lilac), and left venous valve (pink).

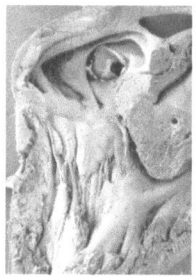

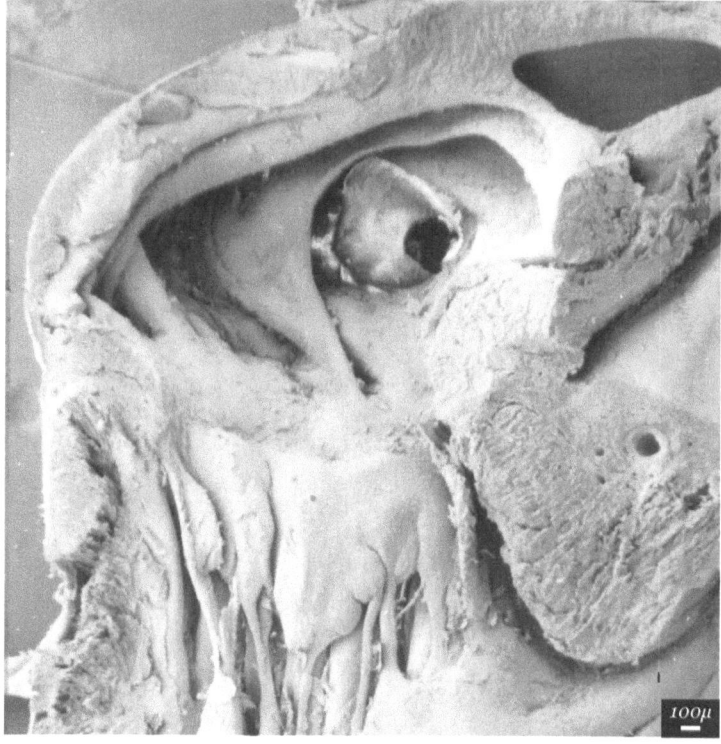

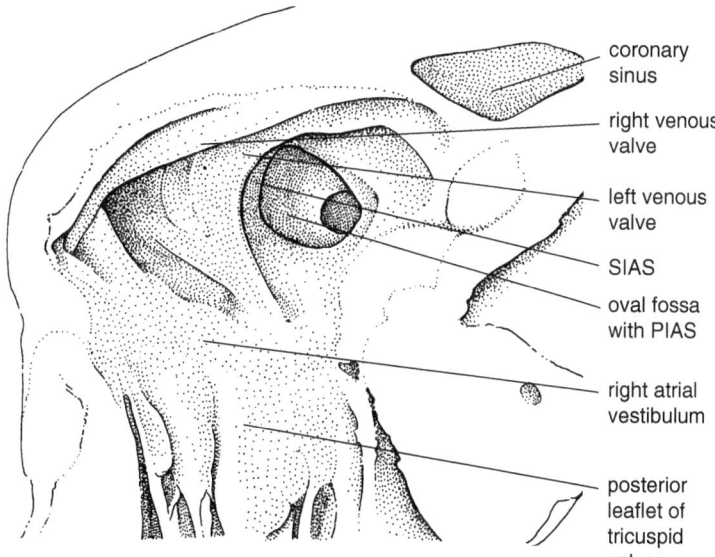

FIGURE 3.35   Sinus venosus and RA (12 weeks), right lateral view. The lateral wall is removed.

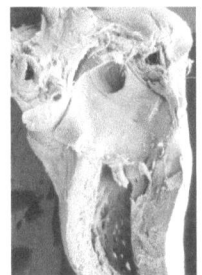

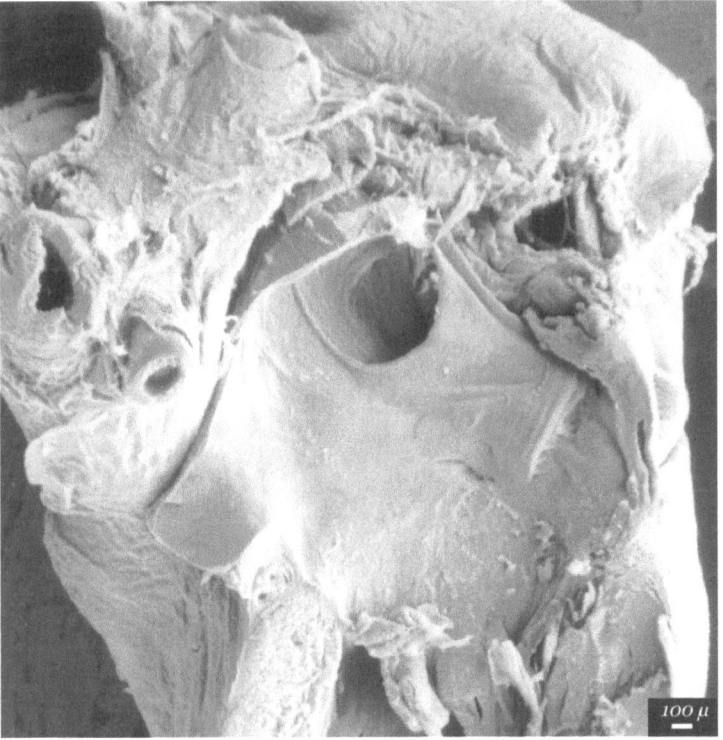

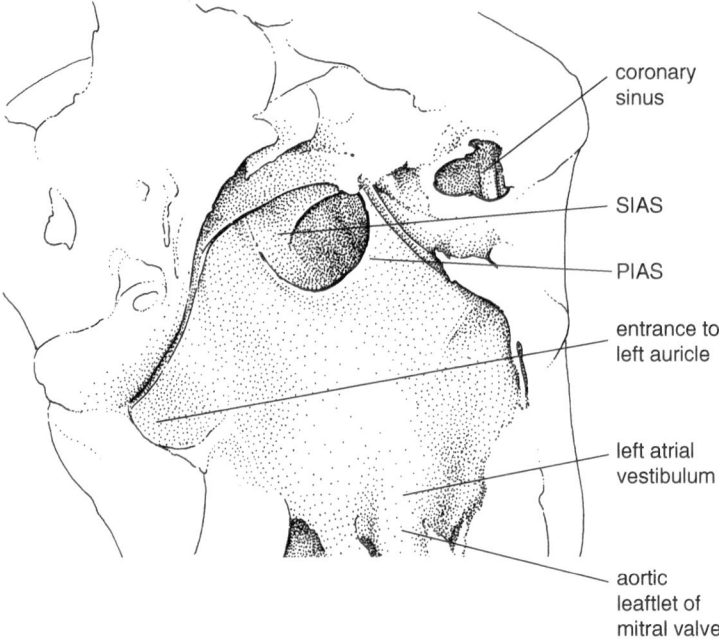

FIGURE 3.36   LA (12 weeks), left lateral view. The lateral wall is removed.

Development and septation of the ventricles and outflow tract

FUNCTIONING OF THE UNSEPTATED HEART

As mentioned in chapter 2, the ventricles balloon out from the greater curvature of the tubular heart at the end of the looping stage by means of expansive apical growth [Harh & Paul, 1975; Steding & Seidl, 1980; Lamers et al., 1992]. As will be discussed in the next chapter, this ballooning is accompanied by the formation of myocardial trabeculation. In between the ventricles a gradually elongating ridge is formed, which is dubbed the (muscular part of the) interventricular septum. Rather than being passively formed by expansion of the trabeculed ventricles, the interventricular septum is an initially fenestrated structure that is formed by aggregation and compaction of apically enlarging trabeculae, as has been demonstrated in chicken embryos [Harh & Paul, 1975]. It should be stressed again that the inner curvature is not involved in the ballooning process but instead retains its primordial tubular phenotype, as do the outer curvature parts of the interjacent segments, being the sinus venosus, the atrioventricular canal and the outflow tract. By now, the primitive heart is on the eve of intricate developmental events which will transform the single heart tube into a double circuited structure that selectively passes the blood from the systemic veins to the pulmonary arteries and the blood from the pulmonary veins to the aorta. To this end, two separate pathways must be formed, which demands that the atria and ventricles will be connected to the proper up- and downstream segments.

From a historical perspective, the region downstream of the atria is divided into four consecutive segments, being the atrioventricular canal, the left ventricle, the right ventricle and the outflow tract, which are considered to be serially connected, meaning that blood from the atria would run through these segments in succession. However, as cardiac development proceeds, this model would run into major conceptual problems with respect to the formation of a right ventricular inlet and a left ventricular outlet. The key issue in dealing with this problem is to understand the nature of the structure that is erroneously named the primary interventricular foramen. Firstly, since the ballooning of the ventricles occurs at the outer curvature and the outermost border of the primary interventricular foramen is the free edge of the interventricular septum, the primary interventricular foramen itself is not positioned interventricularly. Instead, it represents a cross section through the heart tube, bordered ventro-caudally by the interventricular septum and dorso-cranially by a part of the inner curvature of the heart tube known as crista prima [Steding & Seidl, 1980] or bulbo-ventricular flange. Interestingly, the ring of myocardial tissue that surrounds the primary interventricular foramen is a distinguishable structure since it specifically expresses a neuronal marker named GlN2 [Wessels et al., 1992]. This structure is dubbed the primary interventricular ring and in later stages of development it is partly transformed into the atrioventricular part of the cardiac conduction system. This immunohistochemical property makes it possible to persue the structural changes of the primary interventricular ring as development proceeds. Secondly, the name primary interventricular foramen may suggest that blood will pass through this segment from one ventricle to the other, which never happens during normal cardiac development (in contrast to what has been postulated in the past). Instead, blood coming from the atrioventricular canal during the relaxation period of the ventricles (the diastole) directly enters not only the left ventricle but, through the primary interventricular foramen, also the right ventricle. During ventricular contraction (the systole), the outflow tract is filled with blood directly coming not only from the right ventricle but, again by passing the primary interventricular foramen, also from the left ventricle. Thus, during the cardiac cycle, the primary interventricular foramen functions alternately as right ventricular inlet and left ventricular outlet. By relative growth, the atrioventricular outlet and outflow tract inlet will become enlarged in such a way that blood flow to and from the ventricles is facilitated. It is generally assumed that the atrioventricular outlet shifts relatively to the right and the outflow tract inlet shifts relatively to the left. However, once looping of the heart tube is completed both the atrioventricular outlet and the outflow tract inlet retain their initial position throughout development. As a result, both apertures straddle the interventricular foramen only marginally, as can be seen in the pictures. Because of the relative enlargements of the atrioventricular outlet and outflow tract inlet, the primary interventricular ring, initially ring-shaped, becomes distorted and obtains the shape of a cracknel. The upper dorsal quadrant of the ring "moves" to the right, together with the right part of the atrioventricular outlet (the future tricuspid orifice), while the upper ventral quadrant, together with the left part of the outflow tract inlet (the future subaortic infundibulum) "moves" to the left. The remainder of the primary interventricular ring retains its position on the top of the interventricular septum, where it surrounds a part of the primary interventricular foramen that is not involved in the passage of blood streams. It is this part of the primary interventricular foramen that eventually obliterates during the final stages of septation (see next paragraph). Part of the myocardium of the primary interventricular ring transdifferentiates into the atrioventricular conduction system.

SEPTATION OF THE ATRIOVENTRICULAR CANAL AND DEVELOPMENT OF THE ATRIOVENTRICULAR VALVES

In accordance with the peristaltic blood propulsion through the primitive tubular heart, the atrioventricular canal initially has an O-shaped lumen with regular deposition of cardiac jelly. However, with the development of the synchronously contracting myocardium of both the atrial and the ventricular compartments, the atrioventricular canal will assume the function of a sphincter, which means that the lumen must be closed off periodically to prevent regurgitation. To this end two cushion-like proliferations of cardiac jelly appear (see Chapter 5). These cushions are usually dubbed inferior and superior endocardial cushions. Smaller cardiac jelly proliferations appear on both sides of the atrioventricular canal, which form the right and left lateral endocardial cushions. As a consequence the lumen becomes slit-like and eventually H-shaped, which facilitates the haemodynamics of separate left and right blood flows. Since not only the atria and ventricles but also the primary heart tube itself becomes septated, the inferior and superior endocardial cushions grow towards each other and fuse to form a septum, thus creating two separate lumens. The moment of fusion shows remarkable inter-individual variability and may occur between stage 16 and stage 19. Owing to the plane in which the septum is created, one of the lumens is positioned along the inner curvature and the other one is positioned along the outer curvature. The former will become the right atrioventricular (tricuspid) orifice, the latter will become the left atrioventricular (mitral) orifice.

Apart from their involvement in ventricular septation, the endocardial cushions of the atrioventricular canal play an important role in the formation of the leaflets of the atrioventricular valves. From stage 18 onward, the cushions, which cover the basal side of the interventricular septum and the lateral ventricular walls, start to elongate in the direction of the ventricles [Oosthoek et al., 1998]. At the same time, a process called delamination or undermining commences in the ventricular myocardium that is covered by the cushions and proceeds in apical direction [Van Mierop, 1962]. As a result, confluent spaces underneath the cushions appear and freely moving leaflets are formed that remain apically connected to the developing papillary muscles. Initially, these leaflets consist of cushion tissue at their atrial aspect and myocardium at their ventricular aspect [Lamers et al., 1995; Wessels et al., 1996; Oosthoek et al., 1998]. Immunohistochemistry showed that, in contrast to what has been assumed in the past [Van Gils, 1981; Wenink et al., 1986], the forming leaflets receive no contribution from extracardiac mesenchyme of the atrioventricular sulcus [Lamers et al., 1995; Wessels et al., 1996]. In this way, the septal leaflets of the tricuspid and mitral valves are formed largely from the superior and inferior endocardial cushions, whereas the mural leaflets of both valves form from their corresponding lateral endocardial cushions (Figures 4 A–F). The effects of delamination are most pronounced at the mural side of the tricuspid valve. Here the process is accompanied by expansion of the lateral ventricular wall, thus yielding a considerable addition to the right ventricular capacity [De Lange et al., 2004]. The morphogenesis of the central part of the septal leaflet of the mitral valve (i.e. the aortic leaflet) is different in that it is not to covered by myocardium at any time in development [Oosthoek et al., 1998]. At the end of the embryonic period the myocardial layer of the developing leaflets starts to become patchy and eventually disappears completely by the end of the fourteenth week of gestation, leaving both the leaflets and the cords which connect them to the papillary muscles to become entirely fibrous [Lamers et al., 1995; Oosthoek et al., 1998; De Lange et al., 2004].

DEVELOPMENT OF THE OUTFLOW TRACT AND COMPLETION OF SEPTATION

The outflow tract of the embryonic heart is the anterior most part of the primary heart tube, which connects the ventricular region with the aortic sac and its derivatives. However, labelling studies in pre-looped chicken hearts have shown that cells in the anterior part of the heart tube end up in the myocardium of the right ventricle [De la Cruz et al., 1977]. Apparently, the outflow tract is not yet formed in the earliest stages of cardiac development but in stead is added on later [Kelly et al., 2001; Waldo et al., 2001]. Based on the results of animal studies, this process is expected to continue to about stage 13 in human embryos [reviewed by Webb et al., 2003]. During this stage a bend becomes visible in the curved and gradually elongating outflow tract. This bend, which marks the transition between the proximal and distal parts of the outflow tract, is the site where the semilunar valves of the aorta and pulmonary trunk will develop [Steding & Seidl, 1980; Ya et al., 1998; Qayyum et al., 2001; Webb et al., 2003]. Two sets of ridge-shaped cardiac jelly pro-liferations, that have a spiral course, appear in the outflow tract, although the ends of the proximal proliferations run deep into adjacent compartments. These are the superior and inferior endocardial ridges in the distal part of the outflow tract and the parietal (right) and septal (left) endocardial ridges in the proximal part. The superior and inferior ridges in the distal part of the outflow tract fuse with one another in distal to proximal direction. After this septation has been completed, the resulting separate left and right ventricular outflows become the intrapericardial parts of the aorta and pulmonary trunk respectively. The twisting of the pulmonary trunk around the ascending aorta is not caused by an active rotational process, as has been proposed in the past, but merely reflects the initial spiraling course of the outflow tract ridges [Steding & Seidl, 1980; reviewed by Webb et al., 2003]. At the distal end of the outflow tract, the superior and inferior ridges fuse with the ventral and dorsal limbs of the aorticopulmonary septum respectively. This septum, which is supposedly formed by in growth of neural crest derived cells [Waldo et al., 1998], separates the systemic parts of the aortic sac and pharyngeal arch arter-ies form the pulmonary parts. Proximally, the ridges in the distal outflow tract connect with the parietal (right) and septal (left) endocardial ridges in the proxi-mal part, which also fuse with one another in distal to proximal direction. At this level, i.e. the transition between the proximal and distal parts of the outflow tract, the endocardial ridges will form the facing leaflets and sinuses of the aortic and pulmonary semi-lunar valves. Whether these are contributed by the ridges of the distal part of the outflow tract or the proximal part remains a matter of debate. Some investigators consider the proximal and distal ridges to be continuous struc-tures. The non-facing leaflets and sinuses of the semi-lunar valves are derived from two additional endocardial ridges situated in the proximal end of the distal outflow tract: the intercalated ridges (Figure 4 E). The fused parietal and septal ridges in the proximal outflow tract separate an inner curvature lumen, which will become the aortic infundibulum, from the outer curvature lumen, which will become the pulmonary infundibulum. Initially, the whole outflow tract has myocardial walls but from stage 15 onward the myocardium disappears by an as yet unknown mecha-nism, leaving only non-myocardial mesenchymal cells. The border between these two tissues progresses in ventricular direction and by the end of stage 22 only two collars of myocardium remain which encircle the pulmonary and aortic infundibu-lums at the level of the semilunar valves. After septation has completed the non-myocardial portions of the outflow tract will become the intrapericardial parts of the aorta and pulmonary trunk. Eventually, the myocardial component of the aorta disappears completely, whereas the valves of the pulmonary trunk remain sup-ported by a freestanding muscular infundibulum [Thompson et al., 1985].

Septation of the ventricular region comes down to creating an anatomical sepa-ration between the two blood streams that cross at the level of the primary inter-ventricular foramen without shutting off either one of them. If the three septa involved, being the atrioventricular septum, the interventricular septum and the proximal outflow tract septum, would simply grow together, as often depicted in embryological text books, the right ventricle would have no inlet and the left ven-tricle would not have an outlet. To prevent this from happening, only the inferior endocardial cushion and the septal ridge in the proximal outflow tract merge with the interventricular septum. Actually the inferior endocardial cushion grows from the dorsal end of the interventricular septum, over the septum itself to meet, at its ventral end, the septal outflow tract ridge. The superior endocardial cushion only marginally merges with the interventricular septum, thus maintaining a left ventricular outlet. The parietal outflow tract ridge will not reach the interventricular septum. Finally a more or less triangular-shaped opening remains, bordered by the inferior endocardial cushion and both proximal outflow tract ridges (Figures 4 A, B). Theoretically, this opening is a communication between the right ventricular inlet and the left ventricular outlet. With the closure of this opening, which is probably for the main part caused by an outgrowth of the septal outflow tract ridge, cardiac septation is completed. In the mature heart this obliteration can be recognized as the membranous interventricular and atrioventricular septum. The fused ridges in the proximal outflow tract become muscularized [Lamers et al., 1995; Van den Hoff et al., 1999, 2004] and are later to be recognized as the dorsal part of the pulmonary infundibulum and the supraventricular crest.

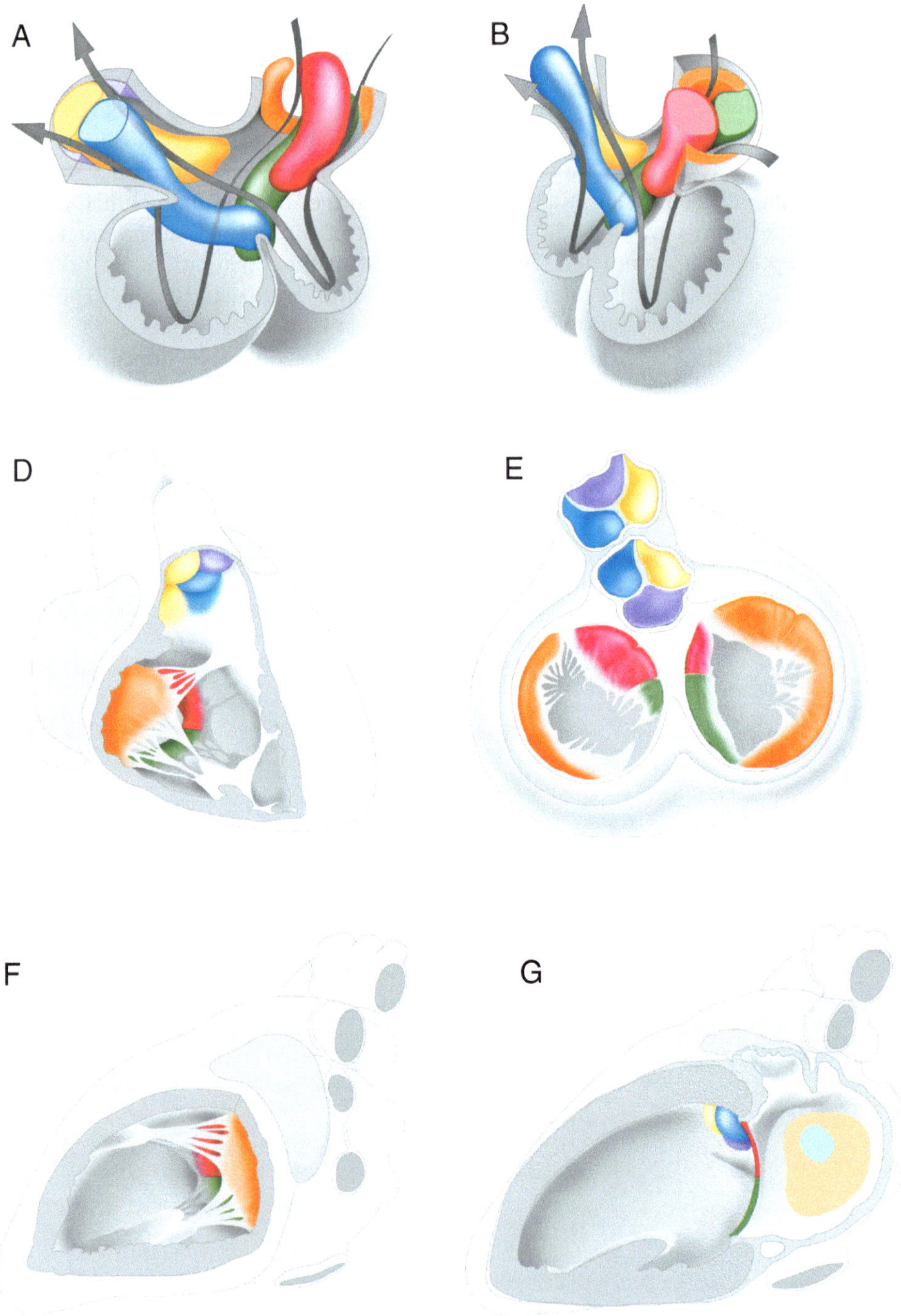

A

B

D

E

F

G

FIGURES 4 A–G   Structures involved in the development and septation of the atrioventricular region and outflow tract, including the superior endocardial cushion (red), inferior endocardial cushion (dark green), right and left lateral endocardial cushions (orange), parietal and superior endocardial ridges (yellow), septal and inferior endocardial ridges (dark blue), and intercalated endocardial ridges (purple). Arrows indicate left and right ventricular inflow and outflow patterns.

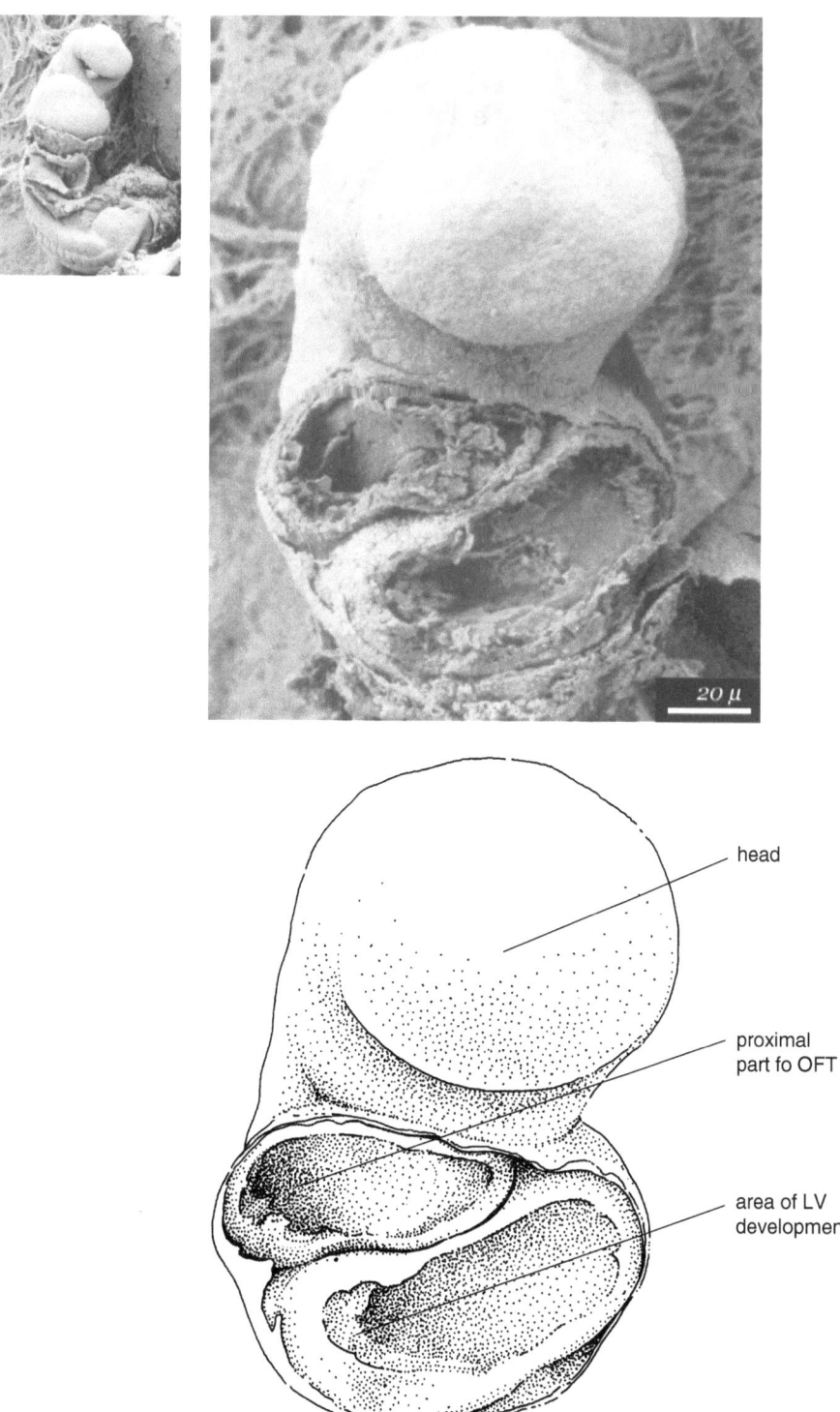

FIGURE 4.1   Complete embryo in situ (stage 11), ventral view. The yolk sac and the amnion are removed. The heart is sectioned in a frontal plane.

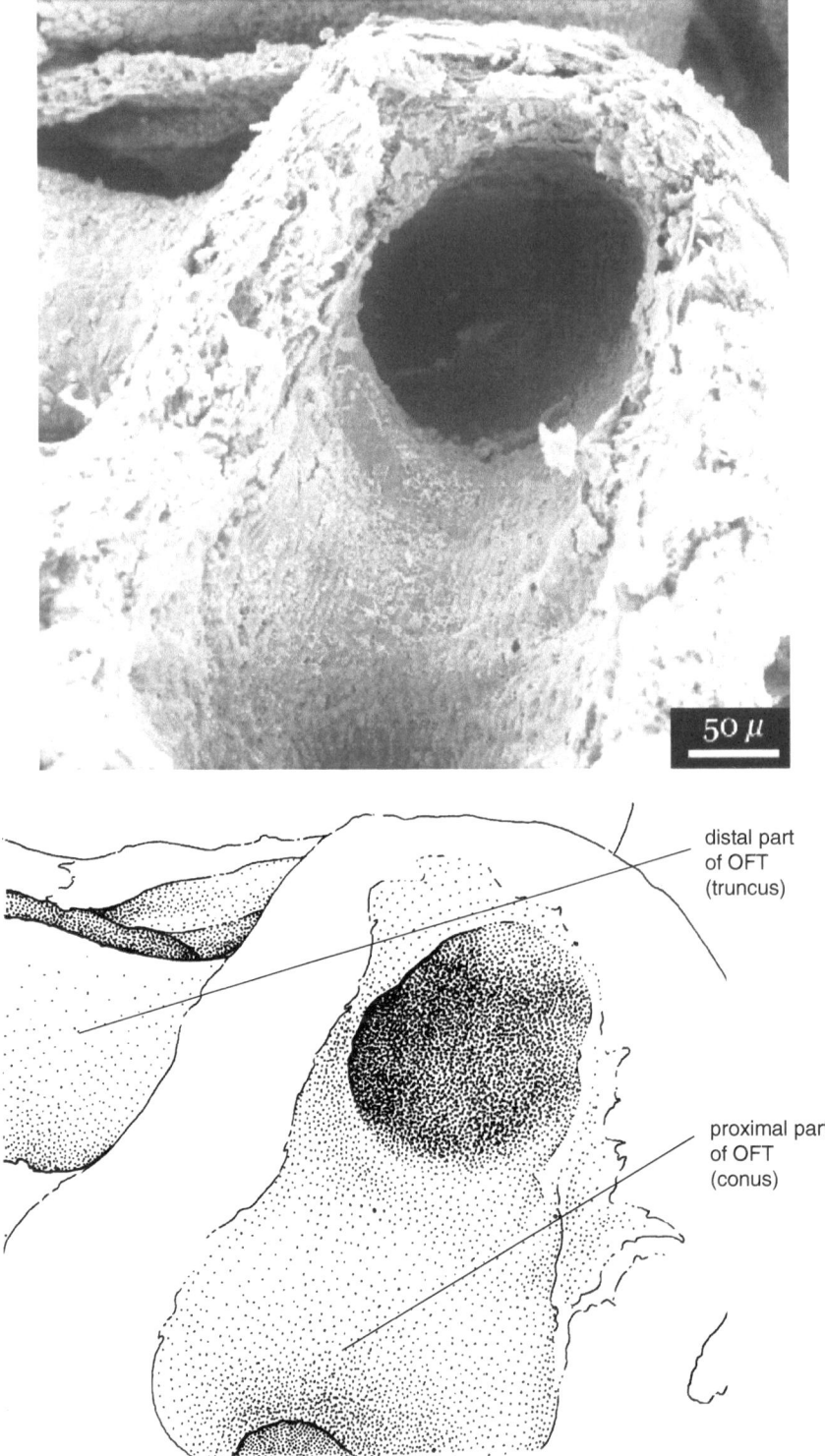

50 μ

distal part
of OFT
(truncus)

proximal part
of OFT
(conus)

FIGURE 4.2   Outflow tract (stage 13), ventral view. The ventral wall of the ventricular region is removed. At this stage the endocardial ridges have not yet been formed.

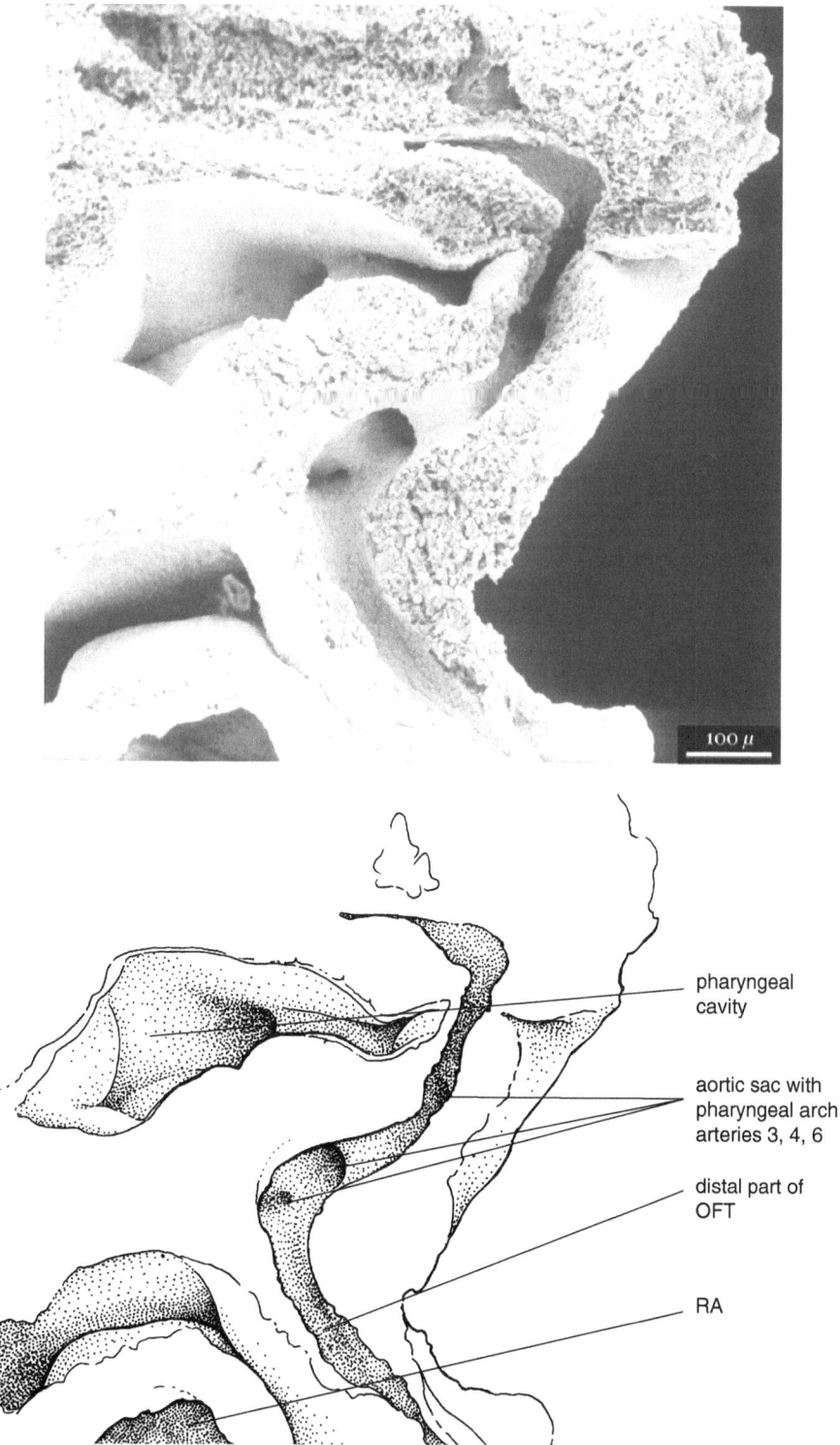

FIGURE 4.3   Embryo, sectioned in a mid sagittal plane (stage 13), right medial view. The distal outflow tract shows no signs of septation yet.

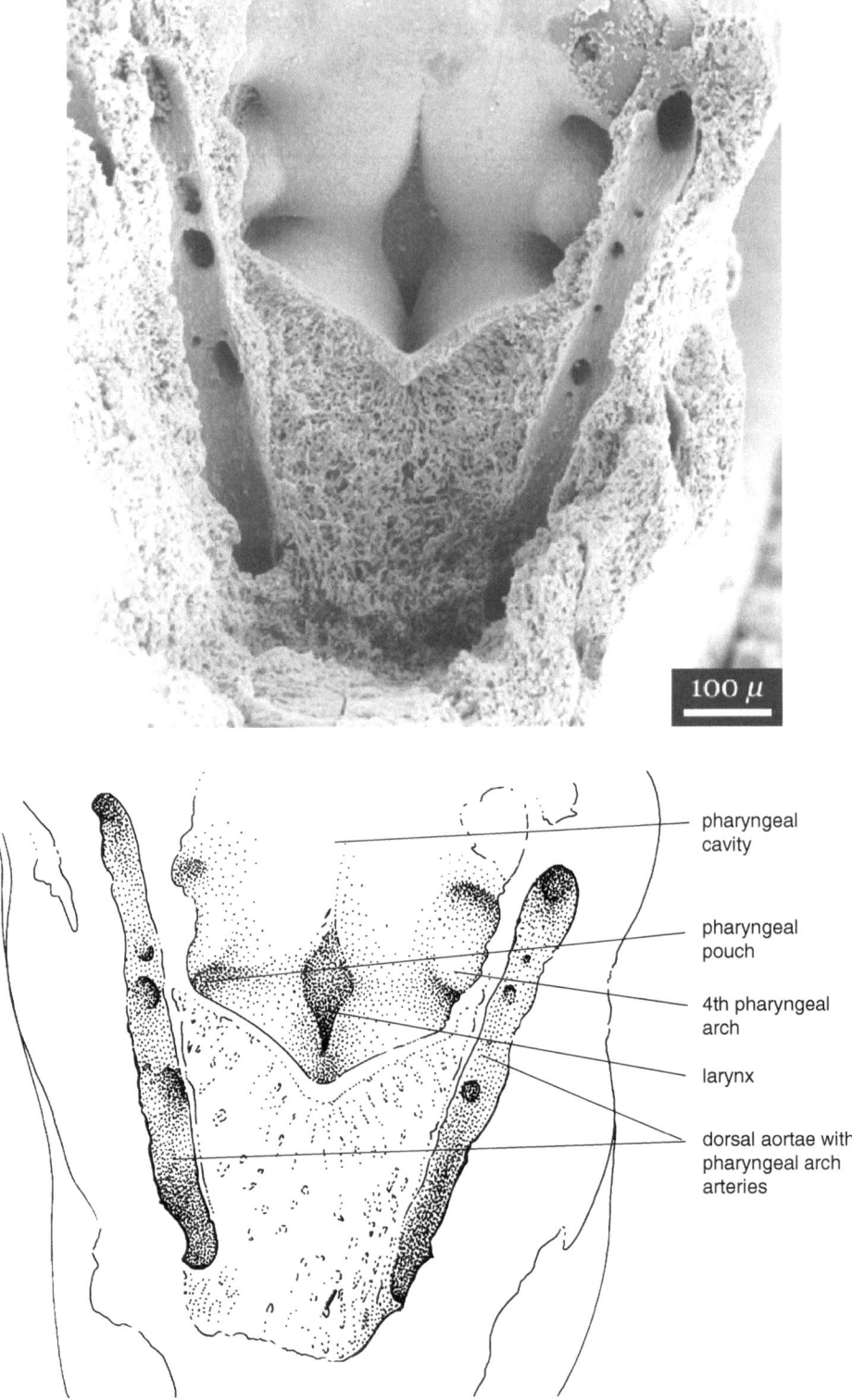

FIGURE 4.4   Embryo, sectioned in a frontal plane (stage 13), dorsal view.

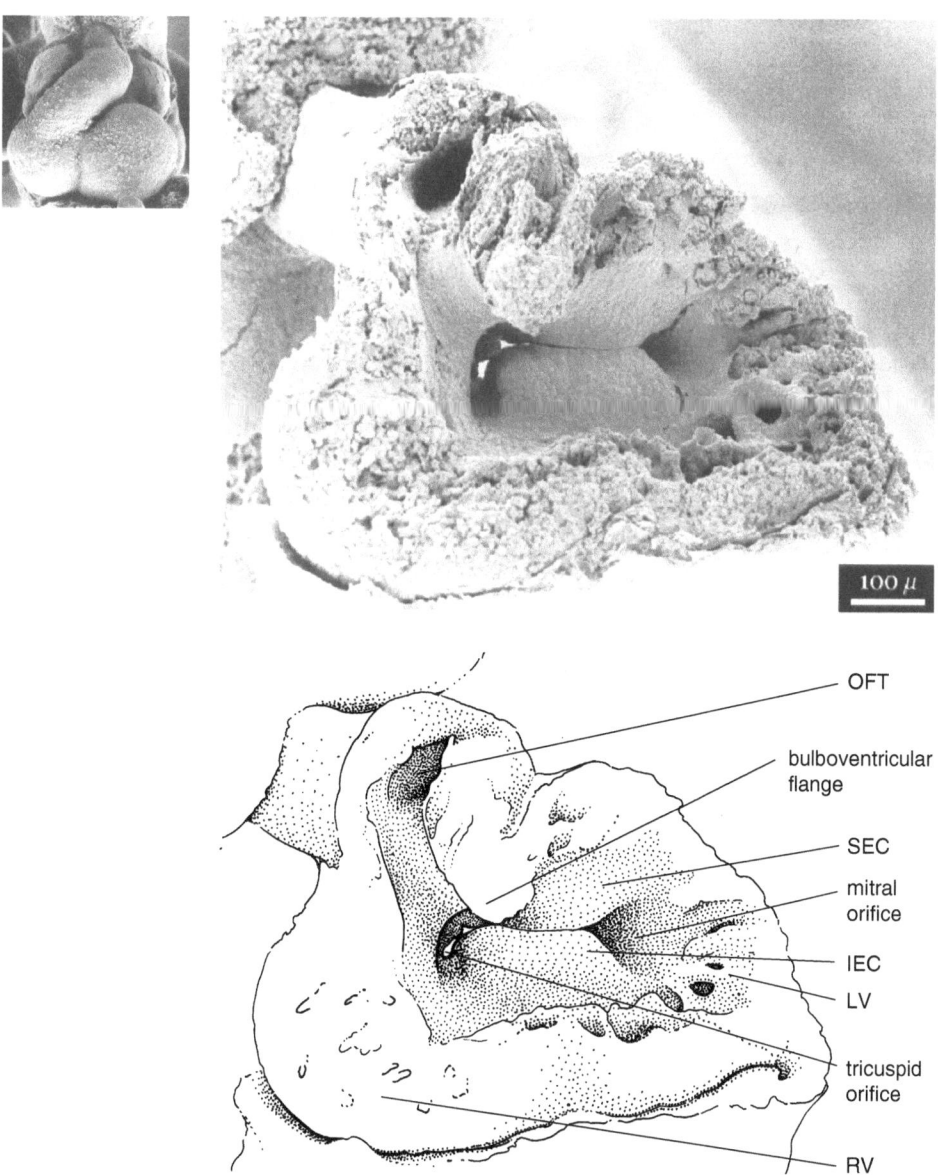

FIGURE 4.5   Atrioventricular canal and outflow tract (stage 14), ventral view. The ventricles are largely removed. The heart is fixed in a contracted state, hence the close apposition of the endocardial cushions in the atrioventricular canal.

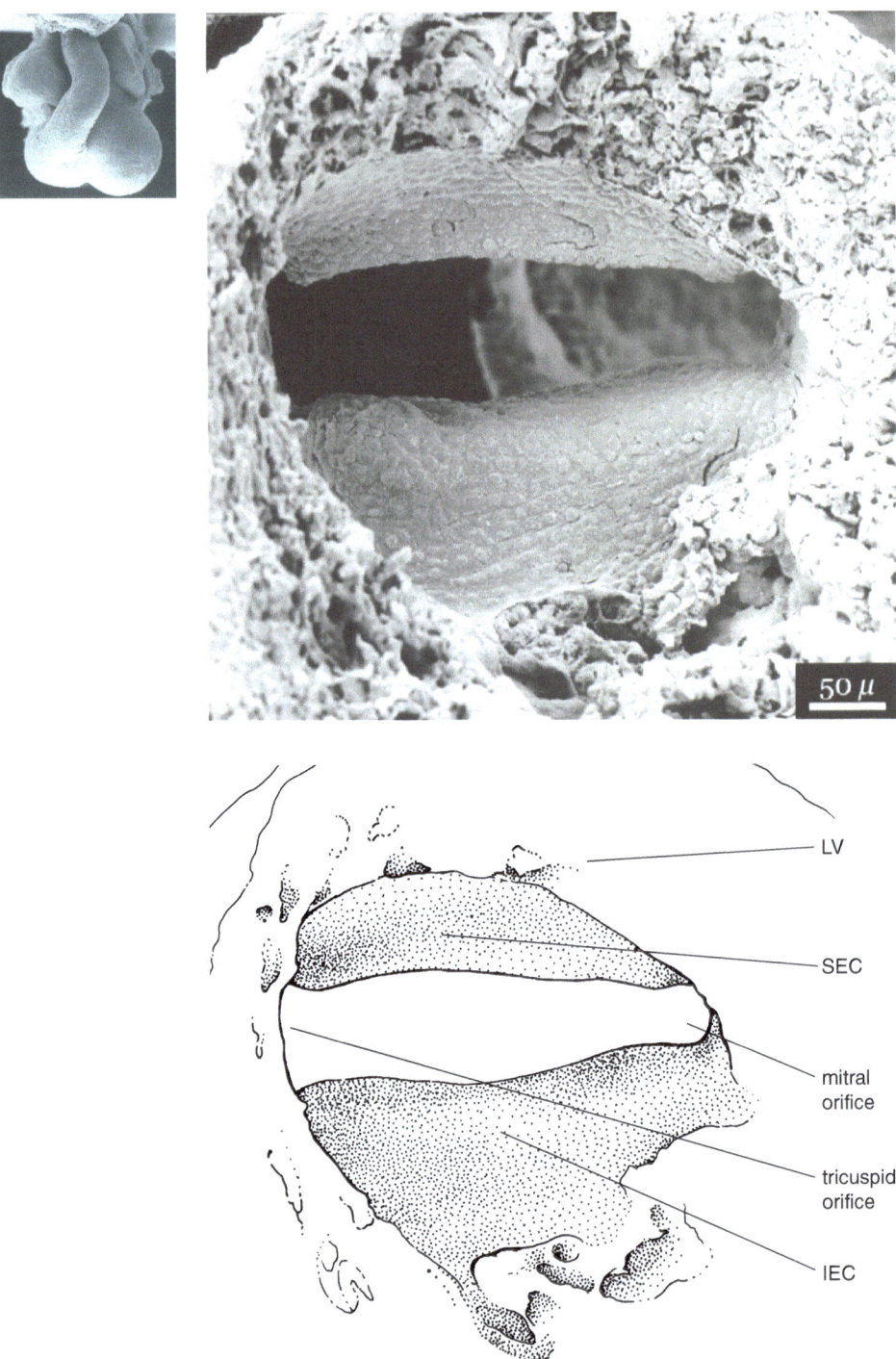

FIGURE 4.6   Atrioventricular canal, frontal section (stage 14), ventral view. The unseptated atrioventricular opening faces mainly the left ventricular inlet.

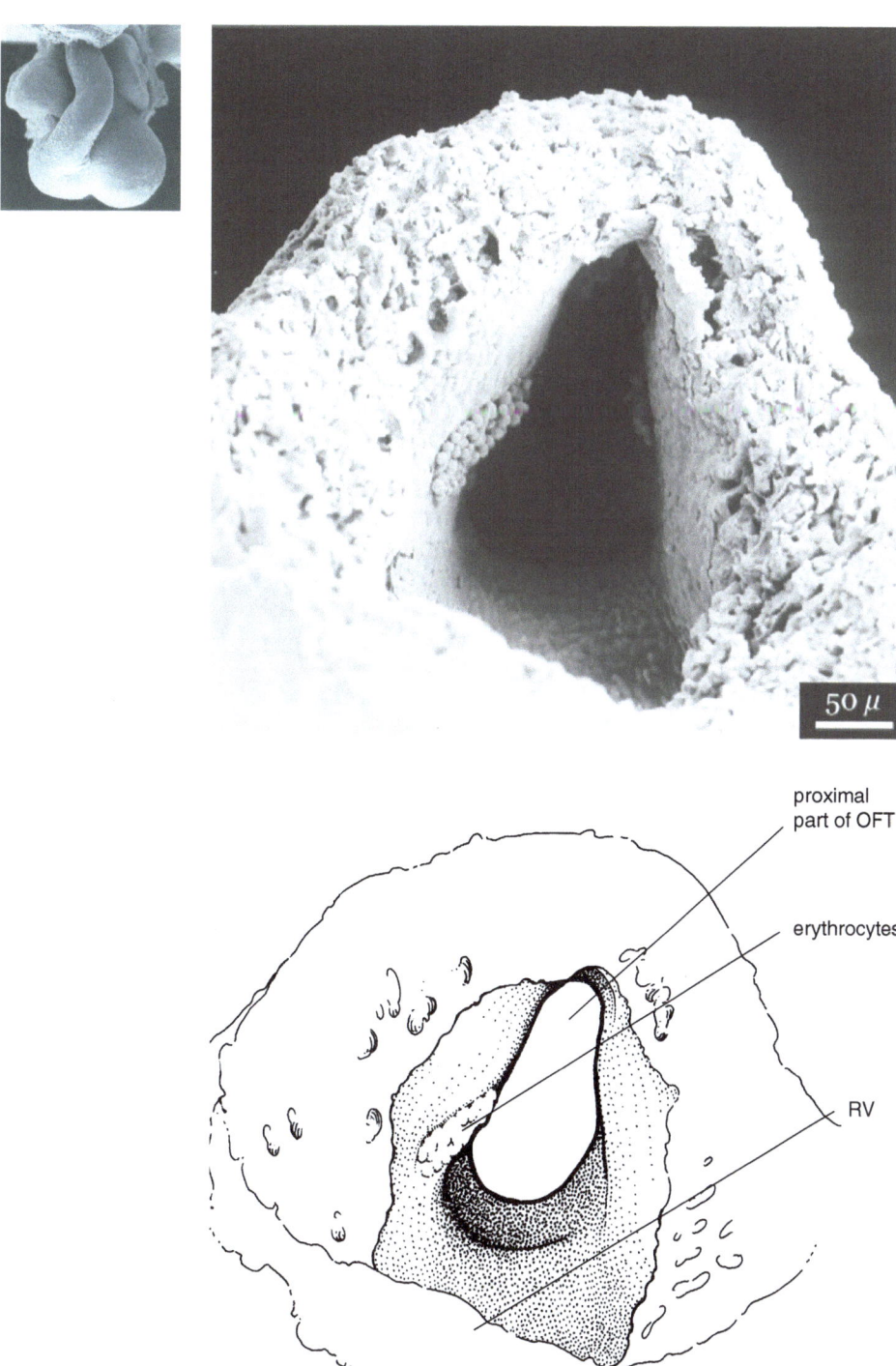

FIGURES 4.7–4.9   Outflow tract and aortic sac (stage 14), ventral and cranial views. The ventral cranial wall is removed. Local thickening of the walls of the proximal part of the outflow tract can be seen, indicating the appearance of endocardial ridges.

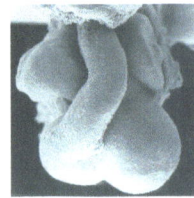

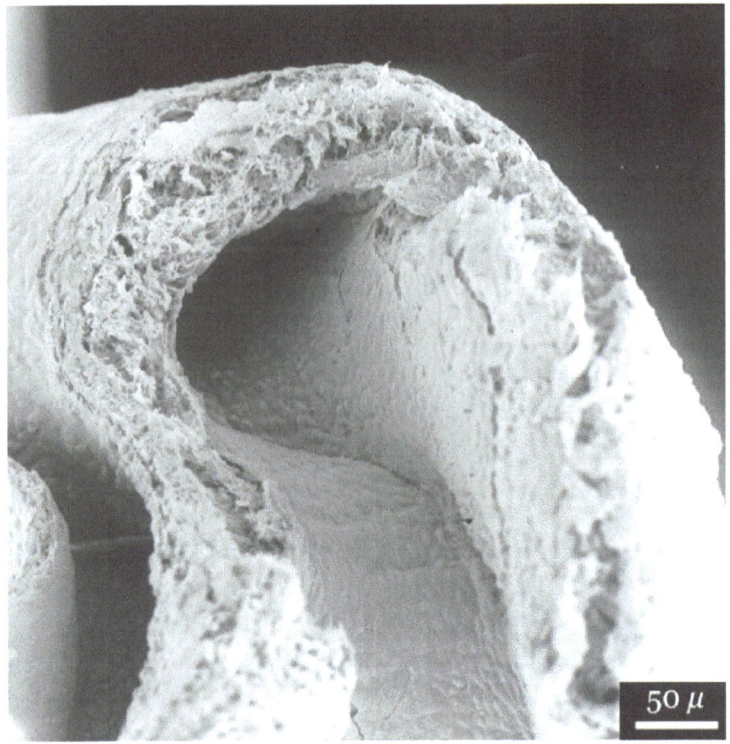

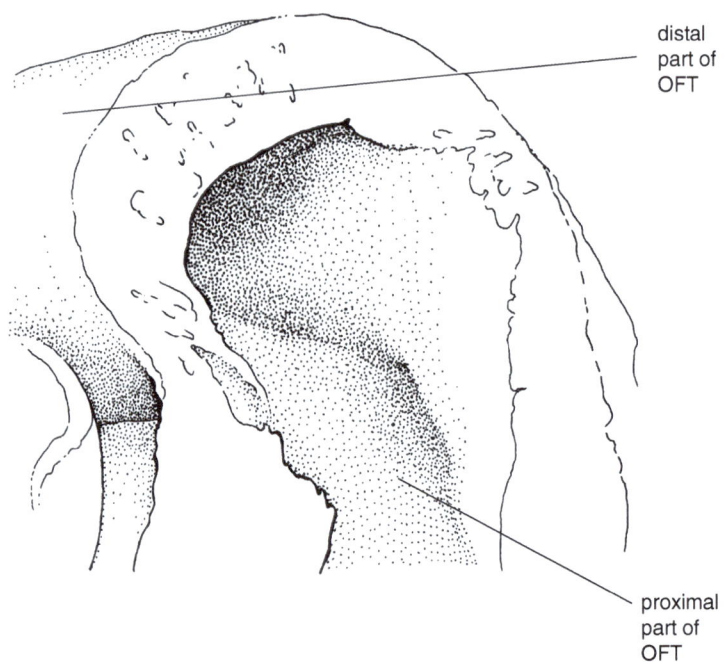

FIGURES 4.7–4.9   *Continued*

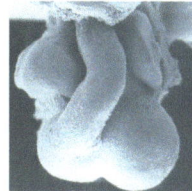

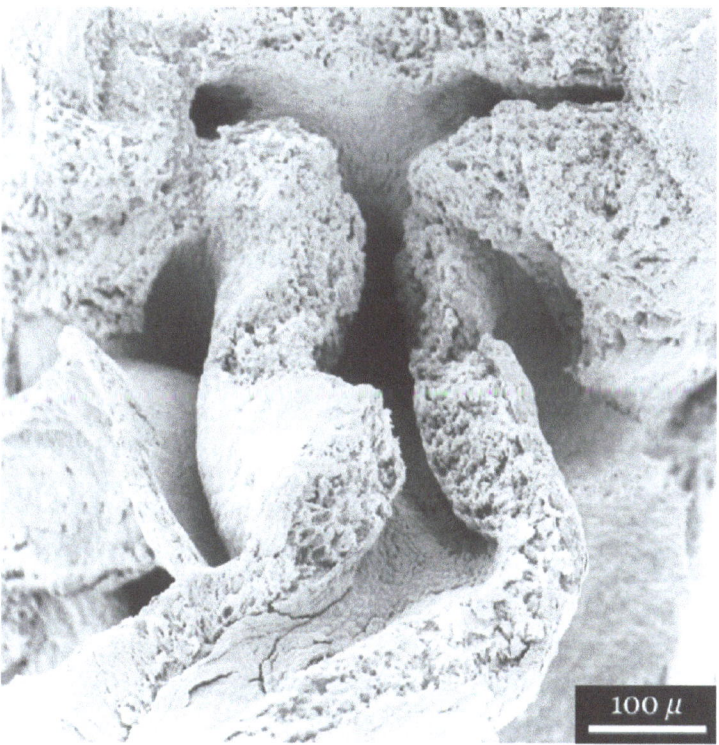

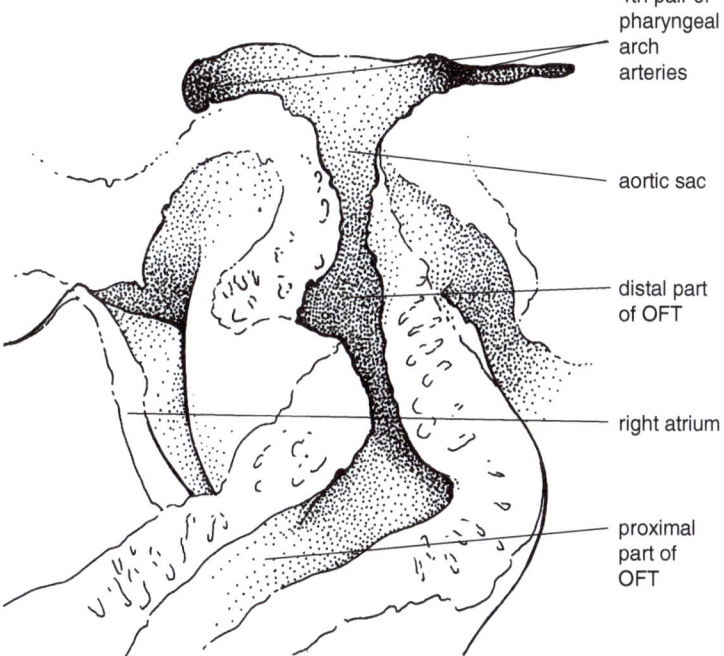

4th pair of pharyngeal arch arteries

aortic sac

distal part of OFT

right atrium

proximal part of OFT

FIGURES 4.7–4.9   *Continued*

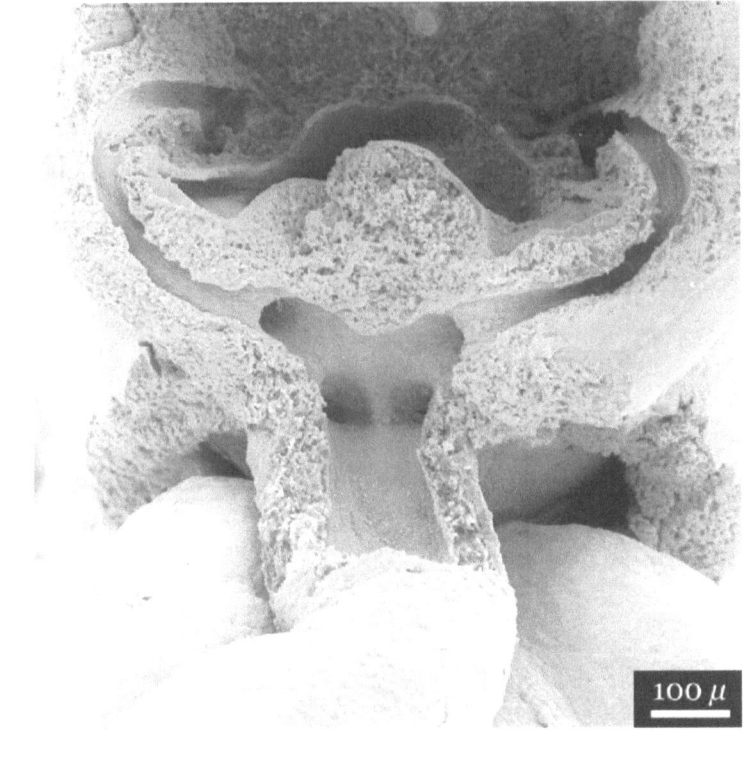

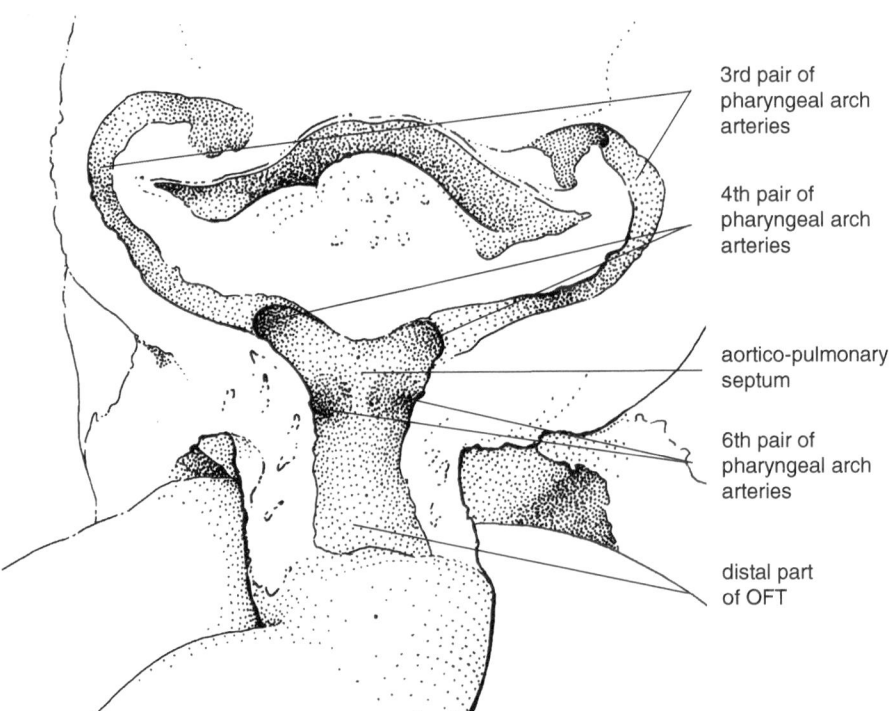

3rd pair of
pharyngeal arch
arteries

4th pair of
pharyngeal arch
arteries

aortico-pulmonary
septum

6th pair of
pharyngeal arch
arteries

distal part
of OFT

FIGURE 4.10   Embryo, sectioned in a frontal plane (stage 14), ventral view.
The ventral wall of the aortic sac is removed.

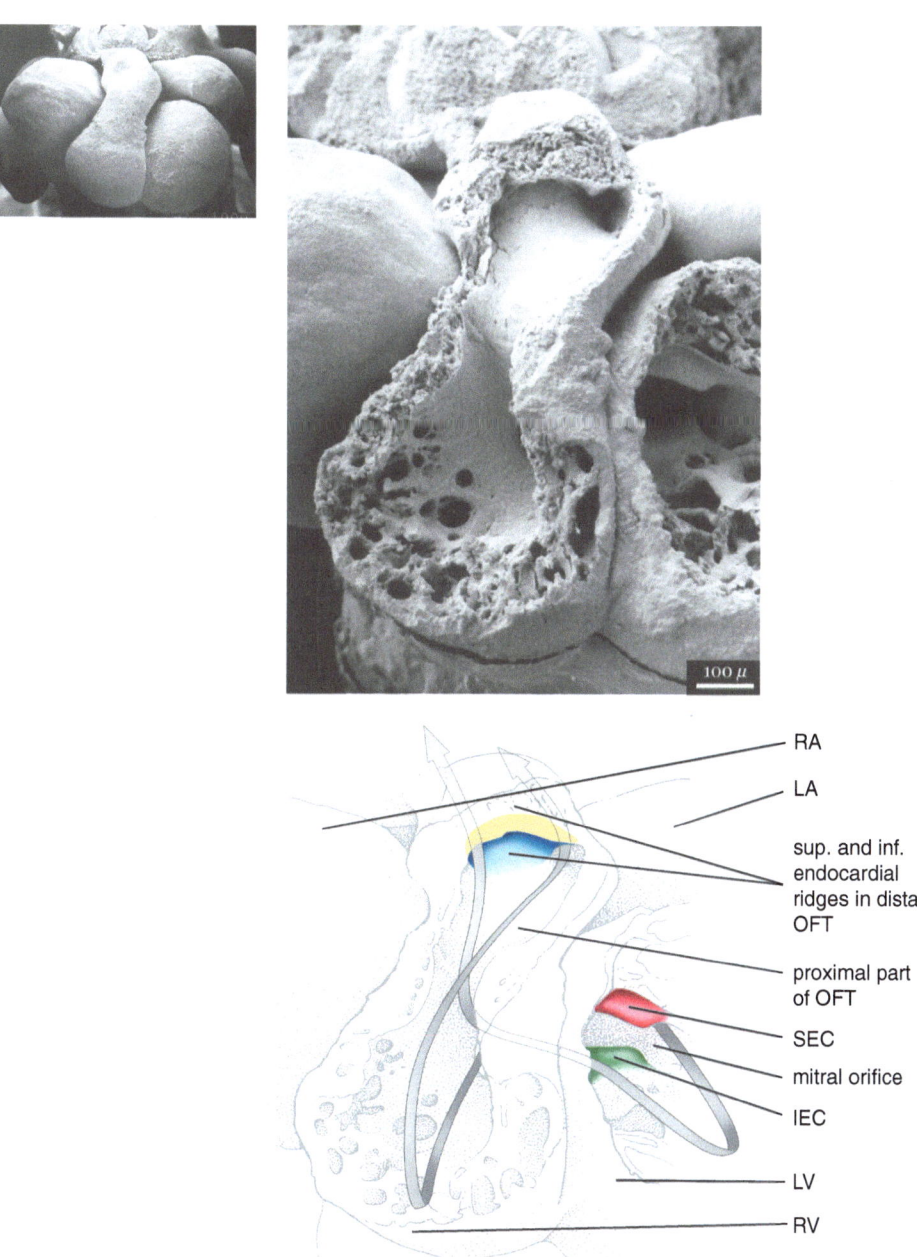

FIGURES 4.11–4.14   Complete heart in situ (stage 15), ventral and detailed views. The ventral wall of the ventricles and outflow tract are removed. The atrioventricular opening faces mainly the left ventricular inlet. The endocardial ridges in the distal outflow tract are already well-developed and have approximated each other, resulting in physical separation of the right and left ventricular blood flow. By contrast the ridges in the proximal outflow tract are only starting to become formed. Colors indicate the superior endocardial cushion (red), inferior endocardial cushion (dark green), superior endocardial ridges (yellow), and inferior endocardial ridge (dark blue). Arrows indicate left and right ventricular inflow and outflow patterns.

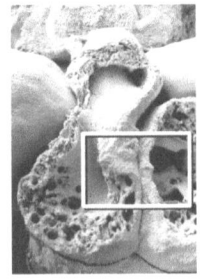

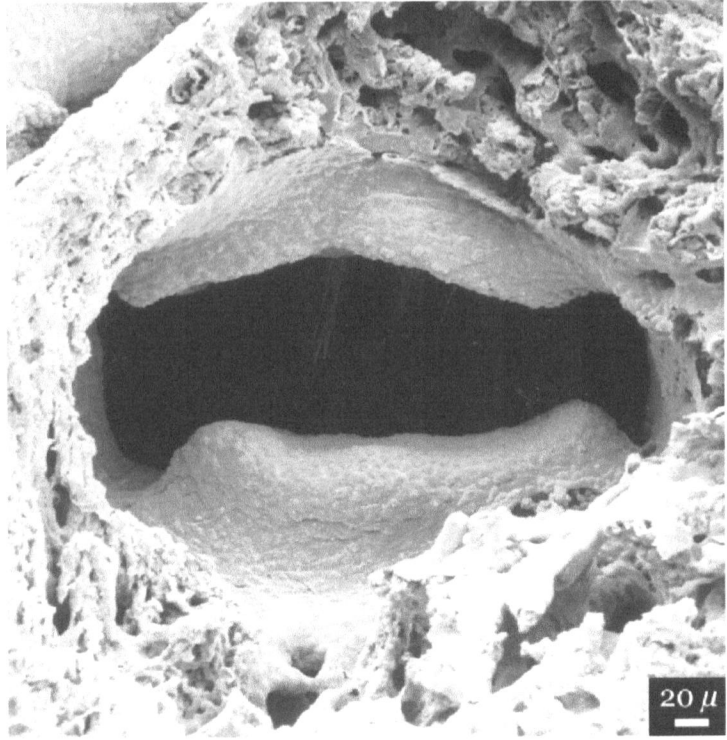

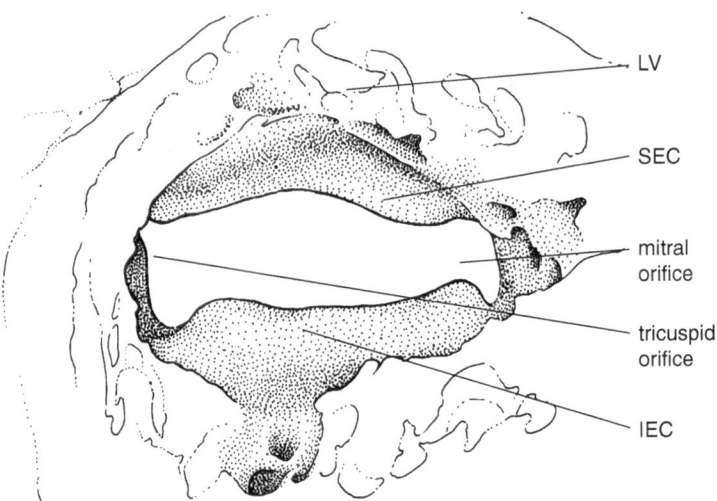

FIGURES 4.11–4.14   *Continued*

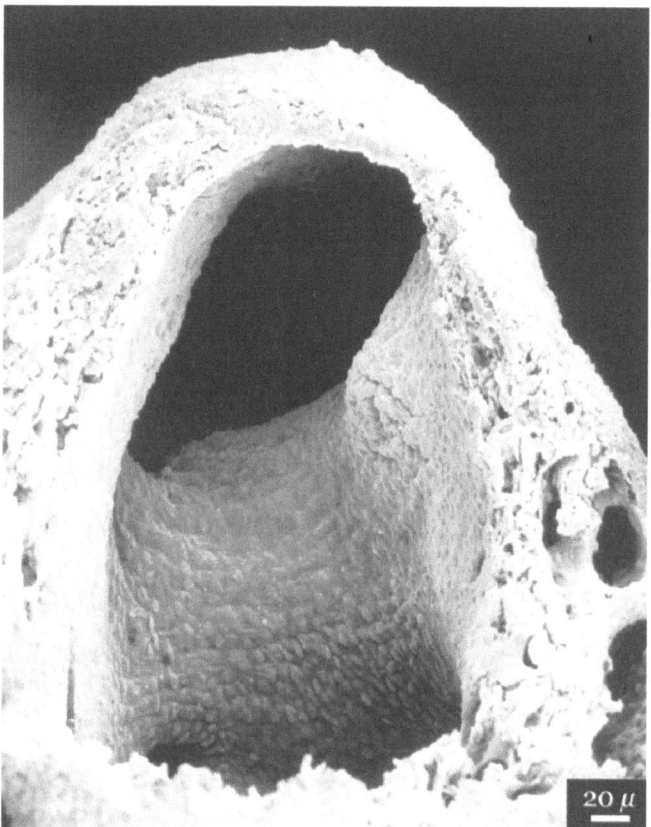

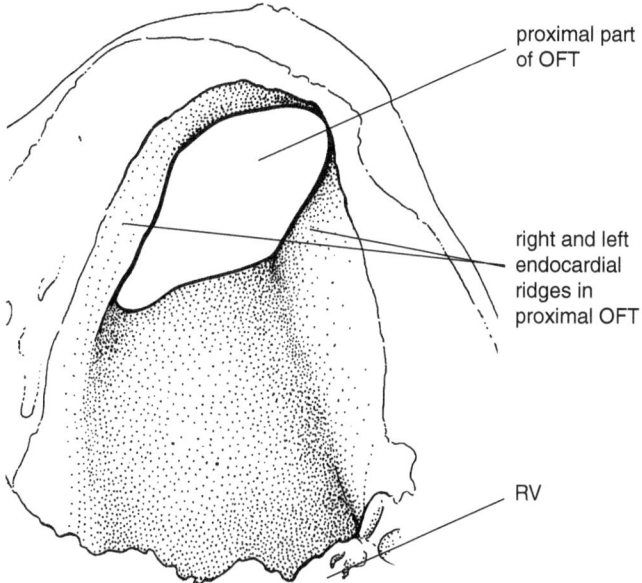

proximal part
of OFT

right and left
endocardial
ridges in
proximal OFT

RV

FIGURES 4.11–4.14   *Continued*

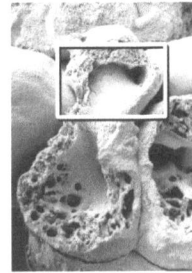

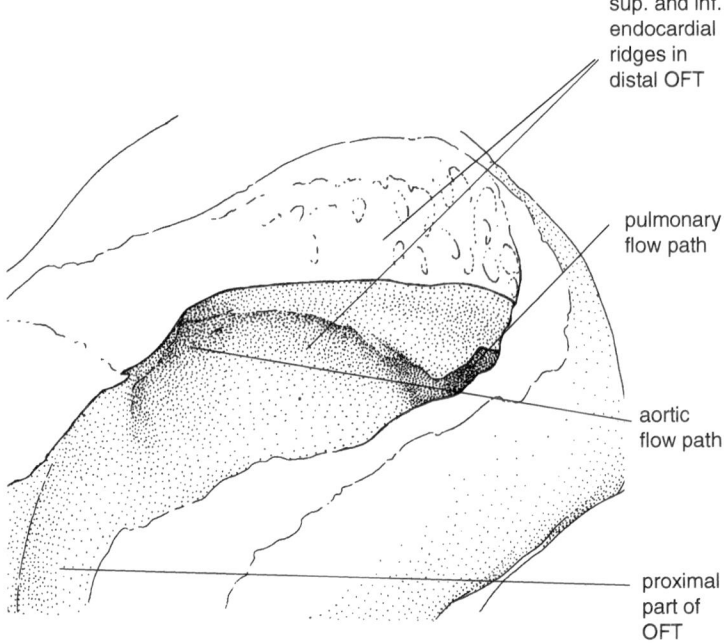

sup. and inf.
endocardial
ridges in
distal OFT

pulmonary
flow path

aortic
flow path

proximal
part of
OFT

FIGURES 4.11–4.14   *Continued*

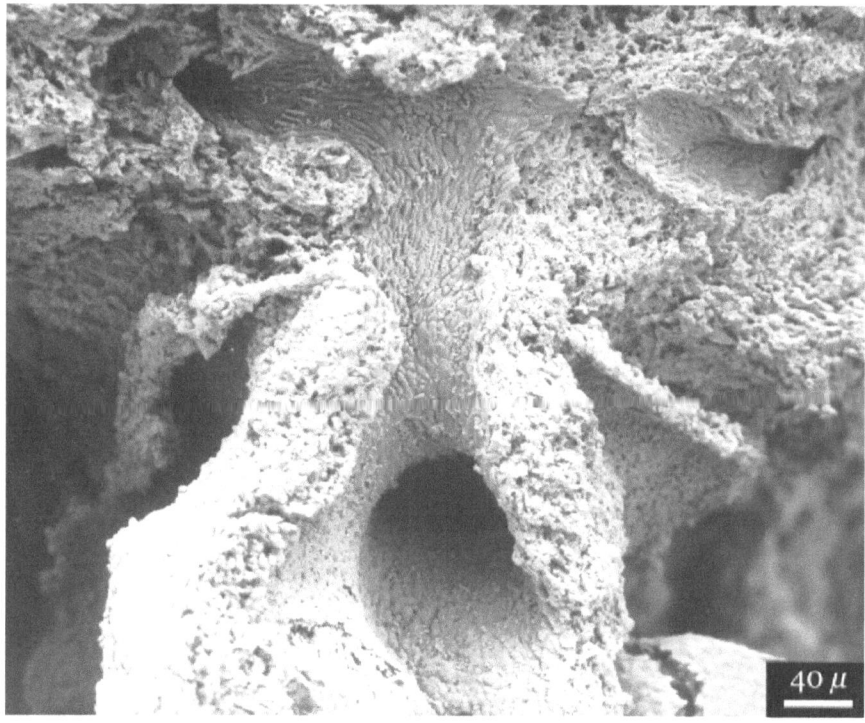

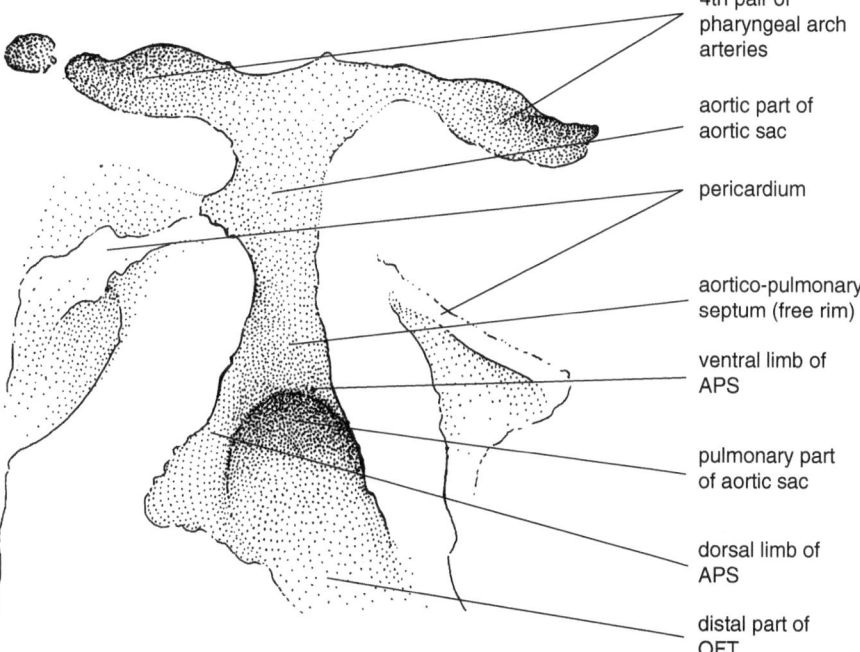

4th pair of
pharyngeal arch
arteries

aortic part of
aortic sac

pericardium

aortico-pulmonary
septum (free rim)

ventral limb of
APS

pulmonary part
of aortic sac

dorsal limb of
APS

distal part of
OFT

FIGURE 4.15   Opened distal outflow tract and aortic sac (stage 15), ventral cranial view. The two limbs of the aortico-pulmonary septum, which separates the systemic from the pulmonary arteries, proceed in proximal direction to meet the endocardial ridges of the distal outflow tract.

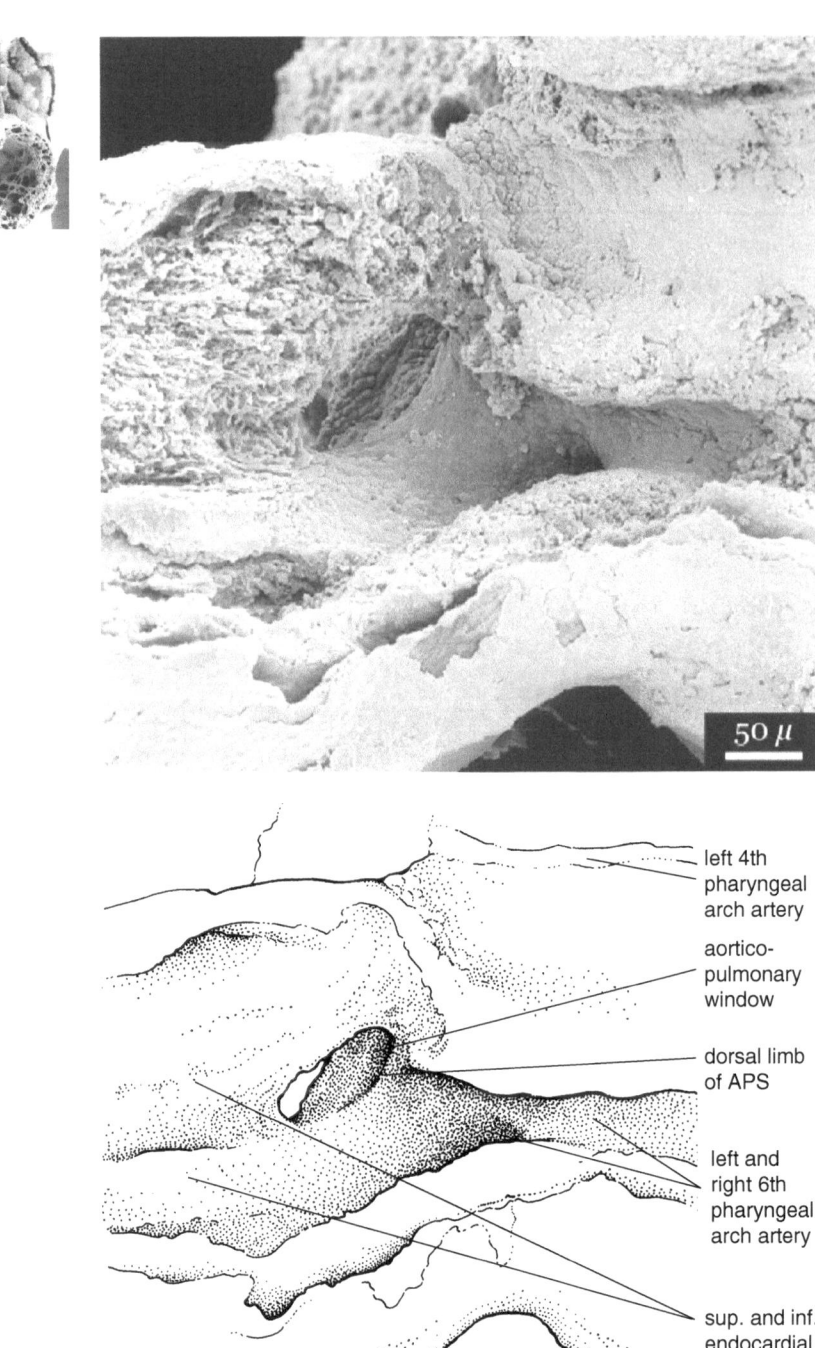

FIGURES 4.16 and 4.17   Opened distal part of the outflow tract and aortic sac (stage 15), left and right lateral views. The endocardial ridges in the outflow tract and the limbs of the aorticopulomnary septum are approaching one another, leaving a temporarily opening (the aortico-pulmonary window).

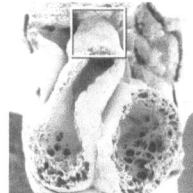

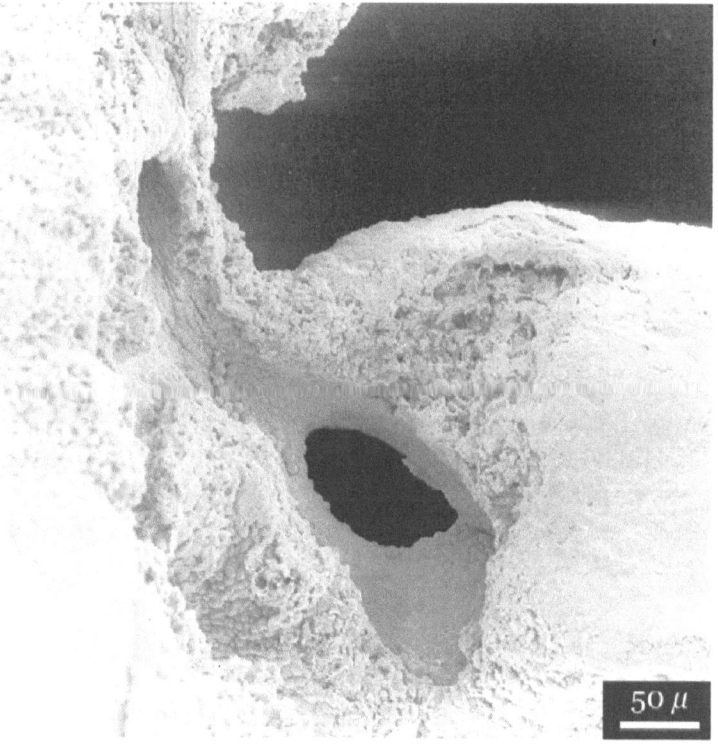

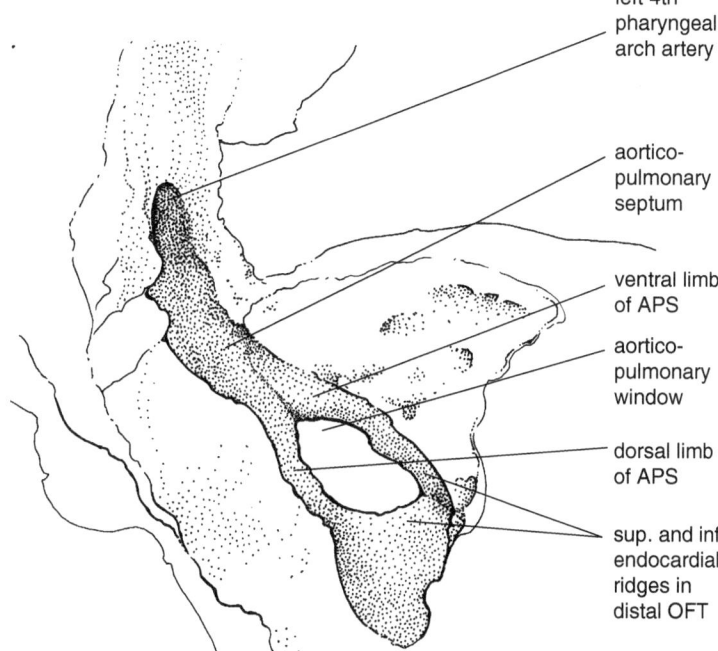

left 4th
pharyngeal
arch artery

aortico-
pulmonary
septum

ventral limb
of APS

aortico-
pulmonary
window

dorsal limb
of APS

sup. and inf.
endocardial
ridges in
distal OFT

FIGURES 4.16 and 4.17   *Continued*

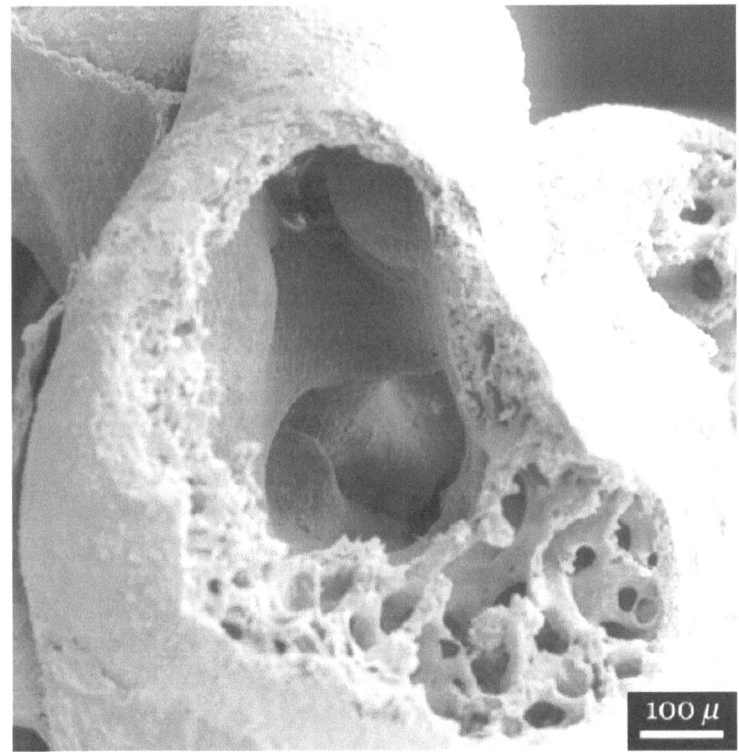

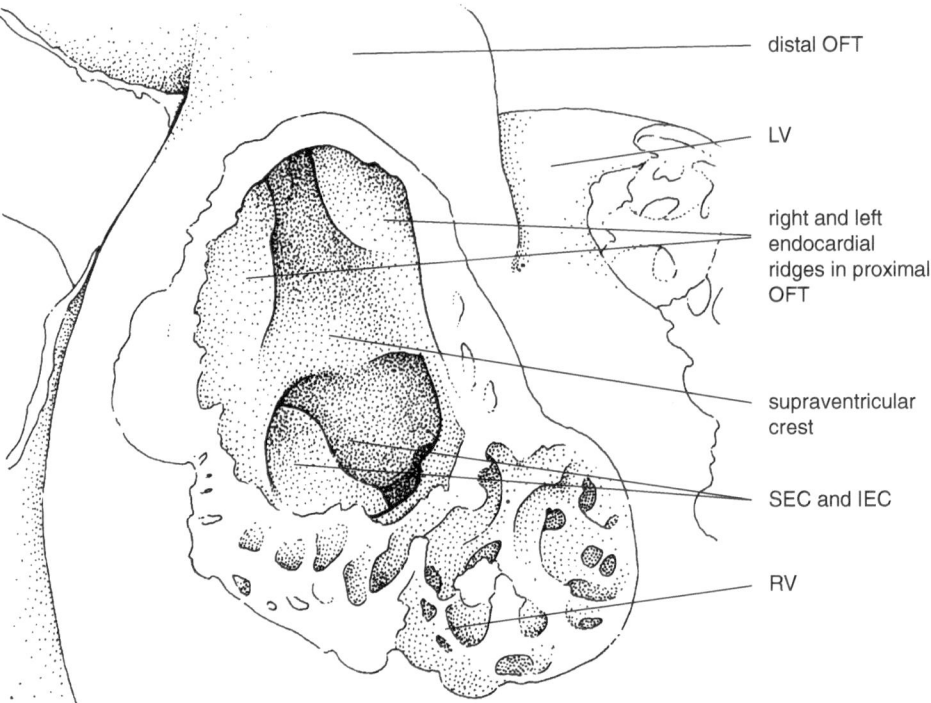

FIGURES 4.18 and 4.19   Opened RV and proximal outflow tract (stage 16), right lateral and caudal views. The endocardial ridges in the proximal outflow tract become increasingly larger.

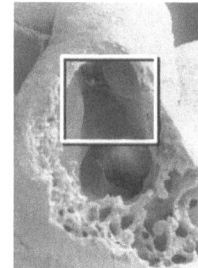

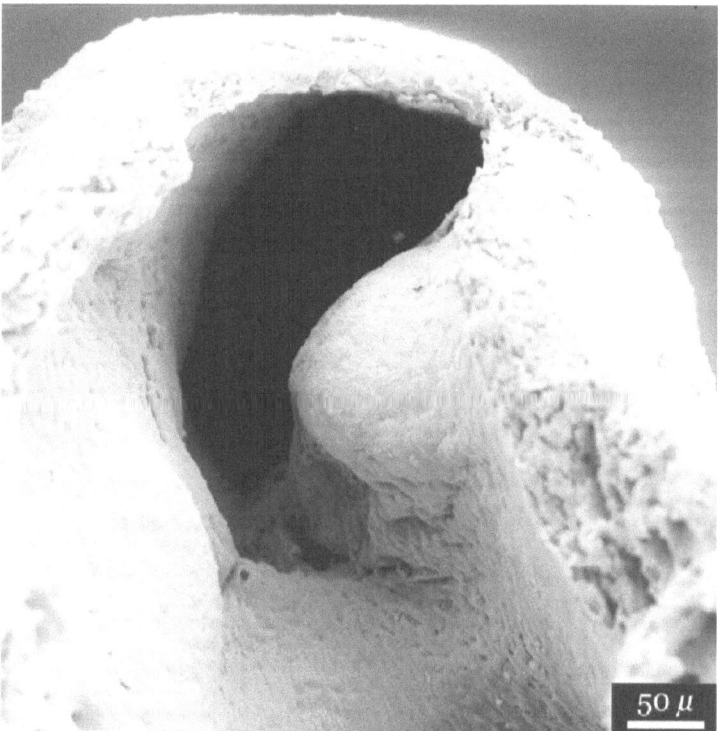

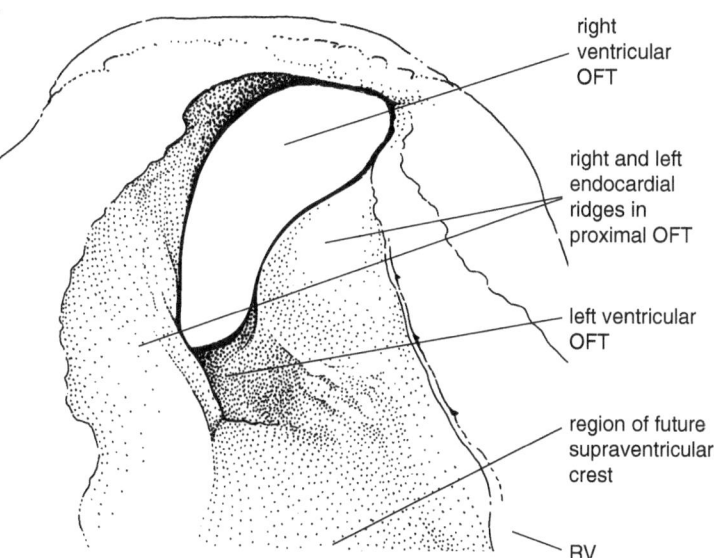

FIGURES 4.18 and 4.19   *Continued*

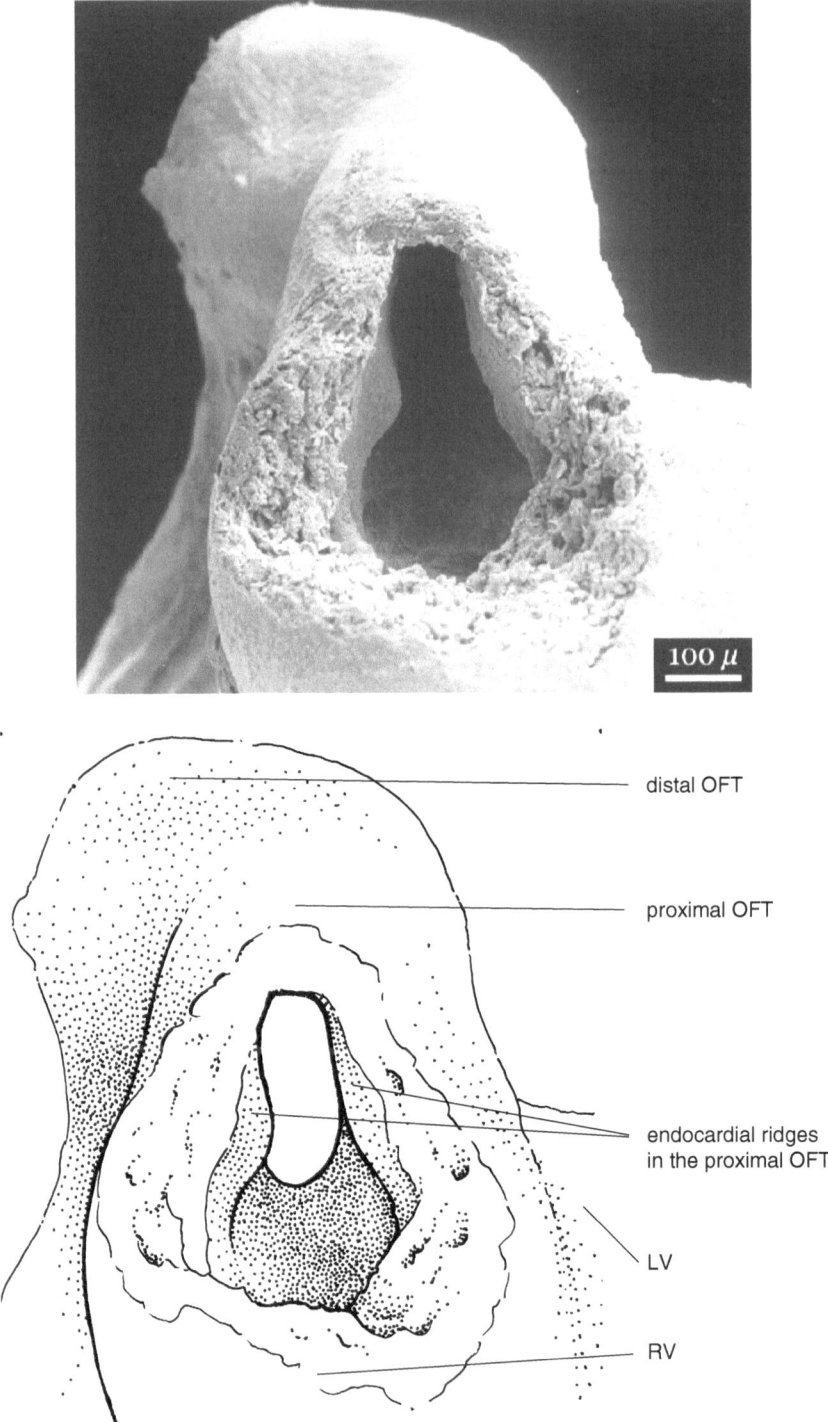

FIGURE 4.20   Complete heart in situ (stage 16), ventral and cranial view. The ventral wall of the RV and the distal most part of the outflow tract are removed. The endocardial ridges in the proximal outflow tract are still in the process of becoming proliferated.

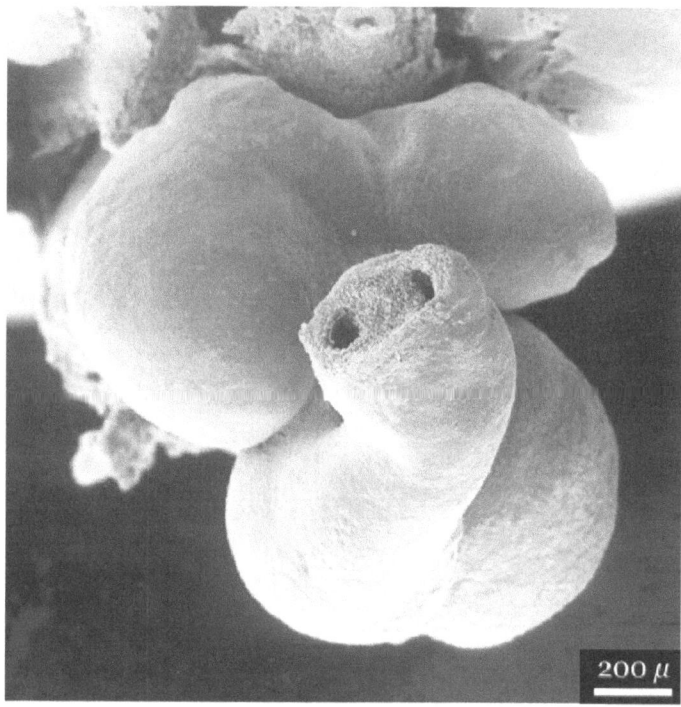

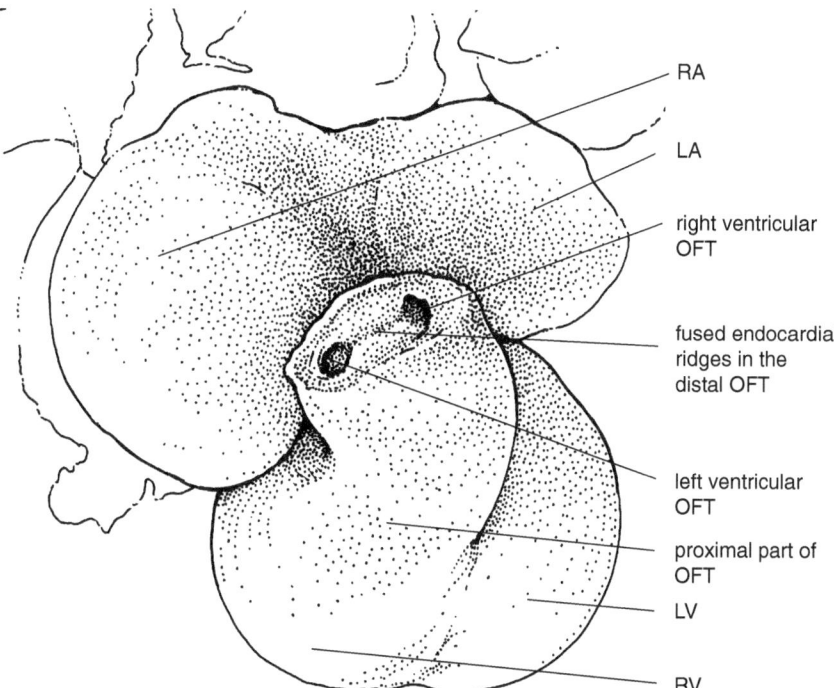

FIGURE 4.21   Complete heart in situ (stage 16), ventral and cranial view. The ventral body wall, the pericardium and the distal most part of the outflow tract are removed. In contrast to its external appearance the distal part of the outflow tract already consists of two separated lumina.

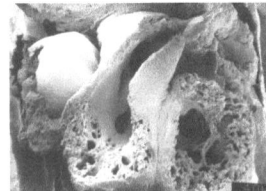

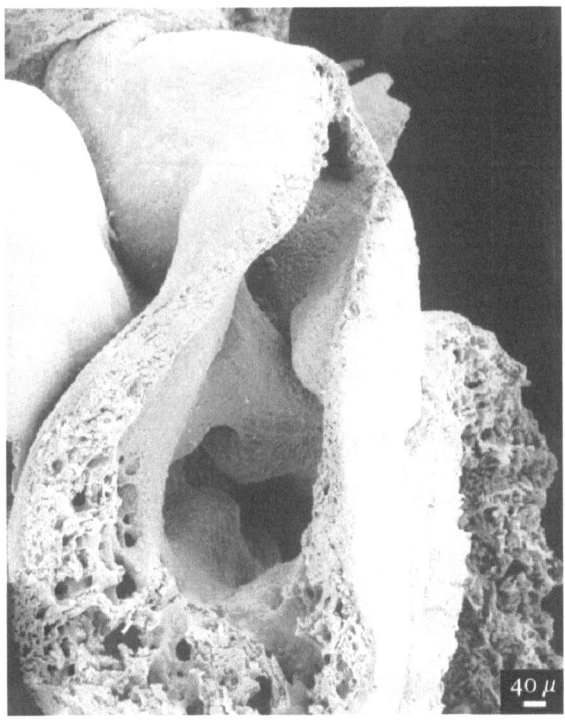

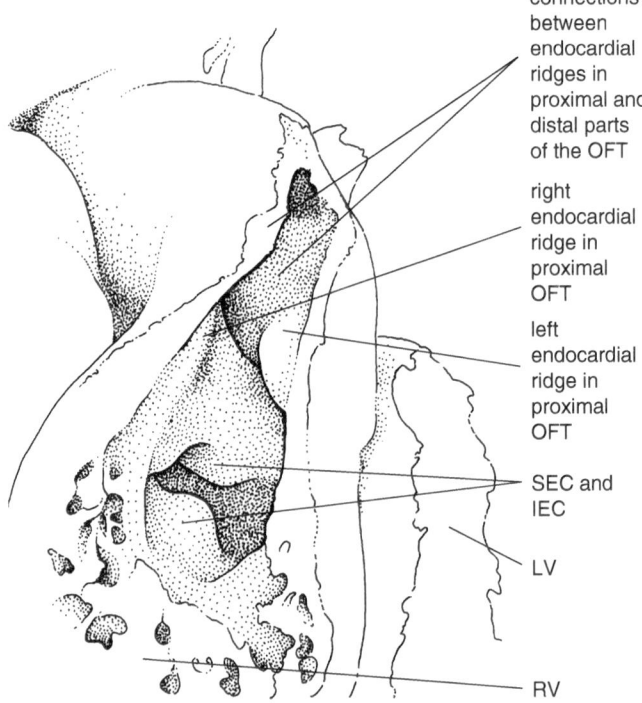

connections
between
endocardial
ridges in
proximal and
distal parts
of the OFT

right
endocardial
ridge in
proximal
OFT

left
endocardial
ridge in
proximal
OFT

SEC and
IEC

LV

RV

FIGURES 4.22 and 4.23   Complete heart (stage 16), ventral and right lateral views. The ventral wall of the ventricles and outflow tract is partially removed.

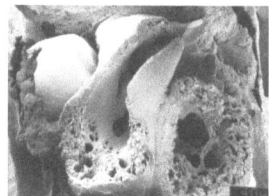

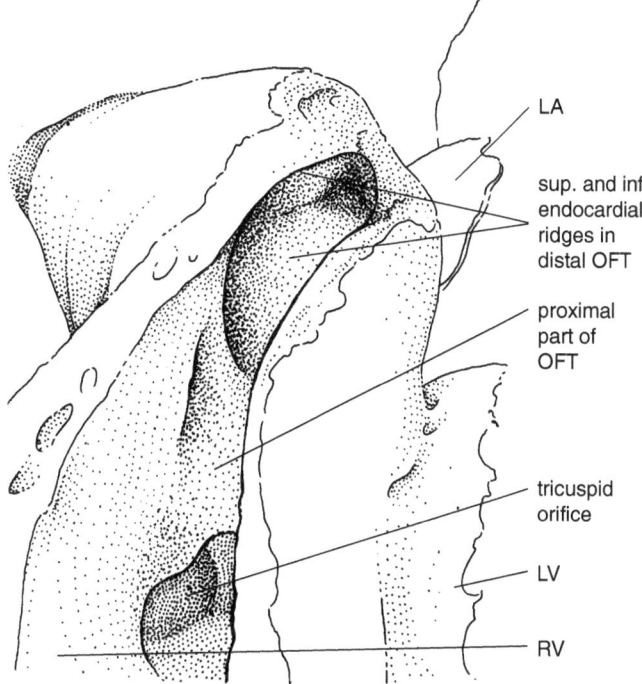

FIGURES 4.22 and 4.23   *Continued*

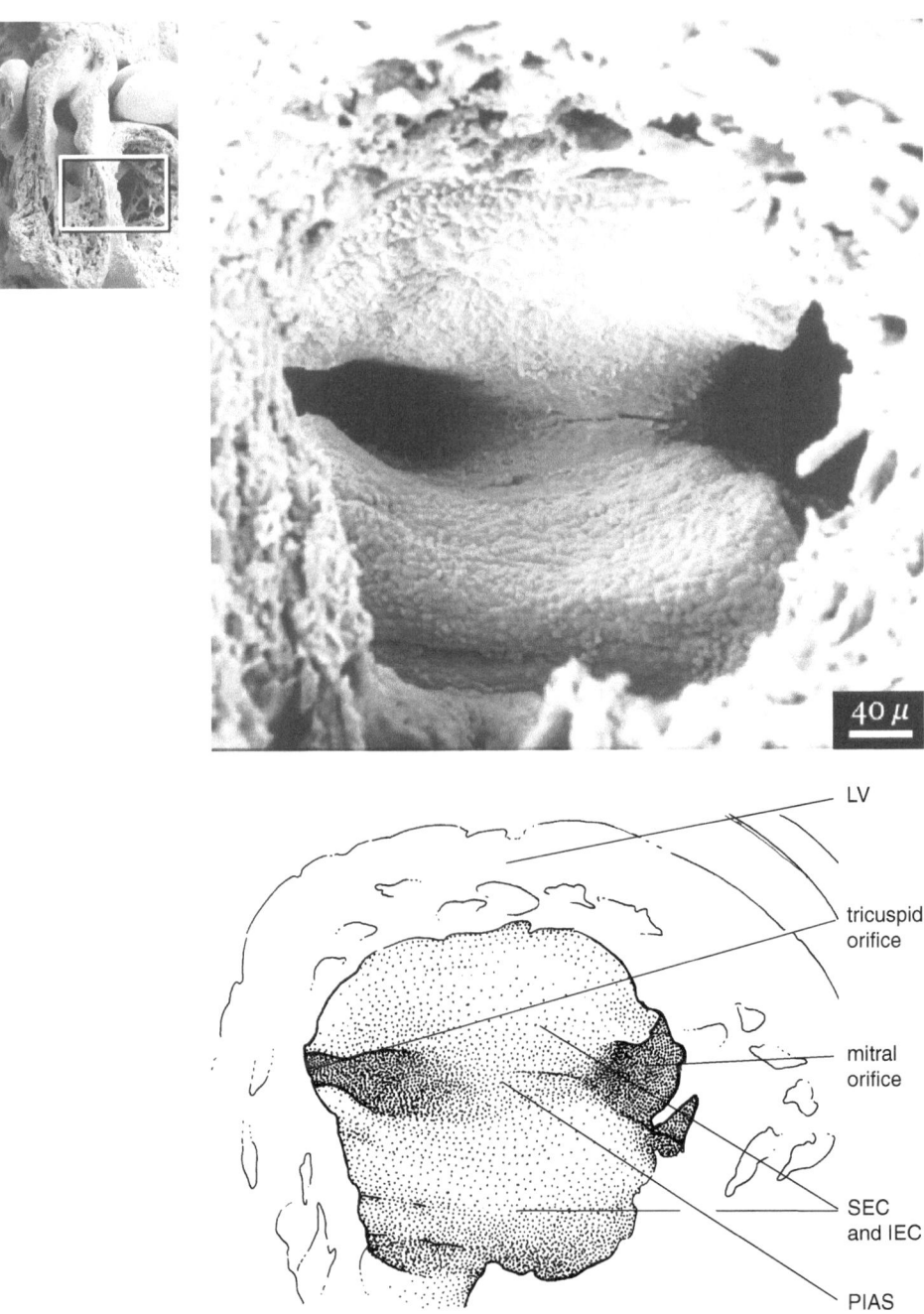

FIGURES 4.24 and 4.25   Tricuspid and mitral orifices (stage 17). There is a marked variability in the timing of the outgrowth, approximation and fusion of the endocardial cushions in the atrioventricular canal. In this specimen, the atrioventricular canal is in relaxation and still has an unseptated H-shaped lumen without signs of the cushions approximating.

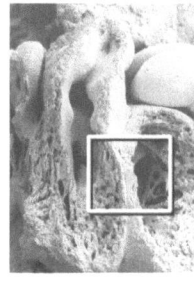

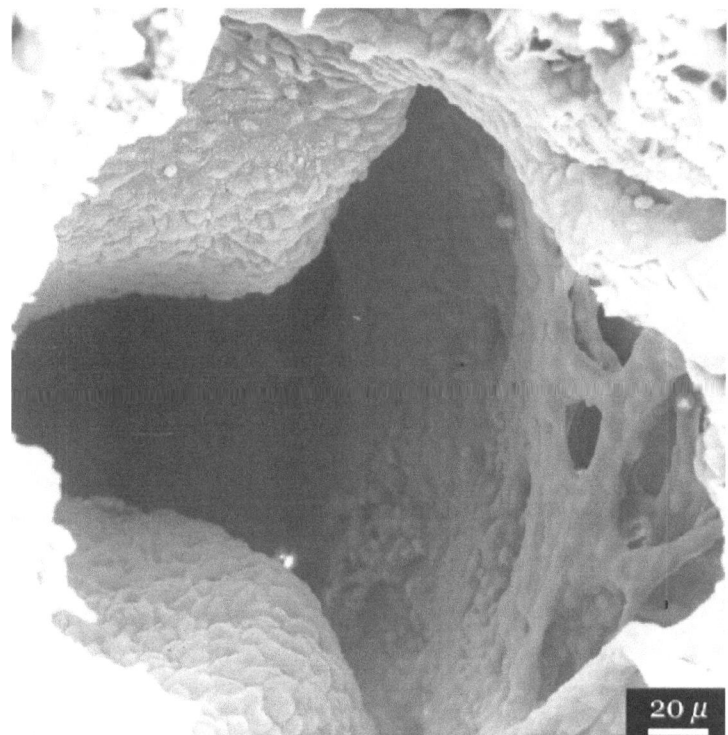

20 μ

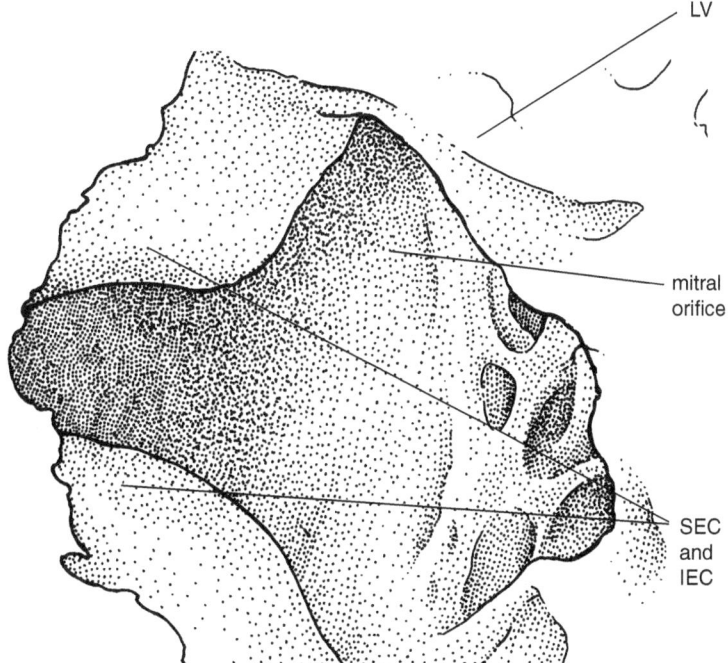

LV

mitral
orifice

SEC
and
IEC

FIGURES 4.24 and 4.25   *Continued*

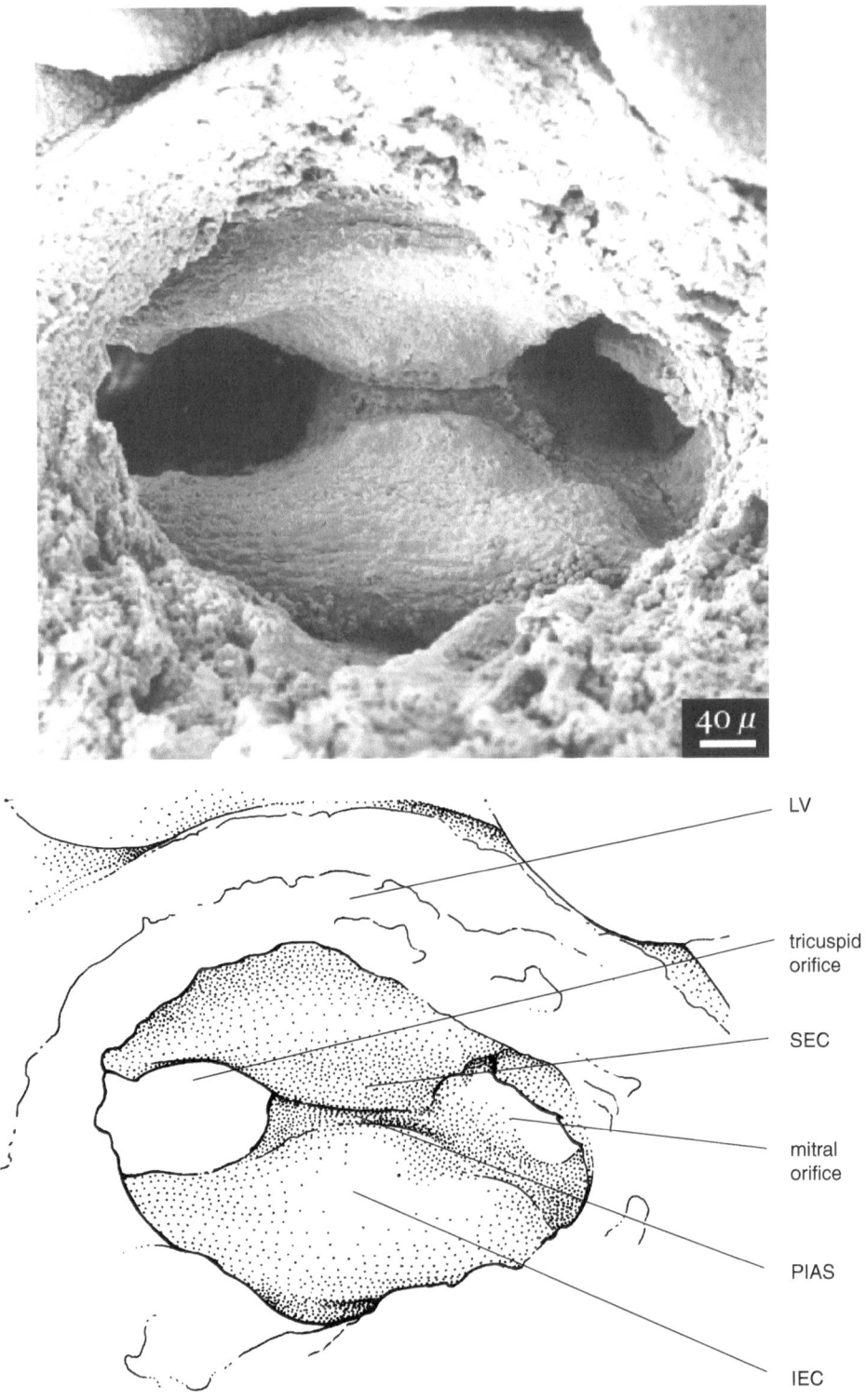

FIGURES 4.26 and 4.27   Tricuspid and mitral orifices (stage 17). In this specimen the cushions are approaching each other but have not yet fused.

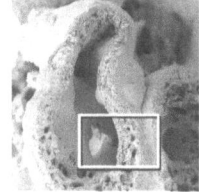

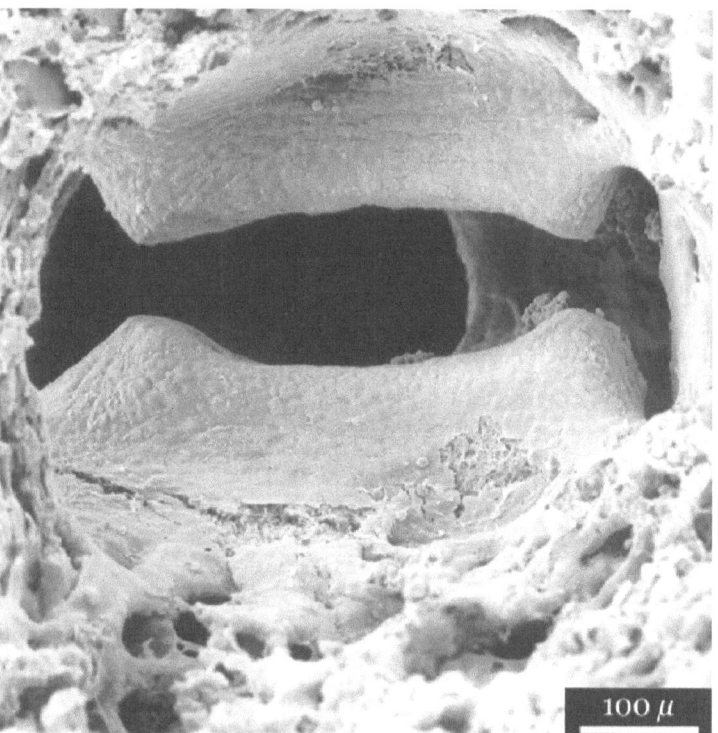

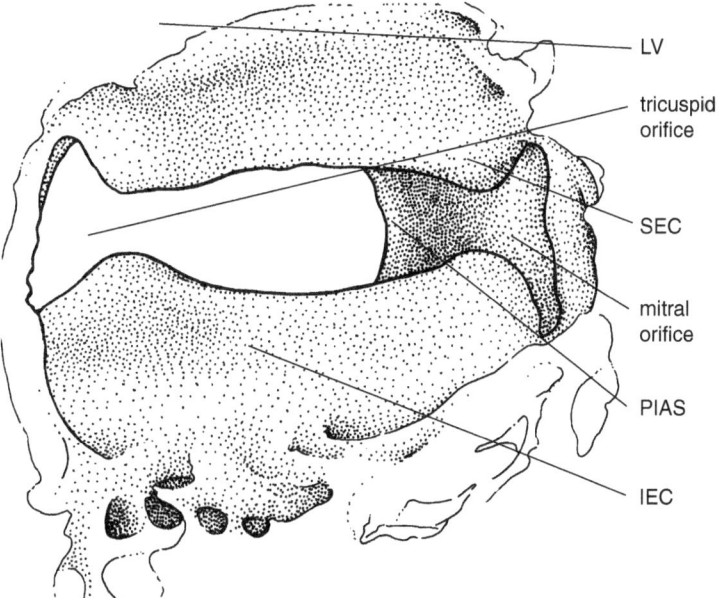

FIGURES 4.26 and 4.27   *Continued*

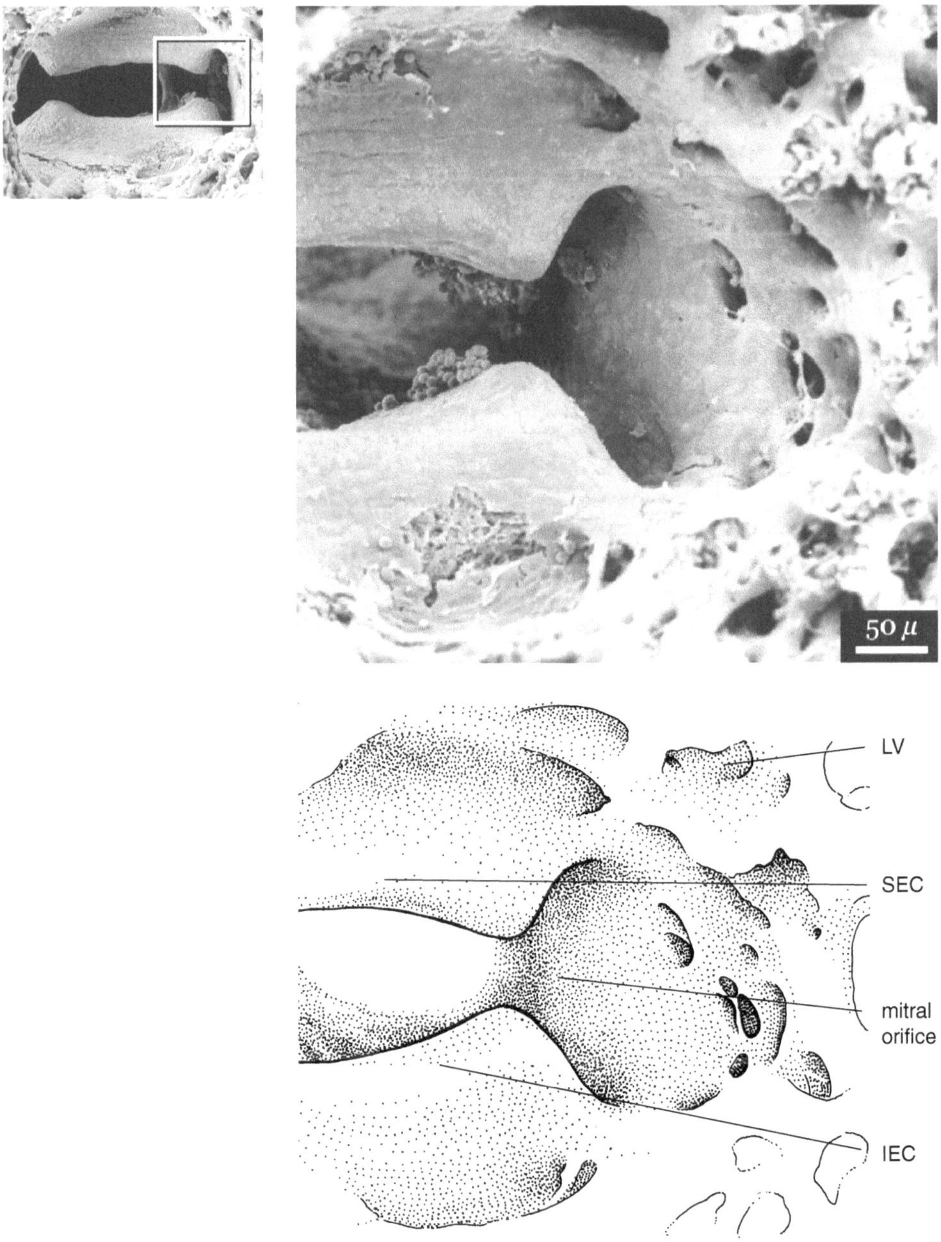

FIGURE 4.28   Tricuspid and mitral orifices (stage 17). In this specimen, the atrioventricular canal is in contraction, resulting in a temporarily contact between the cushions.

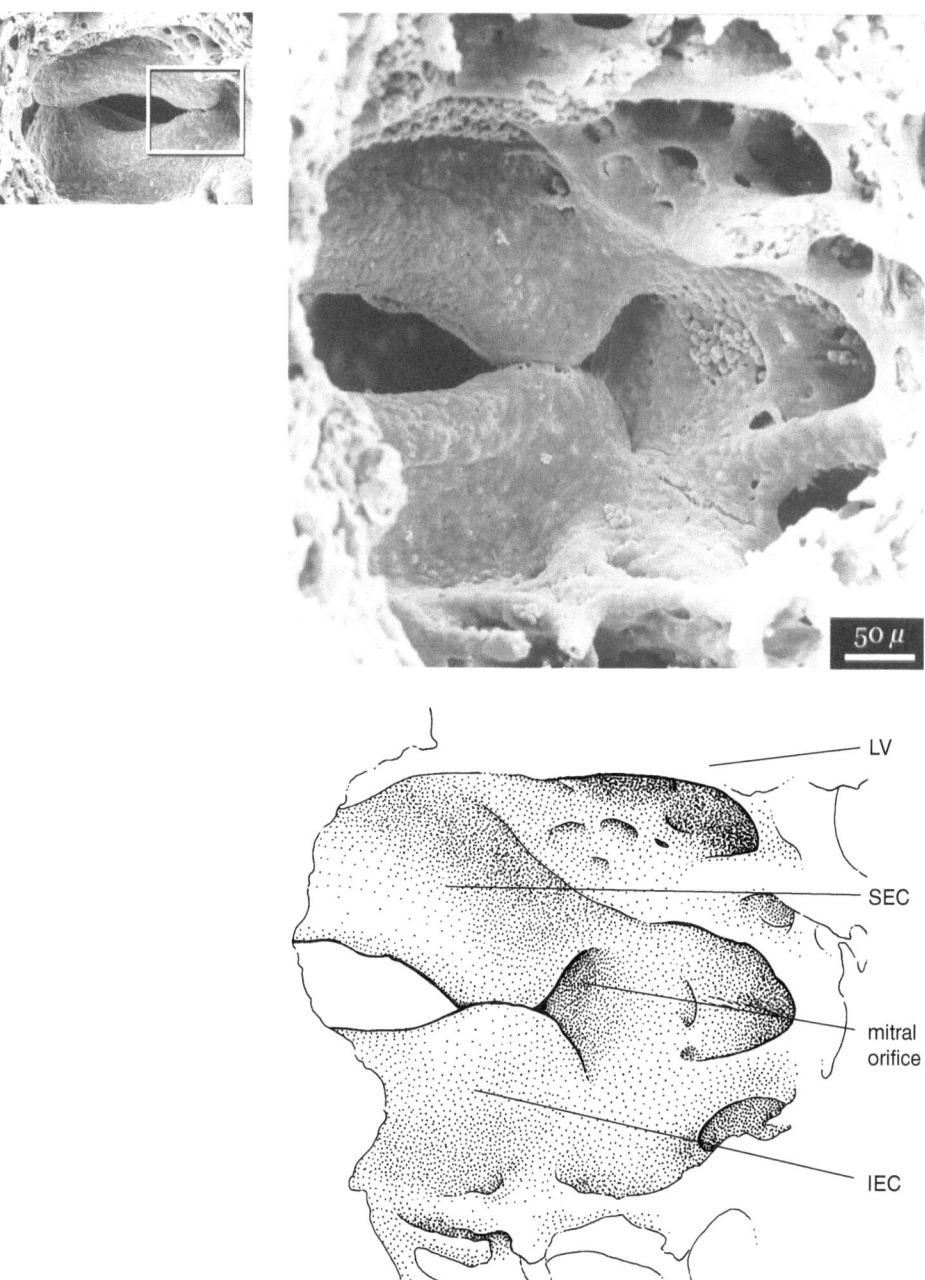

FIGURE 4.29   Tricuspid and mitral orifices (stage 17).

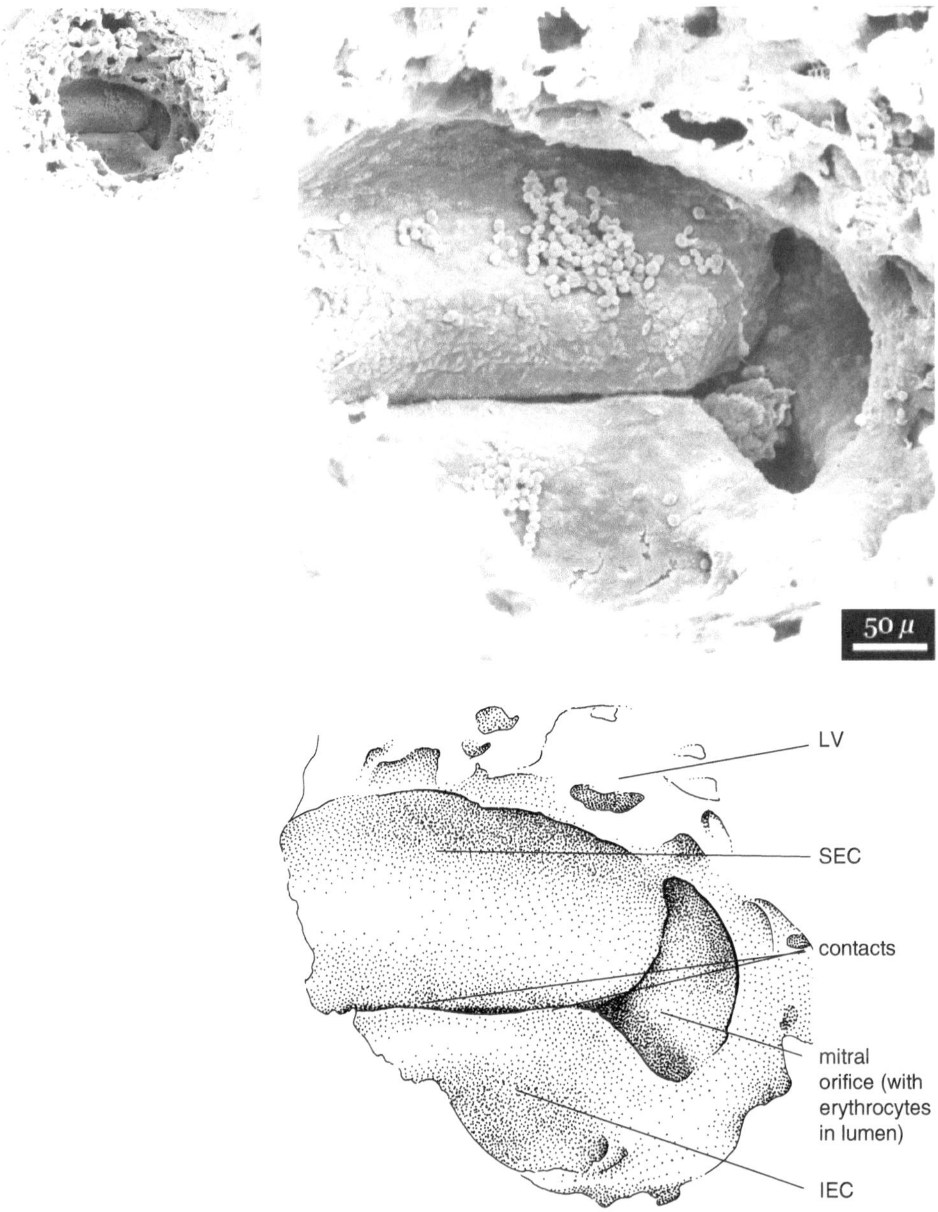

FIGURE 4.30   Tricuspid and mitral orifices (stage 17). In this specimen the H shaped lumen of the atrioventricular canal is about to become permanently separated. The primary interatrial septum is approaching from posterior.

FIGURE 4.31   Opened RV and outflow tract (stage 17), ventral lateral view. The endocardial ridges in the outflow tract give rise to two of the three cusps of both semilunar valves, the remaing ones being formed by intercalated endocardial ridges. The ridges in the proximal part of outflow tract come in contact with those of the distal part and grow proximally in the direction of the atrioventricular cushions. Colors indicate the superior endocardial cushion (red), inferior endocardial cushion (dark green), right and left lateral endocardial cushions (orange), parietal and superior endocardial ridges (yellow), septal and inferior endocardial ridges (dark blue), and intercalated endocardial ridges (purple). Arrows indicate left and right ventricular inflow and outflow patterns.

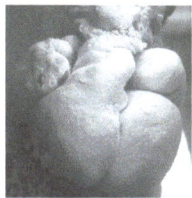

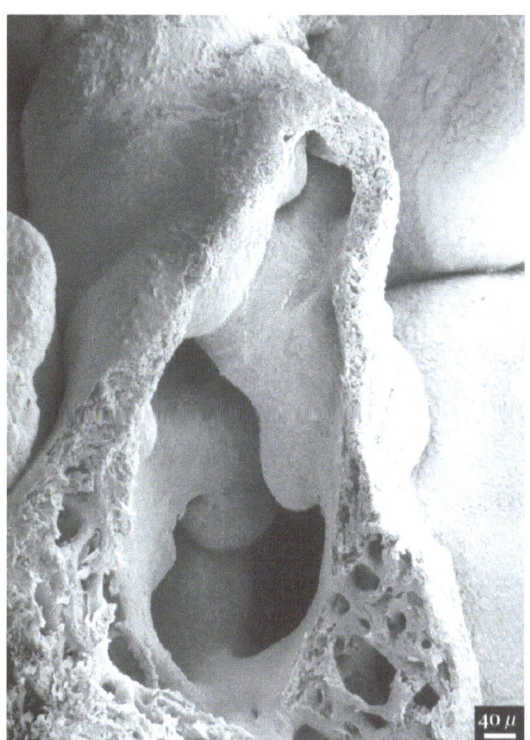

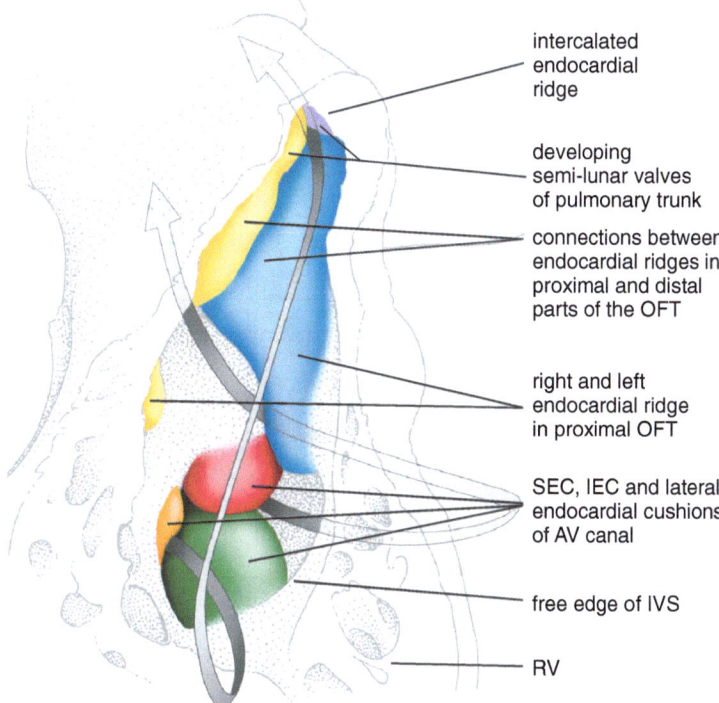

intercalated
endocardial
ridge

developing
semi-lunar valves
of pulmonary trunk

connections between
endocardial ridges in
proximal and distal
parts of the OFT

right and left
endocardial ridge
in proximal OFT

SEC, IEC and lateral
endocardial cushions
of AV canal

free edge of IVS

RV

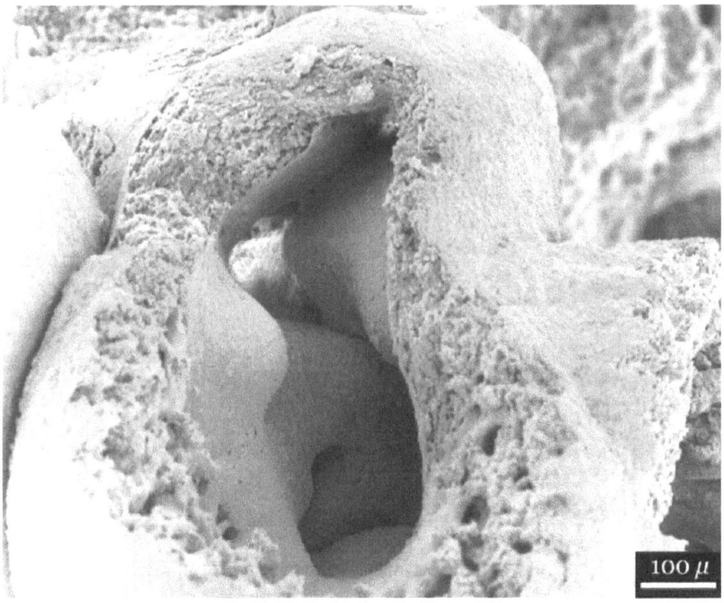

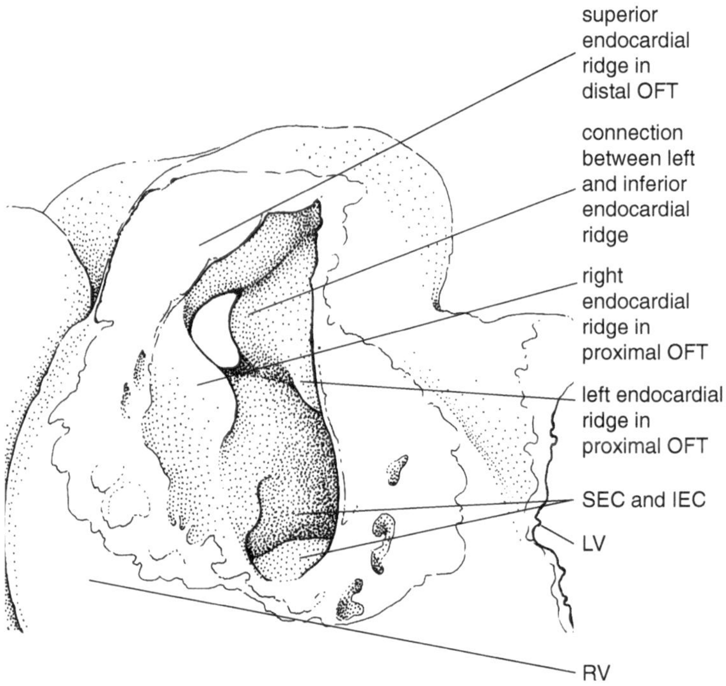

superior
endocardial
ridge in
distal OFT

connection
between left
and inferior
endocardial
ridge

right
endocardial
ridge in
proximal OFT

left endocardial
ridge in
proximal OFT

SEC and IEC

LV

RV

FIGURES 4.32 and 4.33   Opened ventricles and outflow tract (stage 17), ventral and right lateral views.

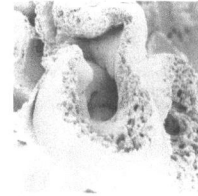

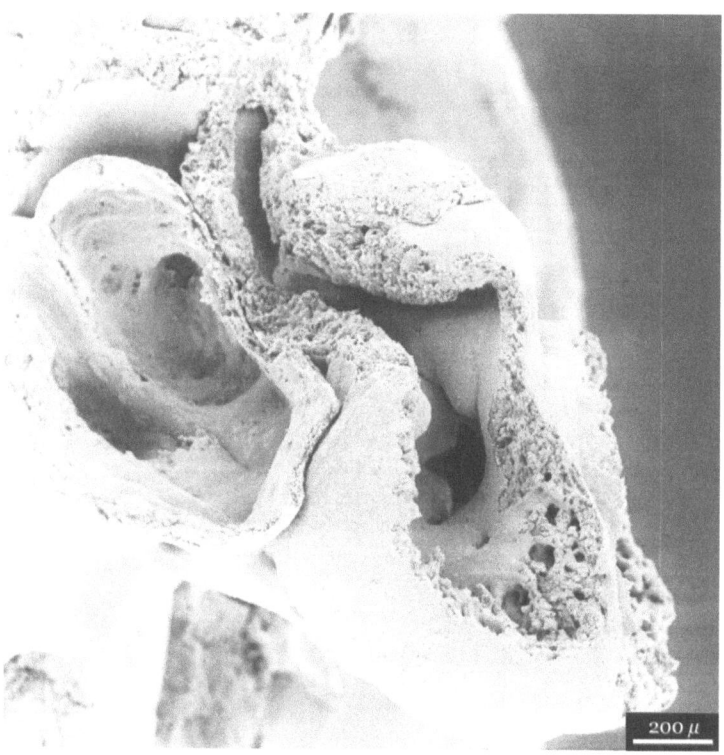

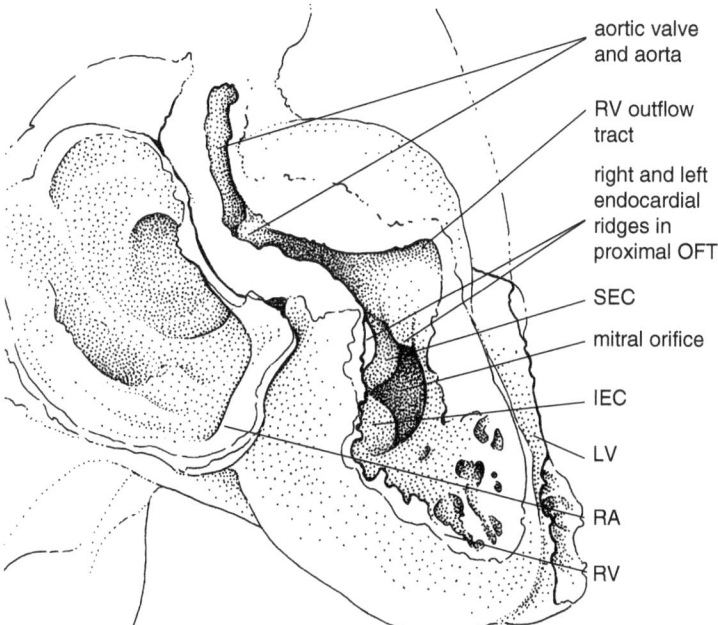

FIGURES 4.32 and 4.33   *Continued*

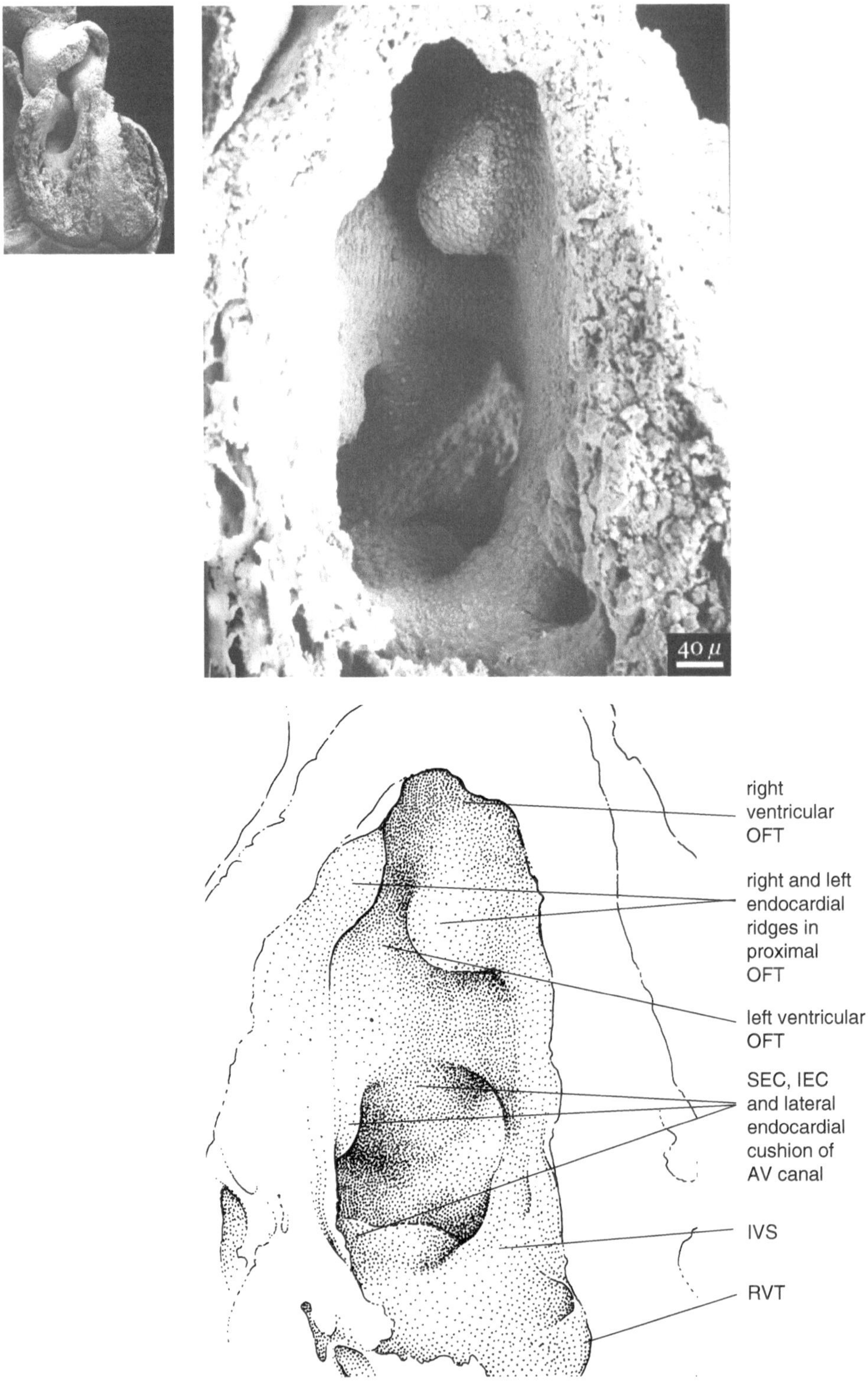

right
ventricular
OFT

right and left
endocardial
ridges in
proximal
OFT

left ventricular
OFT

SEC, IEC
and lateral
endocardial
cushion of
AV canal

IVS

RVT

FIGURE 4.34–4.37   Opened RV and outflow tract (stage 17), right lateral view.

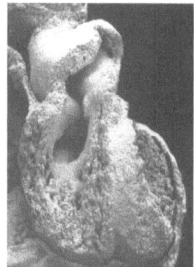

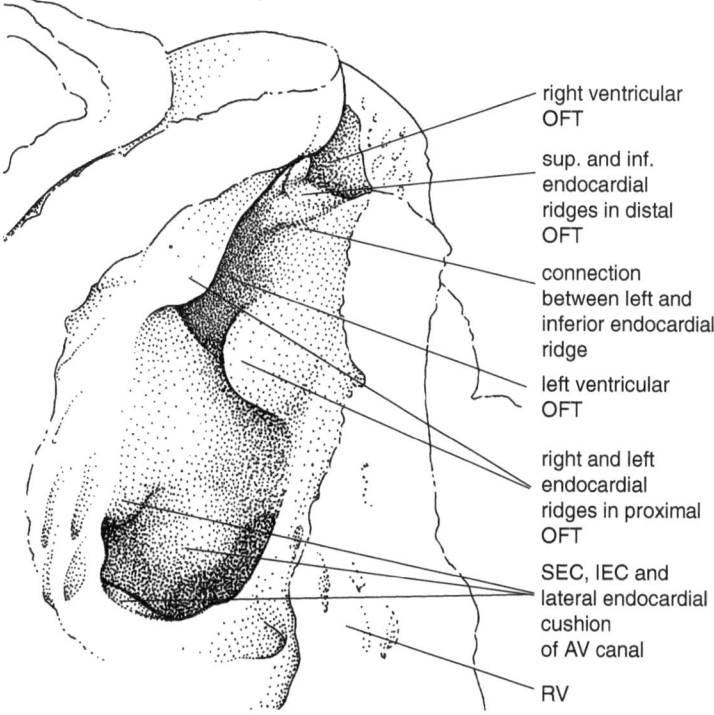

right ventricular
OFT

sup. and inf.
endocardial
ridges in distal
OFT

connection
between left and
inferior endocardial
ridge

left ventricular
OFT

right and left
endocardial
ridges in proximal
OFT

SEC, IEC and
lateral endocardial
cushion
of AV canal

RV

FIGURES 4.34–4.37   *Continued*

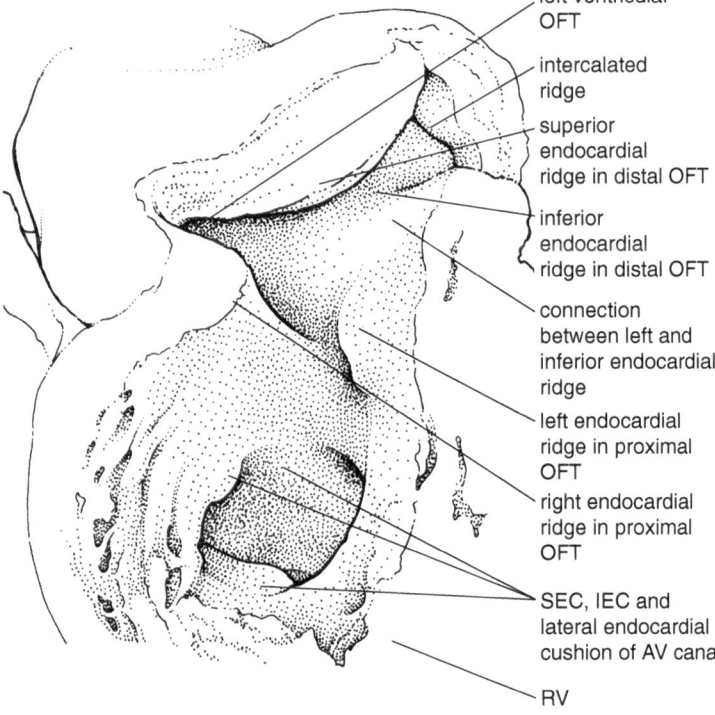

FIGURES 4.34-4.37   *Continued*

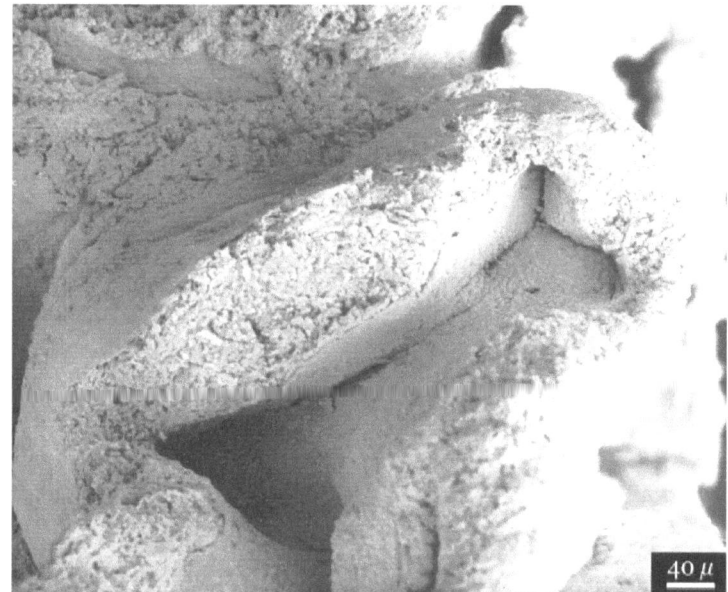

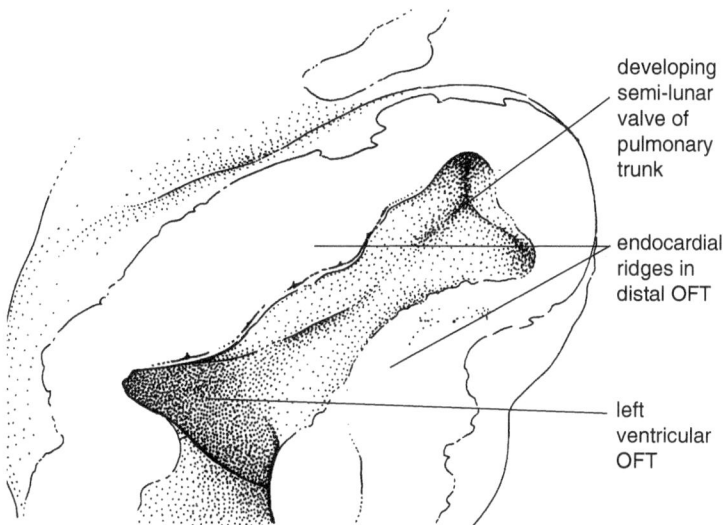

developing
semi-lunar
valve of
pulmonary
trunk

endocardial
ridges in
distal OFT

left
ventricular
OFT

FIGURES 4.34–4.37   *Continued*

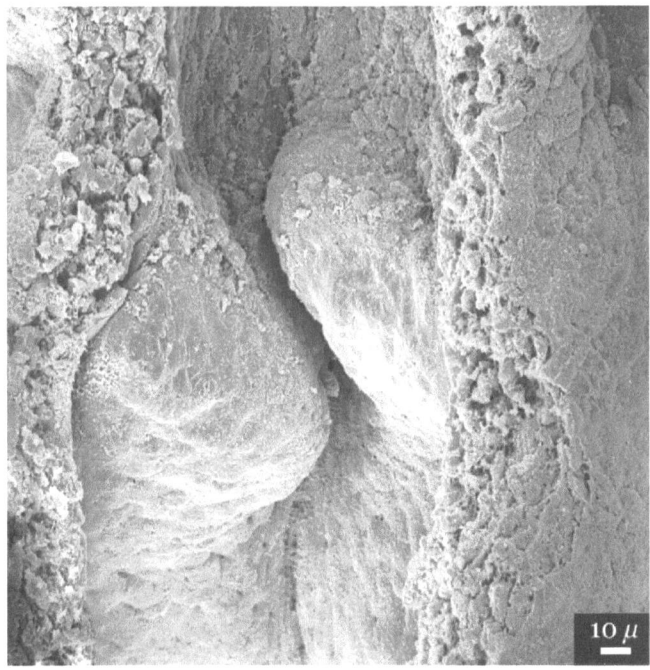

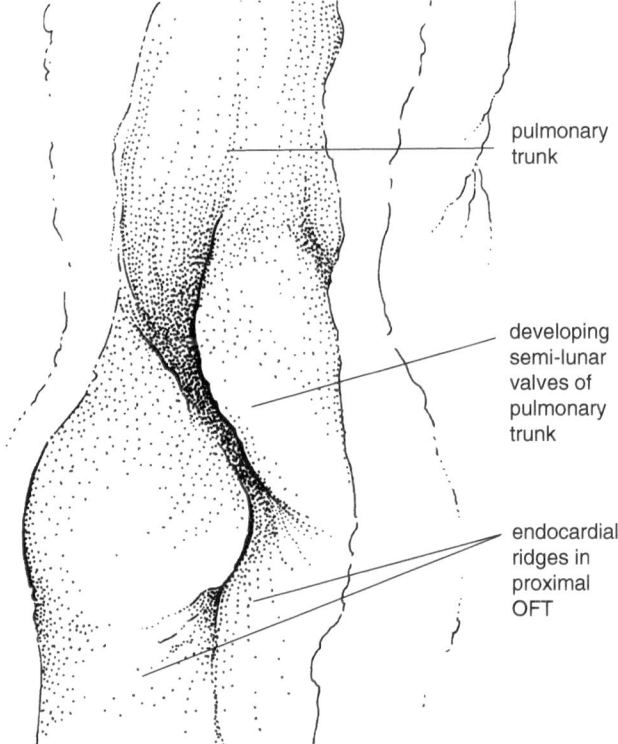

pulmonary
trunk

developing
semi-lunar
valves of
pulmonary
trunk

endocardial
ridges in
proximal
OFT

FIGURE 4.38   Opened RV and outflow tract (stage 17), right lateral view.

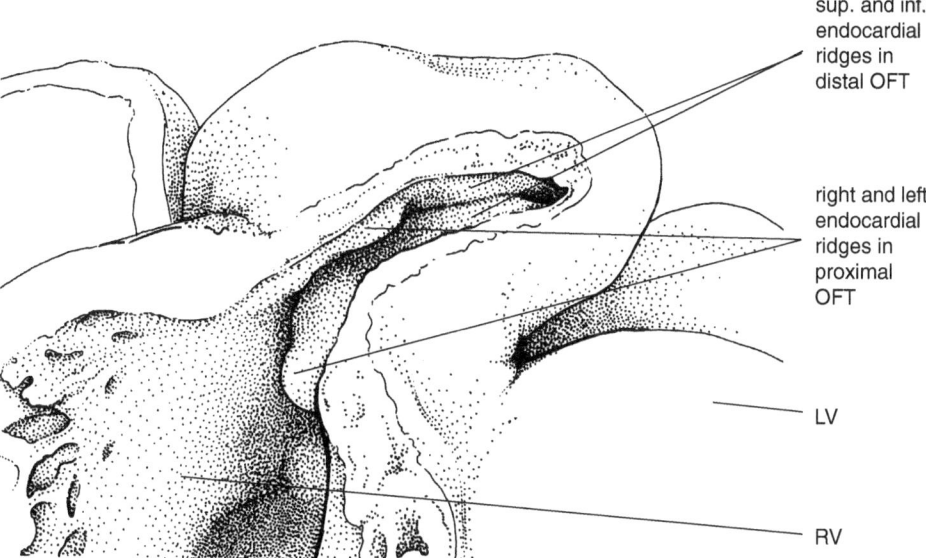

sup. and inf.
endocardial
ridges in
distal OFT

right and left
endocardial
ridges in
proximal
OFT

LV

RV

FIGURE 4.39   Opened RV and outflow tract (stage 17), right lateral view.

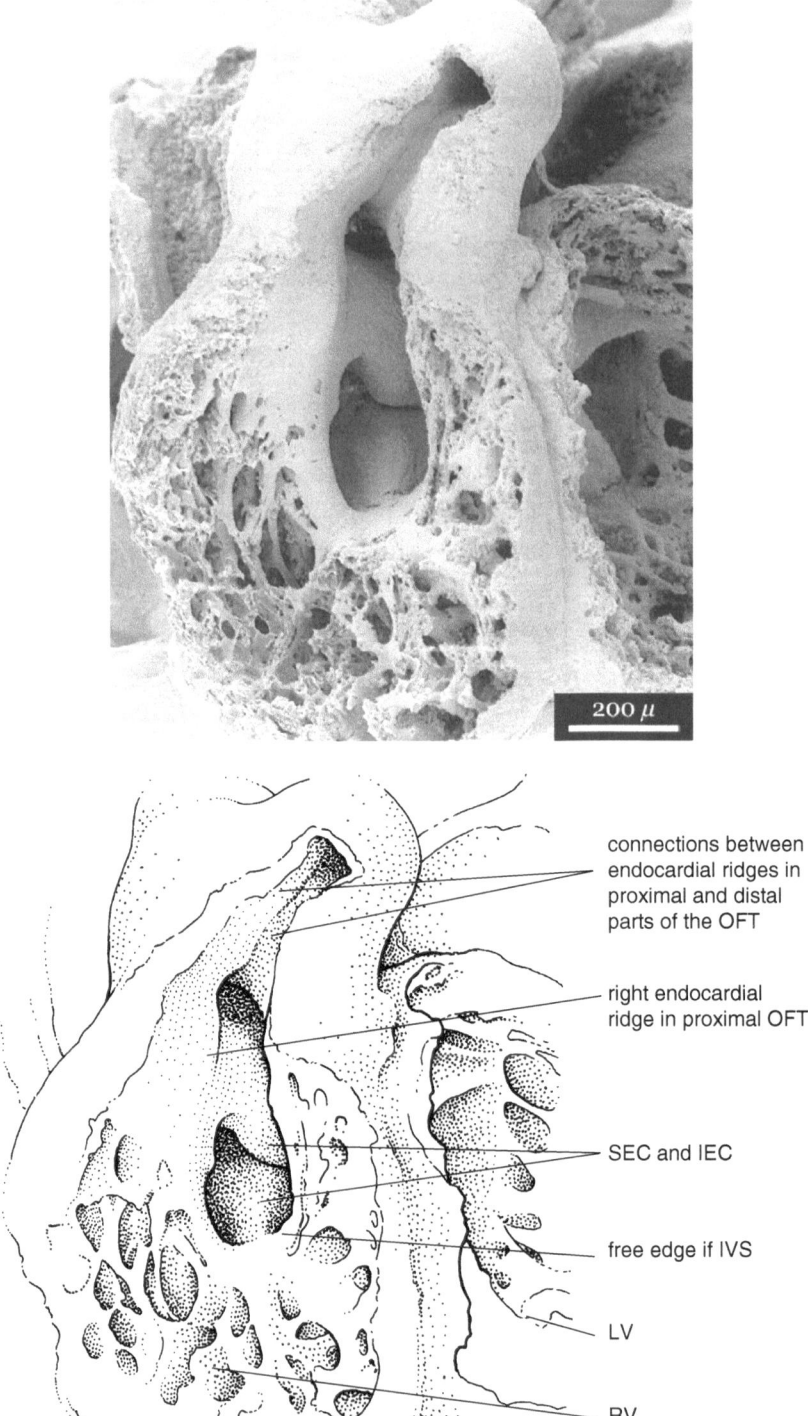

FIGURE 4.40   Opened ventricles and outflow tract (stage 17), ventral view. This specimen clearly shows the rightward position of the interventricular septum in relation to the atrioventricular canal.

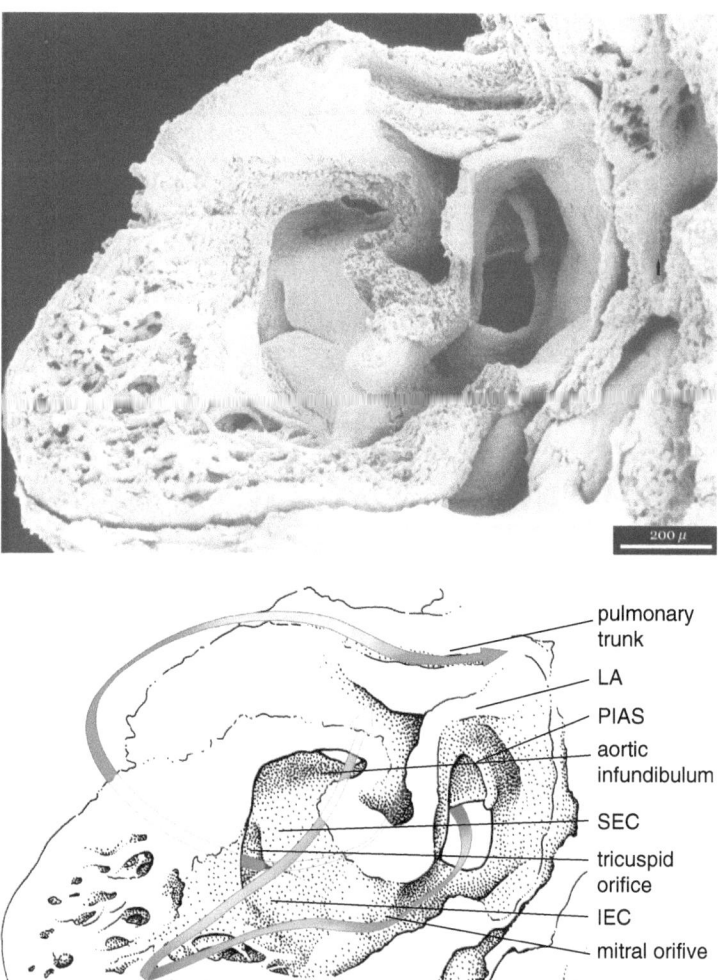

FIGURES 4.41–4.44   Opened atria, ventricles and outflow tract (stage 17), left and right lateral and detailed views. The left ventricular outflow tract is canuled. In this specimen, the endocardial cushions have already fused with each other to a certain extend, as well as the endocardial ridges in the proximal outflow tract. Colors indicate the superior endocardial cushion (red), inferior endocardial cushion (dark green), right and left lateral endocardial cushions (orange), parietal endocardial ridges (yellow), septal endocardial ridges (dark blue), and intercalated endocardial ridges (purple). Arrows indicate left and right ventricular inflow and outflow patterns.

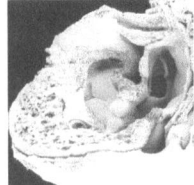

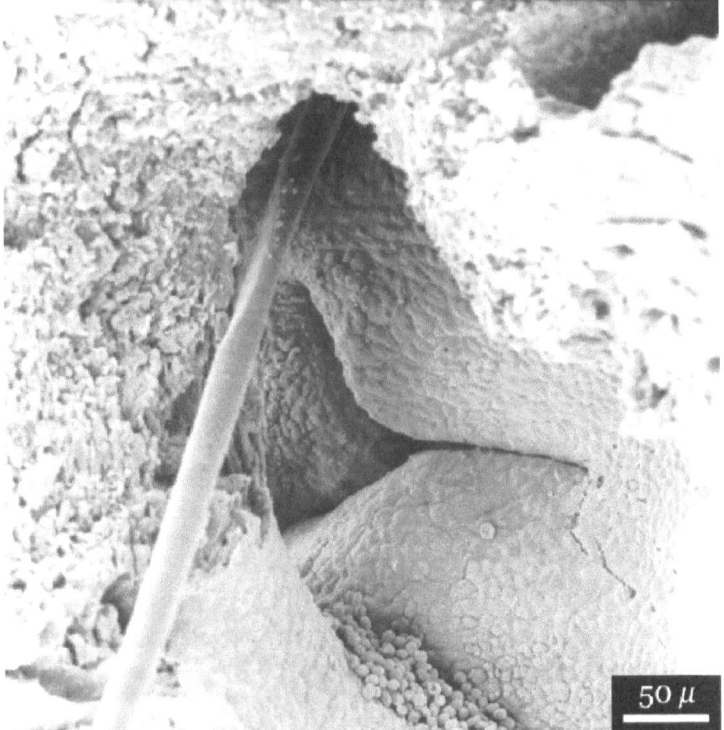

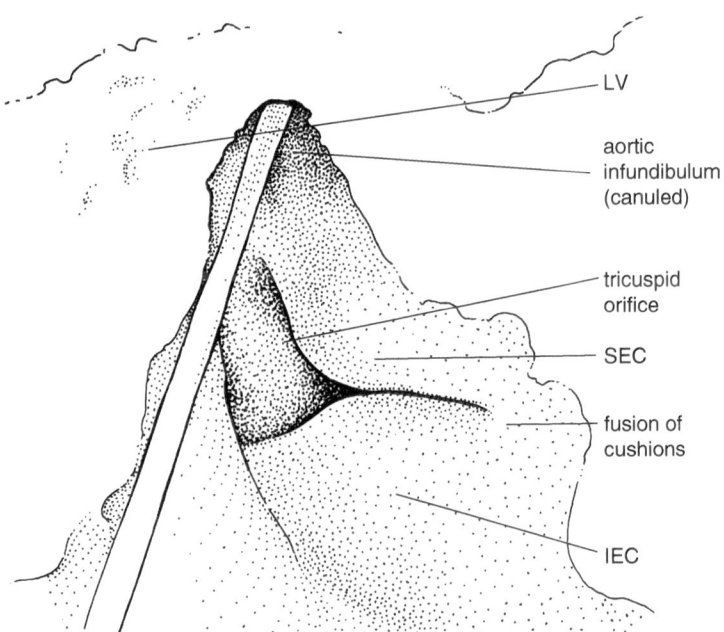

FIGURES 4.41–4.44   *Continued*

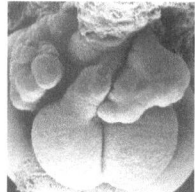

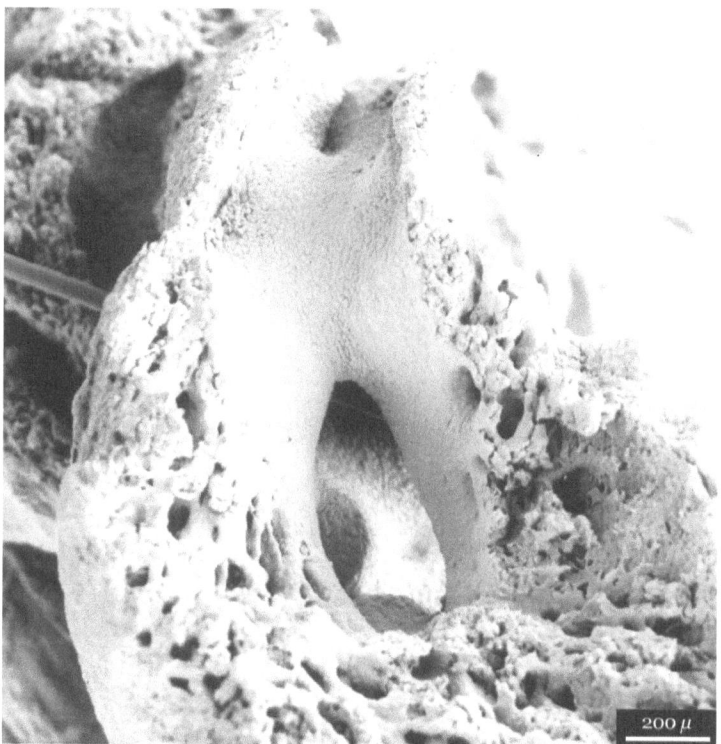

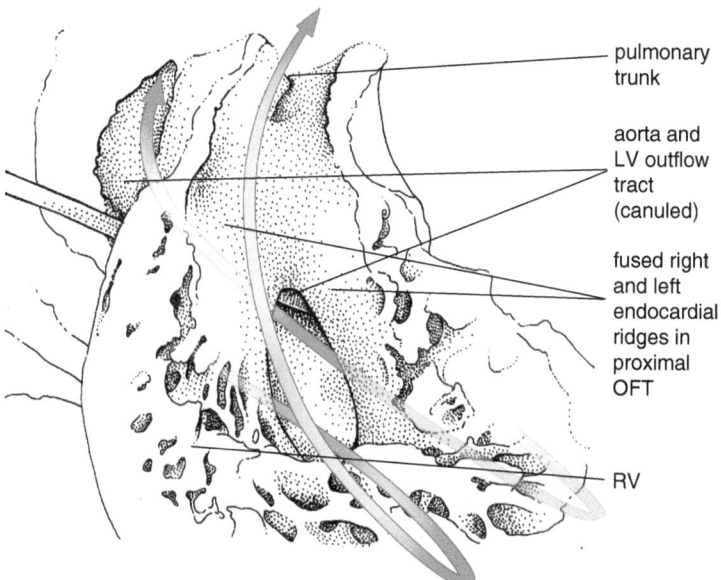

FIGURES 4.41–4.44   *Continued*

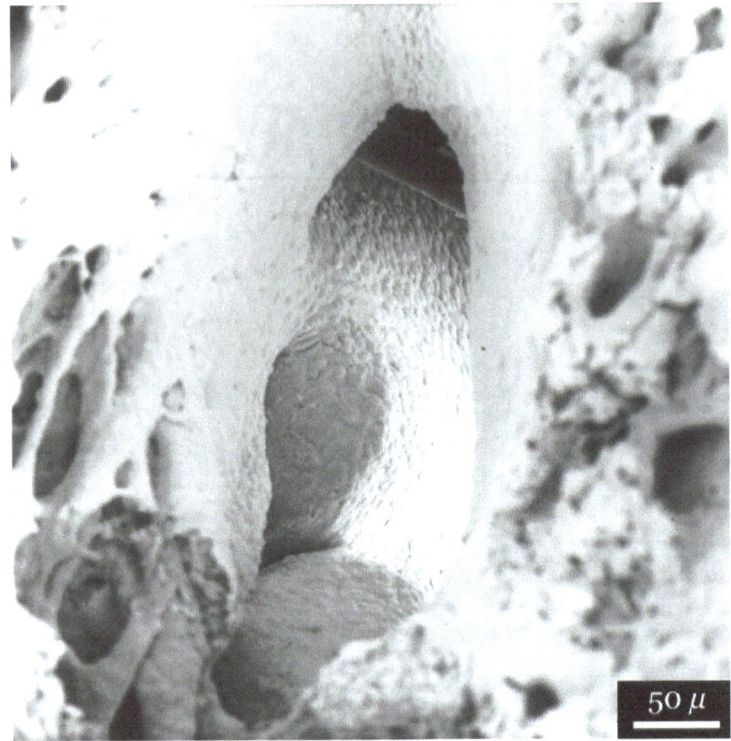

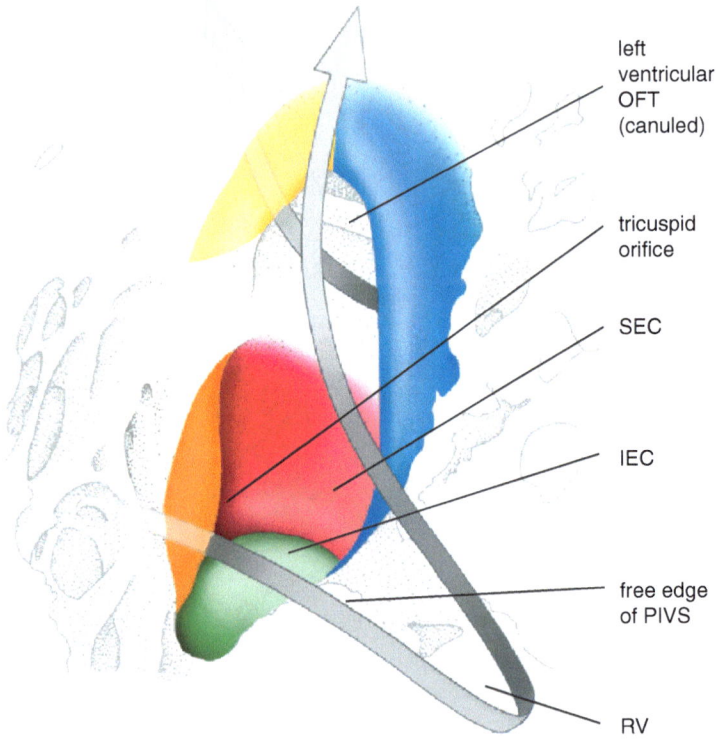

left
ventricular
OFT
(canuled)

tricuspid
orifice

SEC

IEC

free edge
of PIVS

RV

FIGURES 4.41–4.44   *Continued*

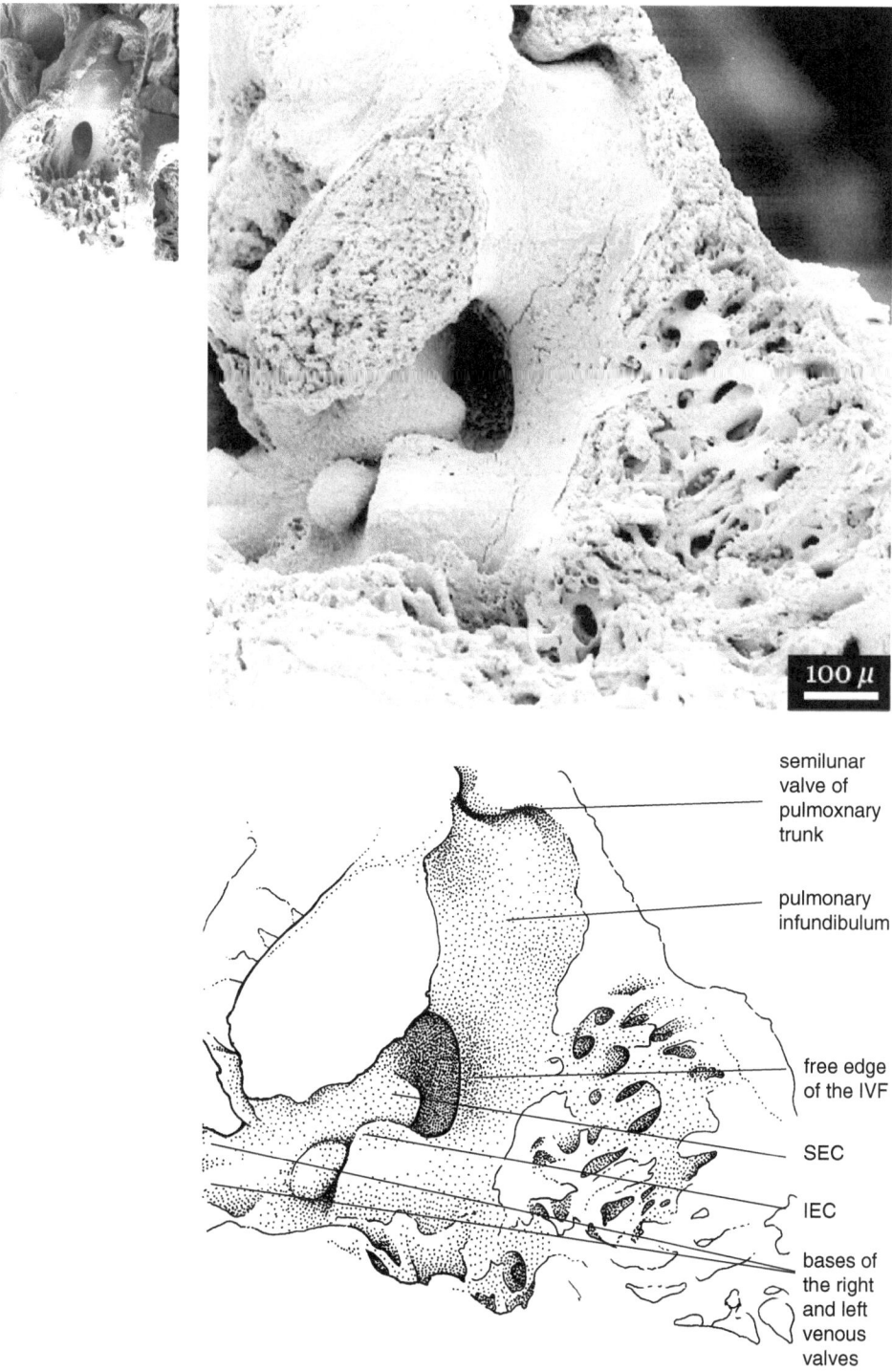

FIGURE 4.45   Opened RV (stage 17), right lateral view.

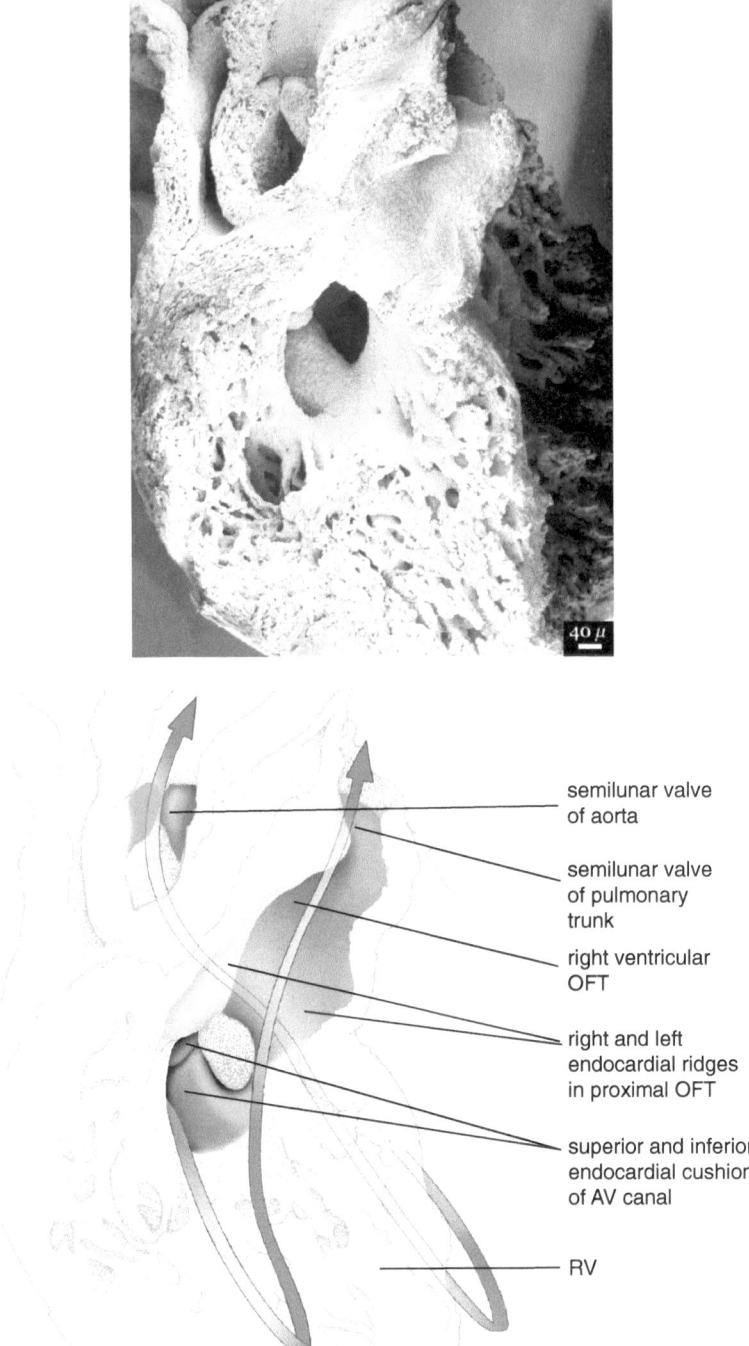

FIGURE 4.46   Opened RV and outflow tract (stage 18), right lateral view. Colors indicate the superior endocardial cushion (red), inferior endocardial cushion (dark green), right and left lateral endocardial cushions (orange), parietal ridges (yellow), and septal endocardial ridges (dark blue). Arrows indicate left and right ventricular inflow and outflow patterns.

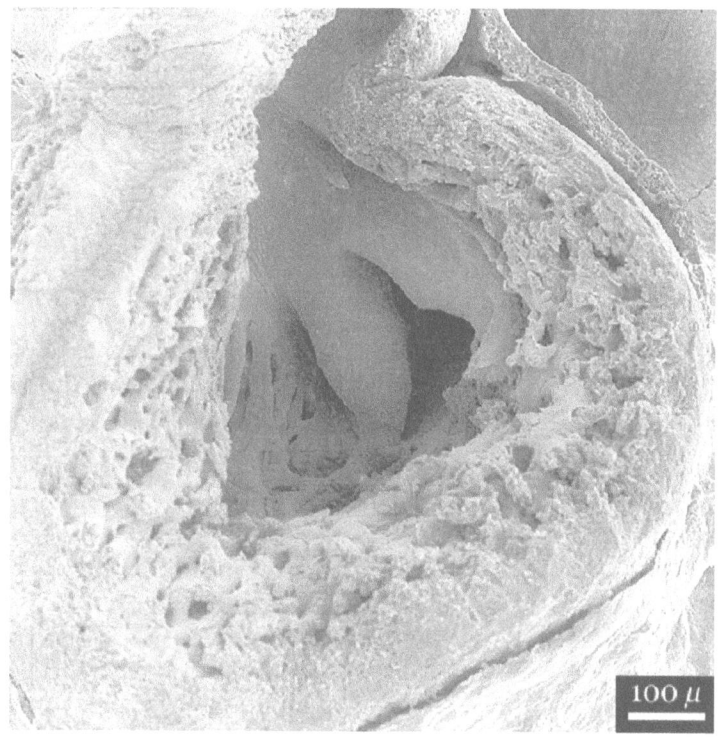

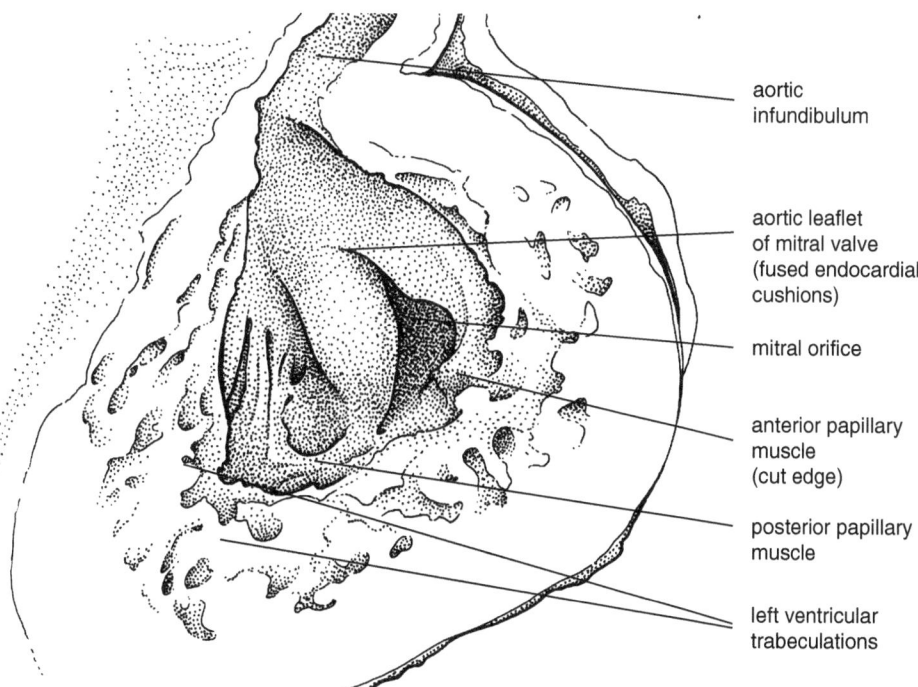

aortic
infundibulum

aortic leaflet
of mitral valve
(fused endocardial
cushions)

mitral orifice

anterior papillary
muscle
(cut edge)

posterior papillary
muscle

left ventricular
trabeculations

FIGURE 4.47   Opened LV (stage 18), left lateral view. The endocardial cushions, which contribute to the formation of the aortic leaflet of the mitral valve, have not yet fused completely.

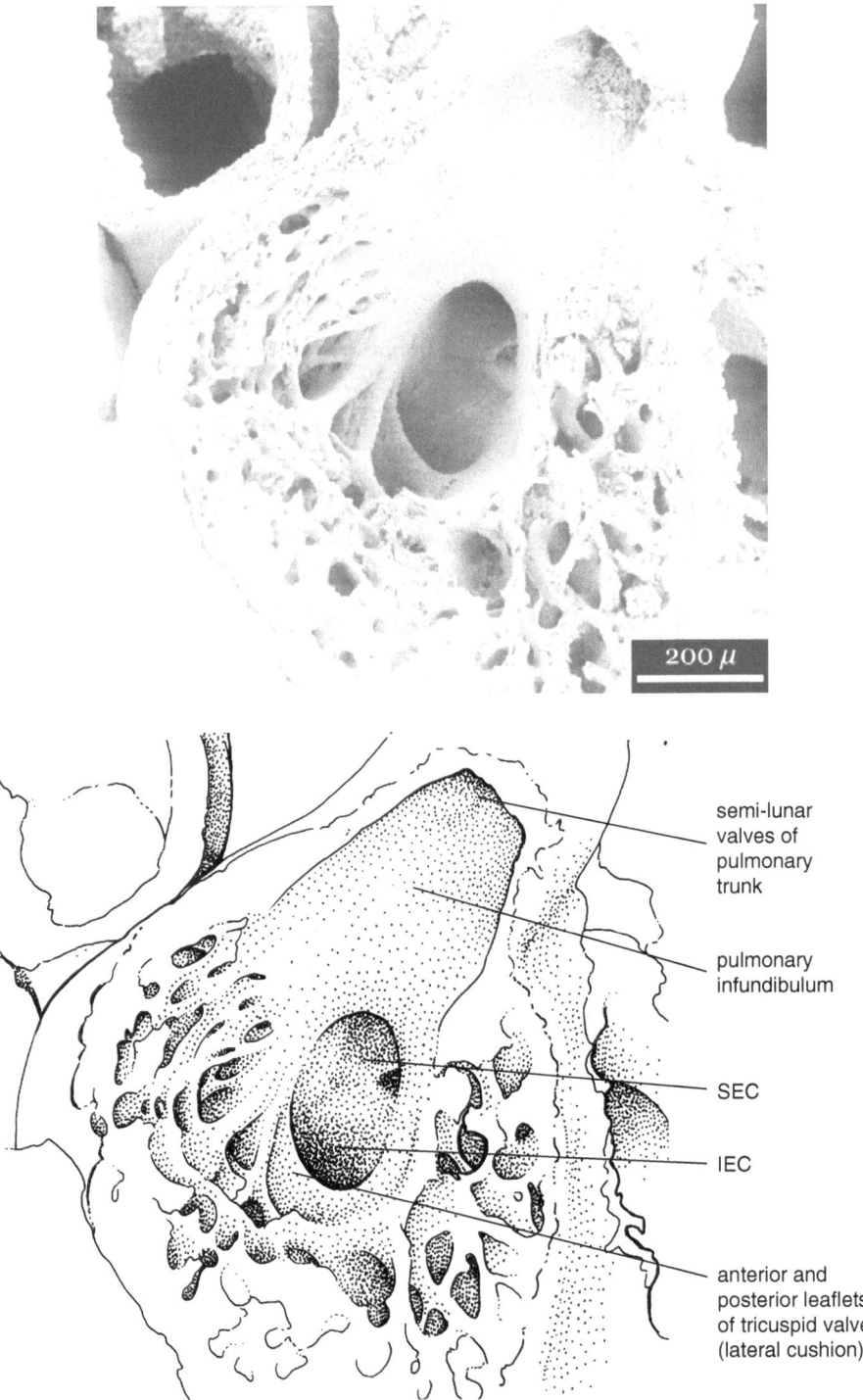

semi-lunar
valves of
pulmonary
trunk

pulmonary
infundibulum

SEC

IEC

anterior and
posterior leaflets
of tricuspid valve
(lateral cushion)

FIGURES 4.48 and 4.49   Opened RV and LV (stage 18), right and left lateral views. In this specimen the endocardial ridges have fused completely to form the infundibular septum. Closure of the secondary interventricular foramen still has to be completed. The superior and inferior endocardial cushions have also fused for the greater part.

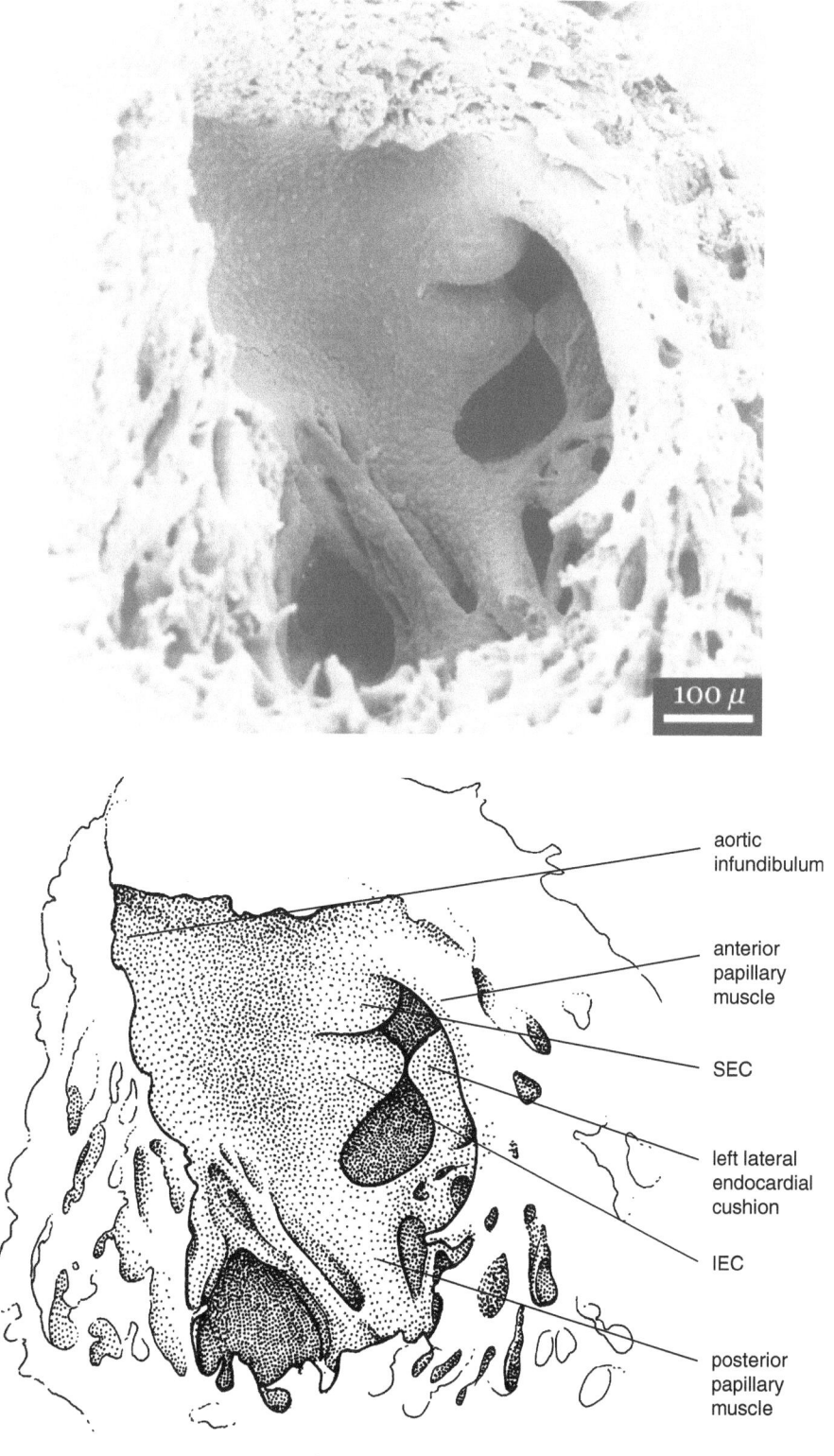

FIGURES 4.48 and 4.49   *Continued*

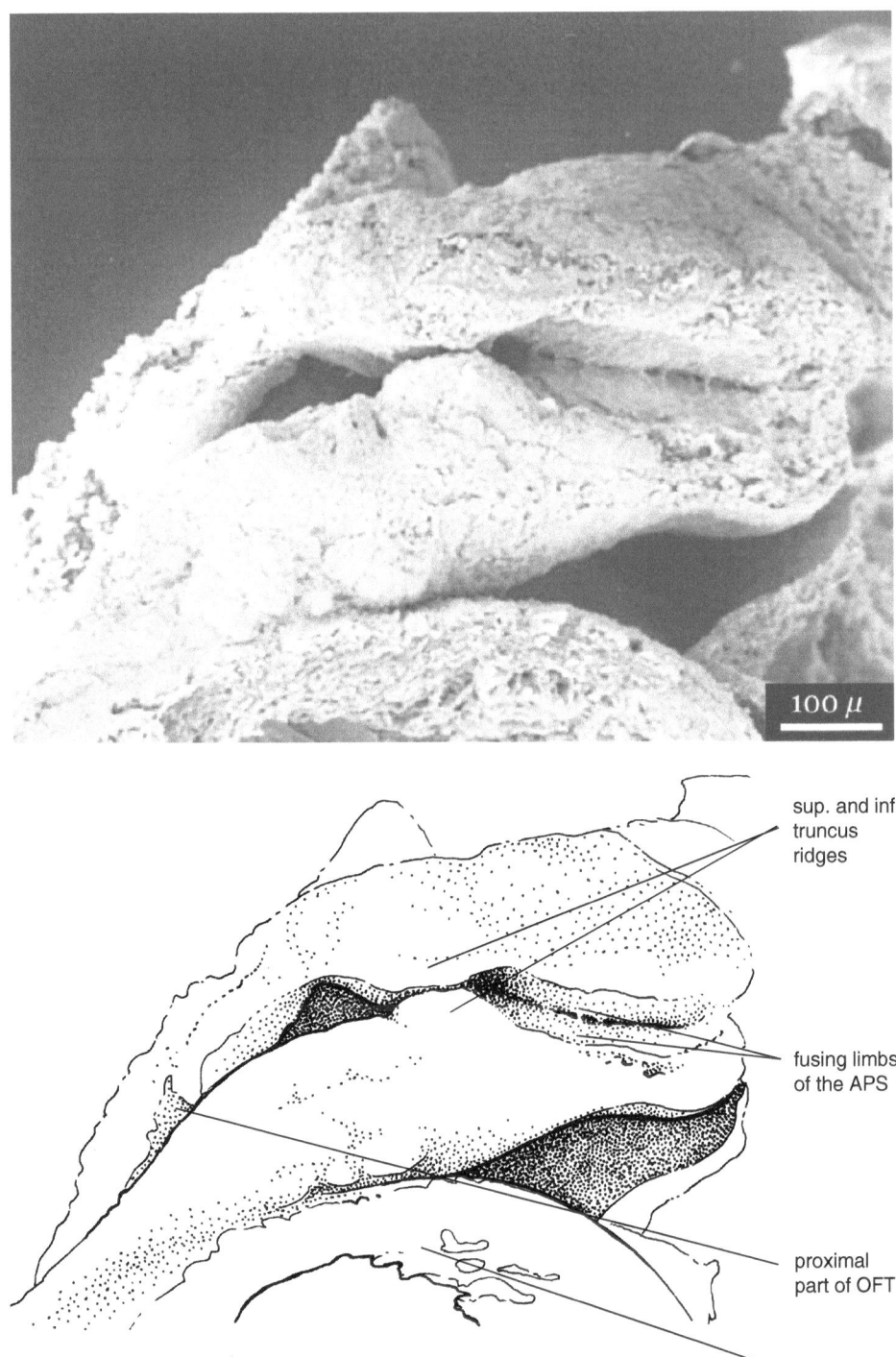

100 μ

sup. and inf.
truncus
ridges

fusing limbs
of the APS

proximal
part of OFT

LV

FIGURES 4.50 and 4.51   Opened proximal and distal parts of the outflow tract (stage 18), left lateral and detailed view. The distal ends of the endocardial ridges in the proximal part of the outflow tract start to form semilunar valves and connect with the fusing ridges in the distal part of the outflow tract.

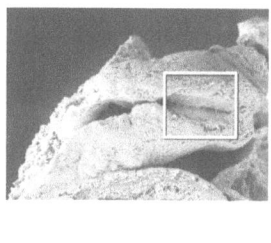

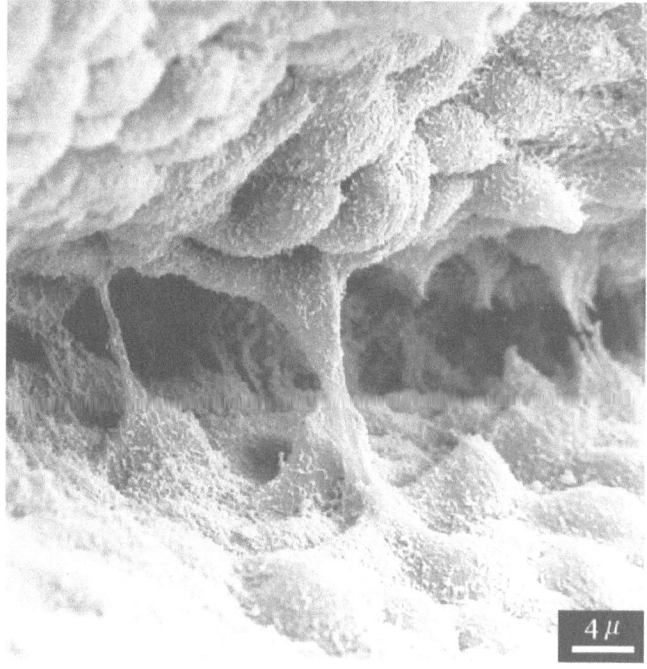

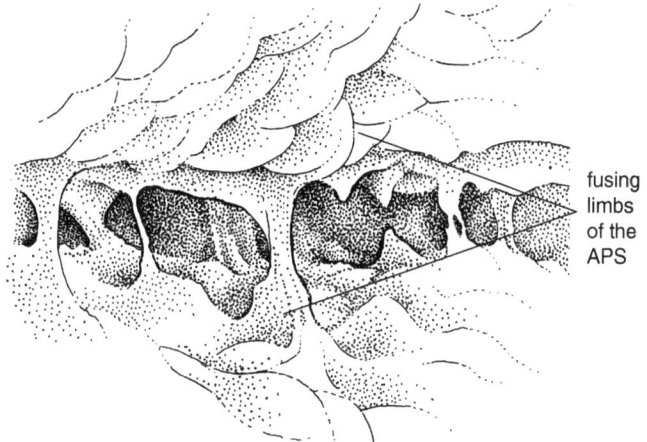

FIGURES 4.50 and 4.51   *Continued*

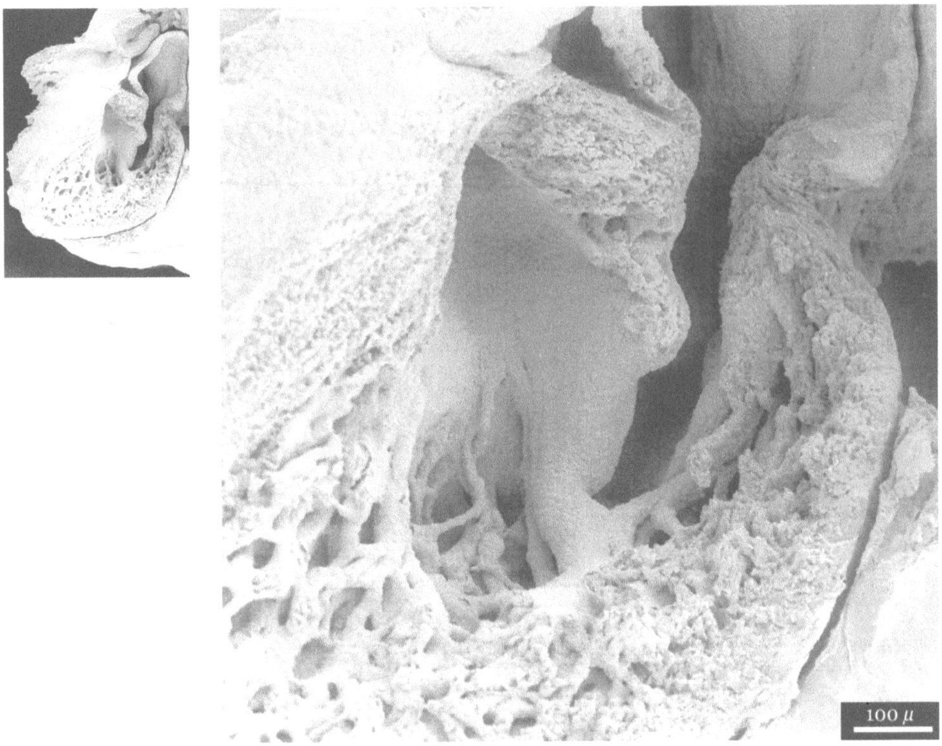

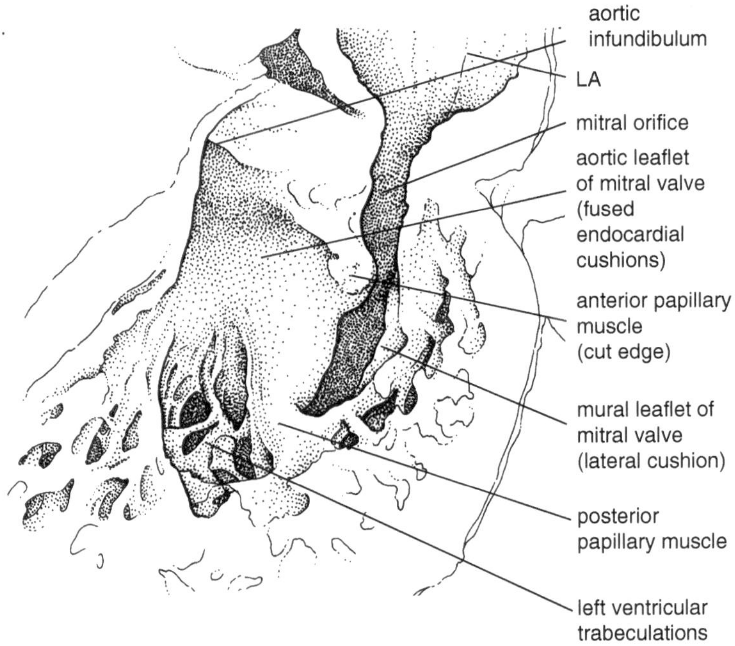

aortic
infundibulum

LA

mitral orifice

aortic leaflet
of mitral valve
(fused
endocardial
cushions)

anterior papillary
muscle
(cut edge)

mural leaflet of
mitral valve
(lateral cushion)

posterior
papillary muscle

left ventricular
trabeculations

FIGURES 4.52 and 4.53   Opened LA ,LV and pulmonary trunk (stage 19); left lateral and detailed views. Here, the superior and inferior endocardial cushions have fused completely and their left lateral part contributes to the aortic leaflet of the mitral valve. The left lateral endocardial cushion gives rise to the mural leaflet.

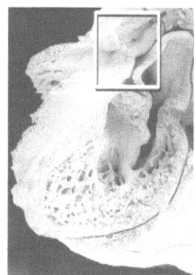

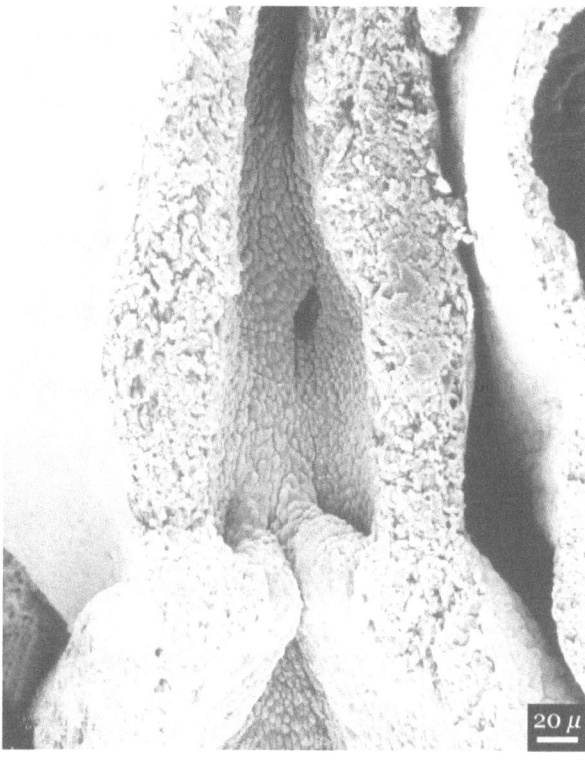

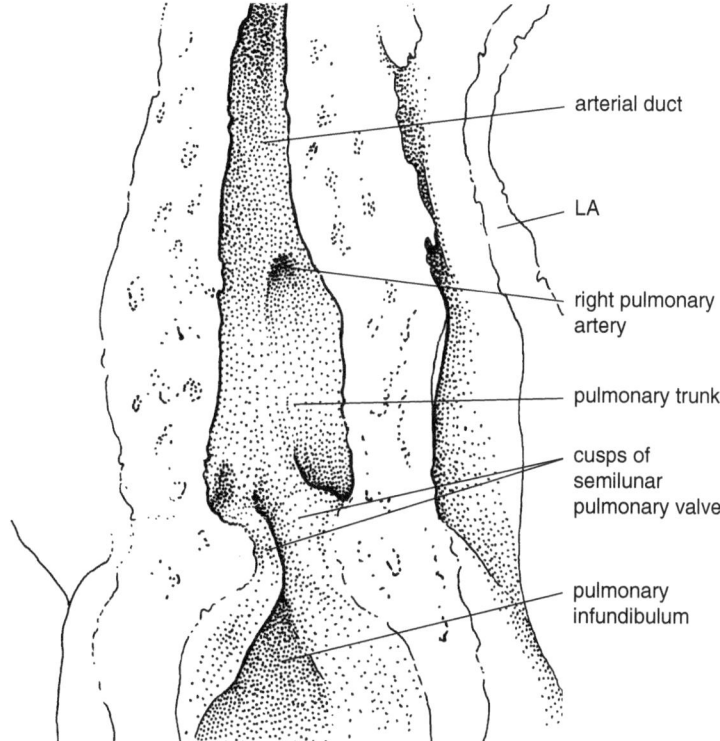

arterial duct

LA

right pulmonary
artery

pulmonary trunk

cusps of
semilunar
pulmonary valve

pulmonary
infundibulum

FIGURES 4.52 and 4.53   *Continued*

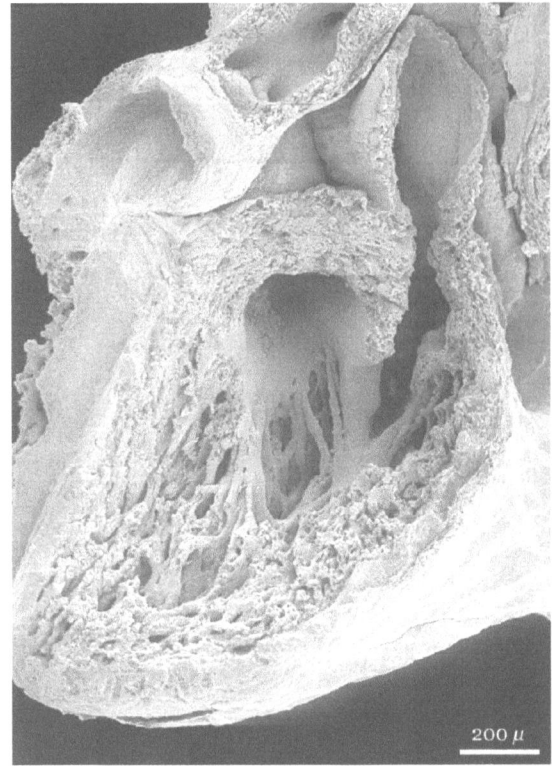

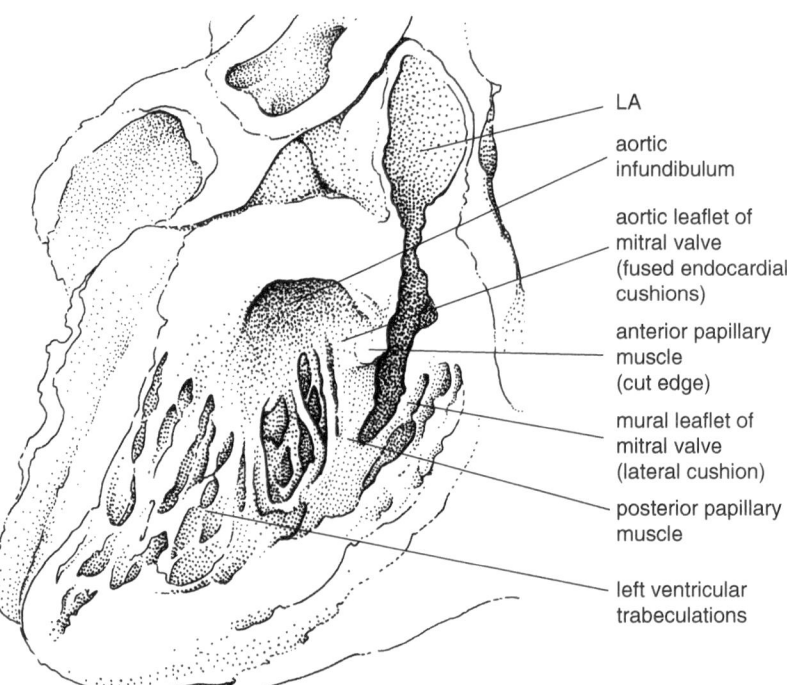

FIGURES 4.54 and 4.55   Opened LV, outflow tract and great arteries (stage 19), left lateral and detailed views.

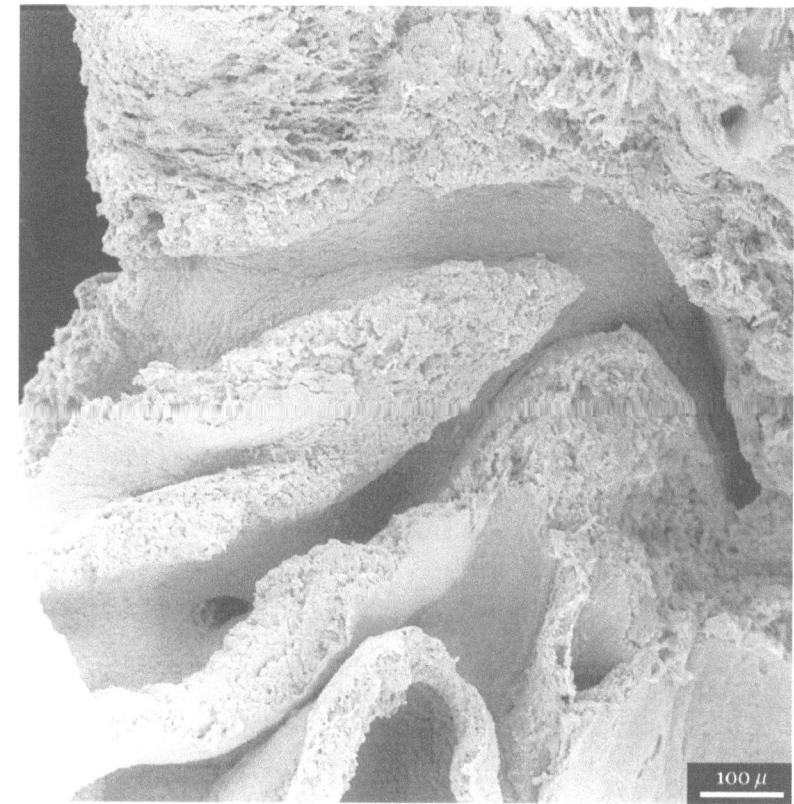

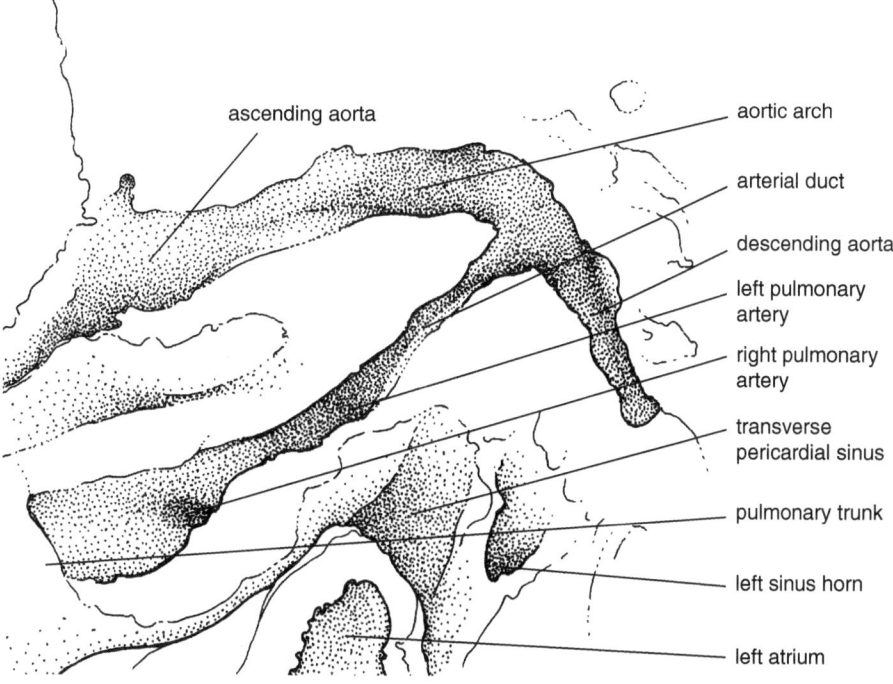

ascending aorta

aortic arch

arterial duct

descending aorta

left pulmonary artery

right pulmonary artery

transverse pericardial sinus

pulmonary trunk

left sinus horn

left atrium

FIGURES 4.54 and 4.55   *Continued*

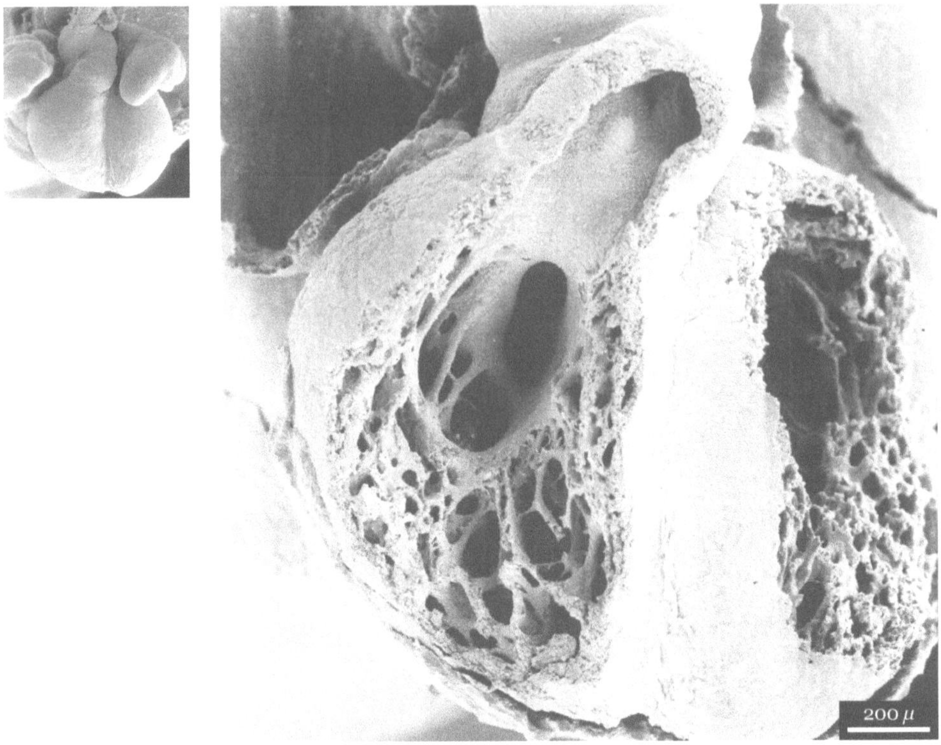

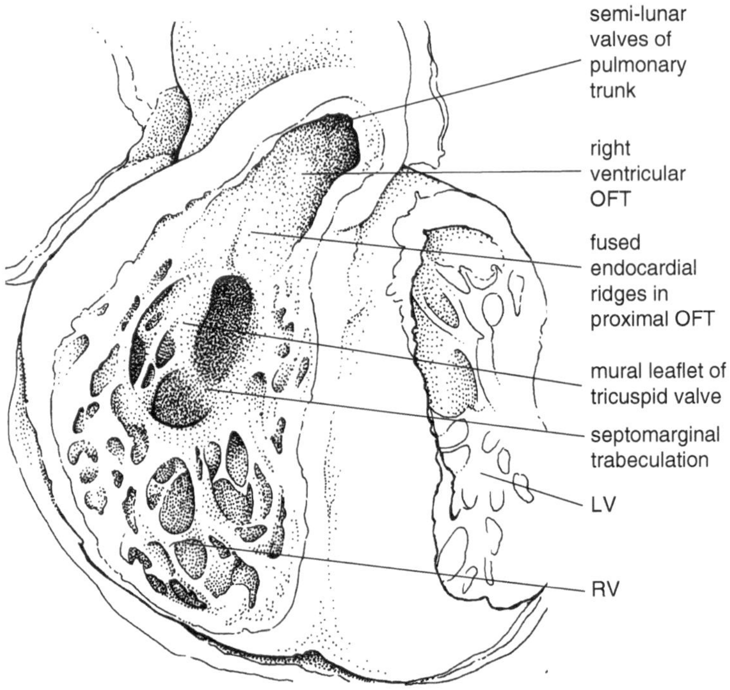

semi-lunar
valves of
pulmonary
trunk

right
ventricular
OFT

fused
endocardial
ridges in
proximal OFT

mural leaflet of
tricuspid valve

septomarginal
trabeculation

LV

RV

FIGURES 4.56 and 4.57   Opened RV and LV (stage 19), ventral and right lateral views.

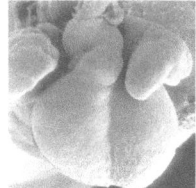

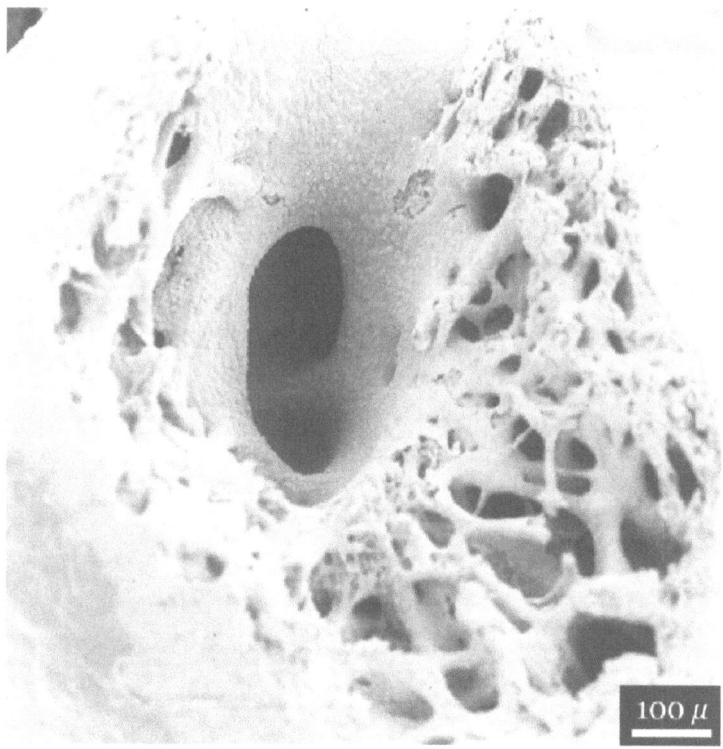

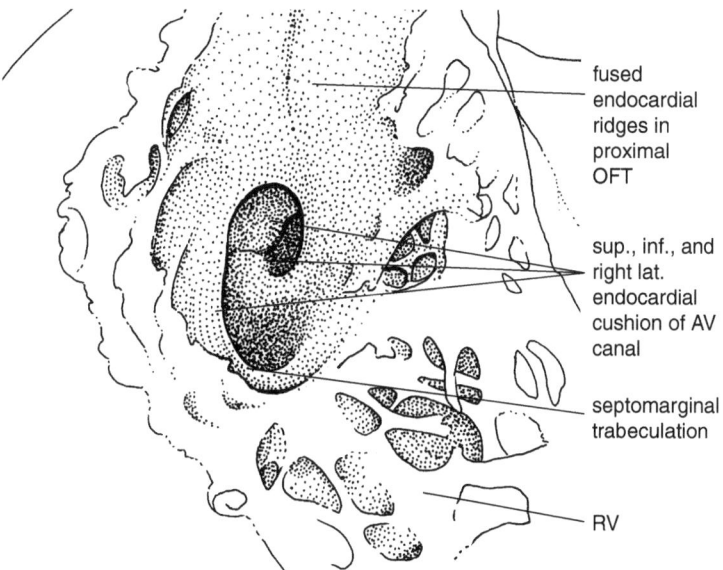

fused
endocardial
ridges in
proximal
OFT

sup., inf., and
right lat.
endocardial
cushion of AV
canal

septomarginal
trabeculation

RV

FIGURES 4.56 and 4.57   *Continued*

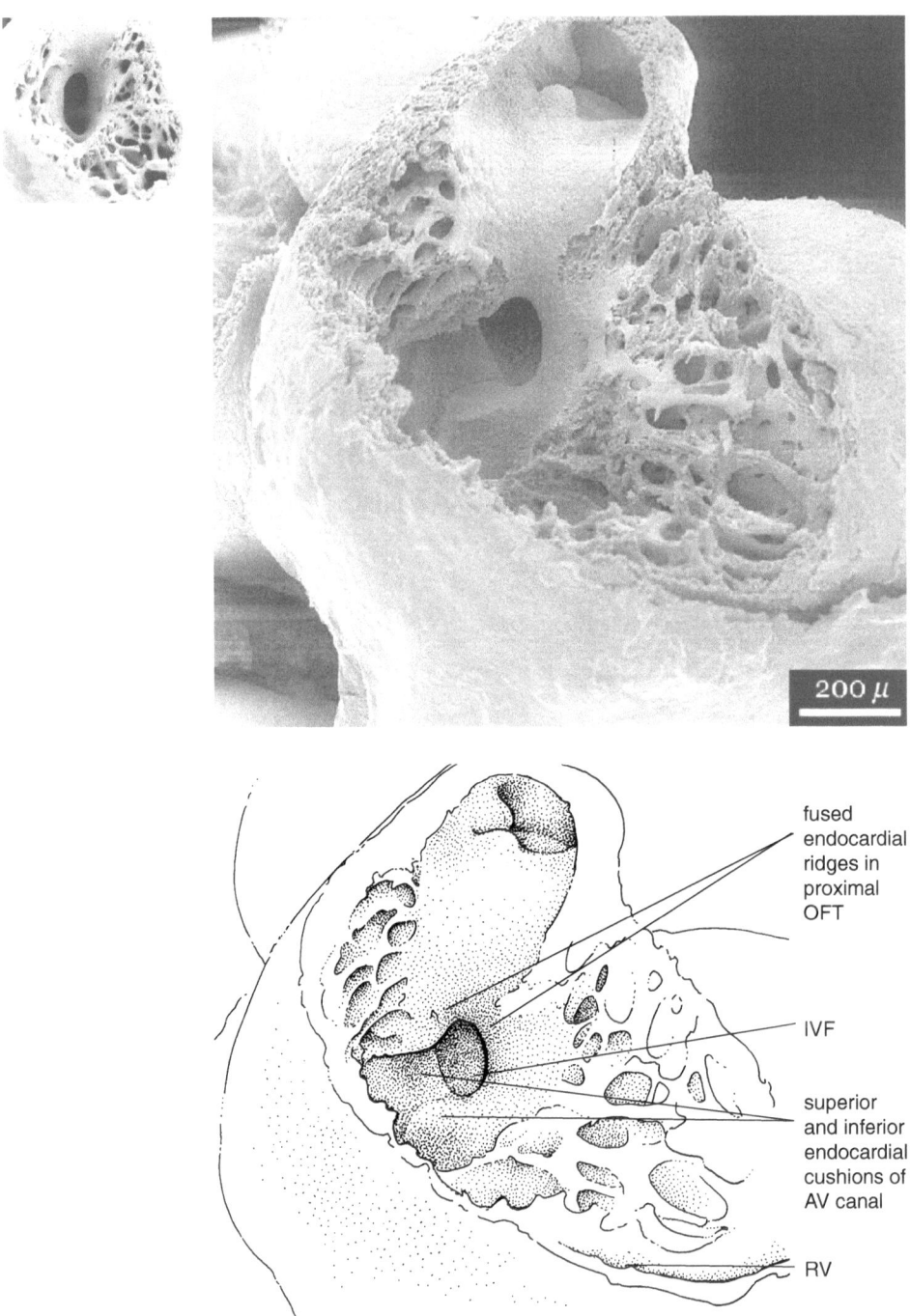

FIGURES 4.58–4.60   Opened RV and LV (stage 19), right and left lateral and detailed views. The right lateral wall, including the right lateral endocardial cushion, is partly removed.

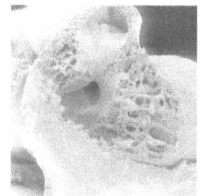

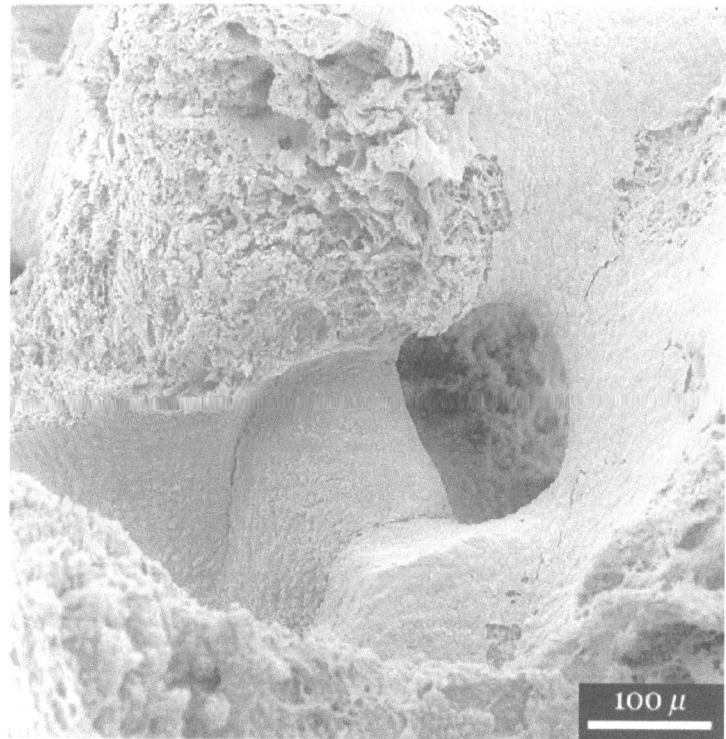

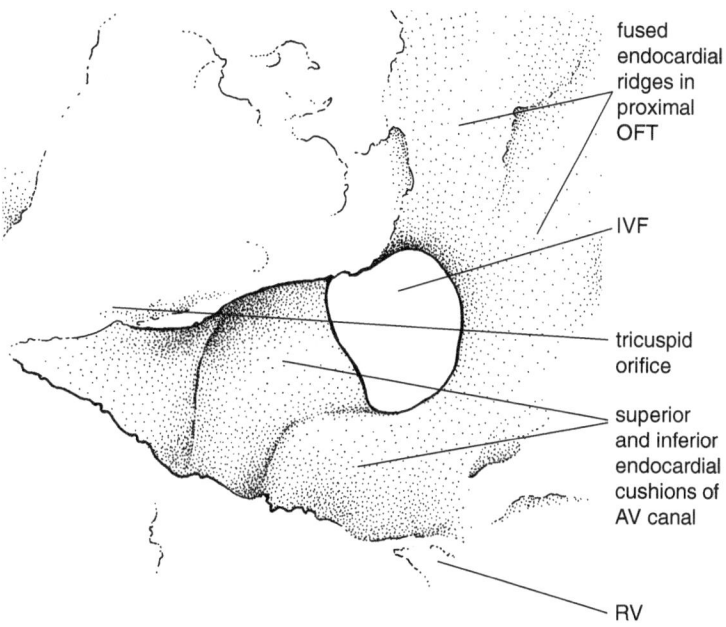

fused
endocardial
ridges in
proximal
OFT

IVF

tricuspid
orifice

superior
and inferior
endocardial
cushions of
AV canal

RV

FIGURES 4.58–4.60   *Continued*

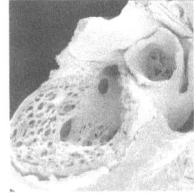
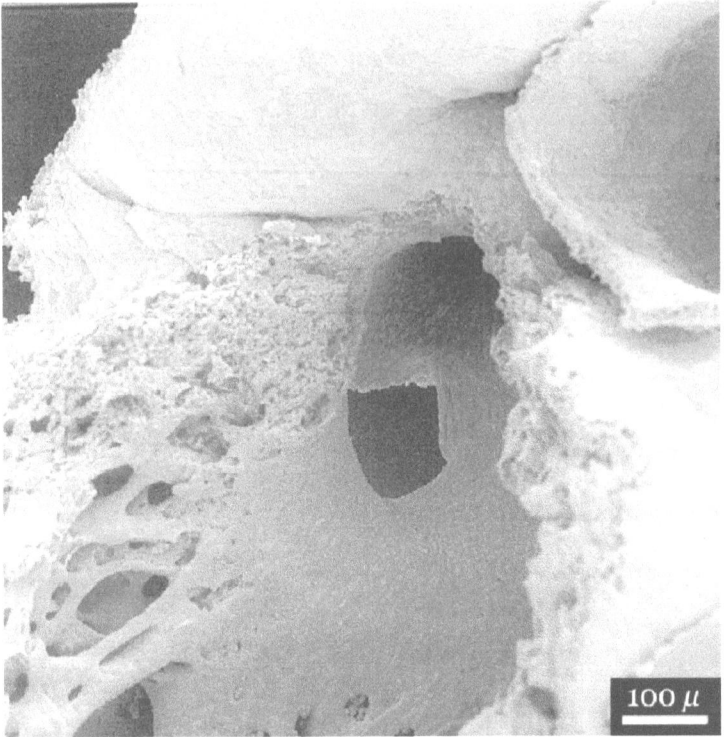

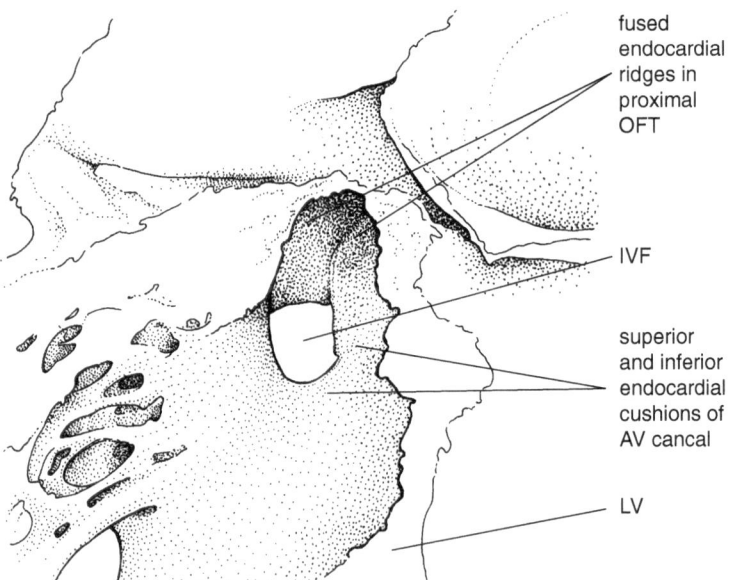

fused
endocardial
ridges in
proximal
OFT

IVF

superior
and inferior
endocardial
cushions of
AV cancal

LV

FIGURES 4.58–4.60   *Continued*

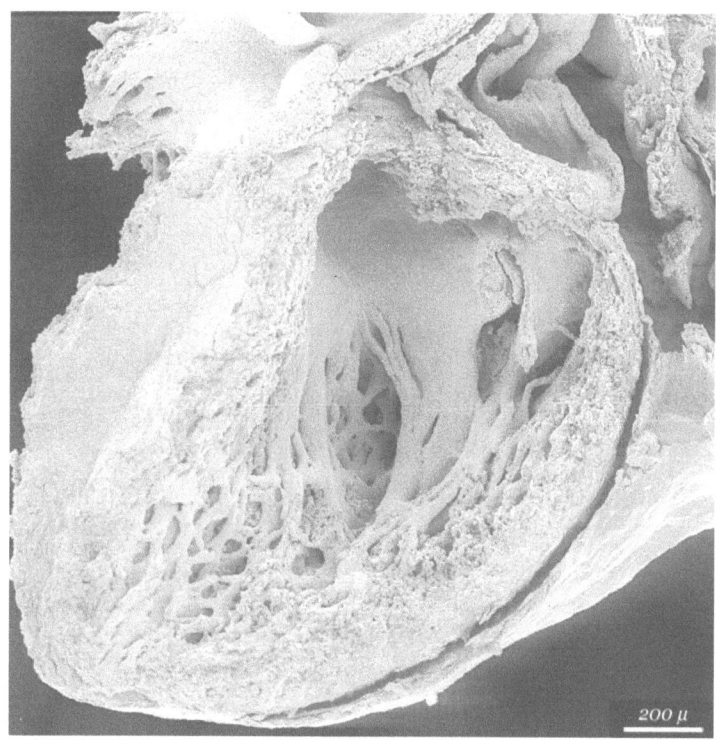

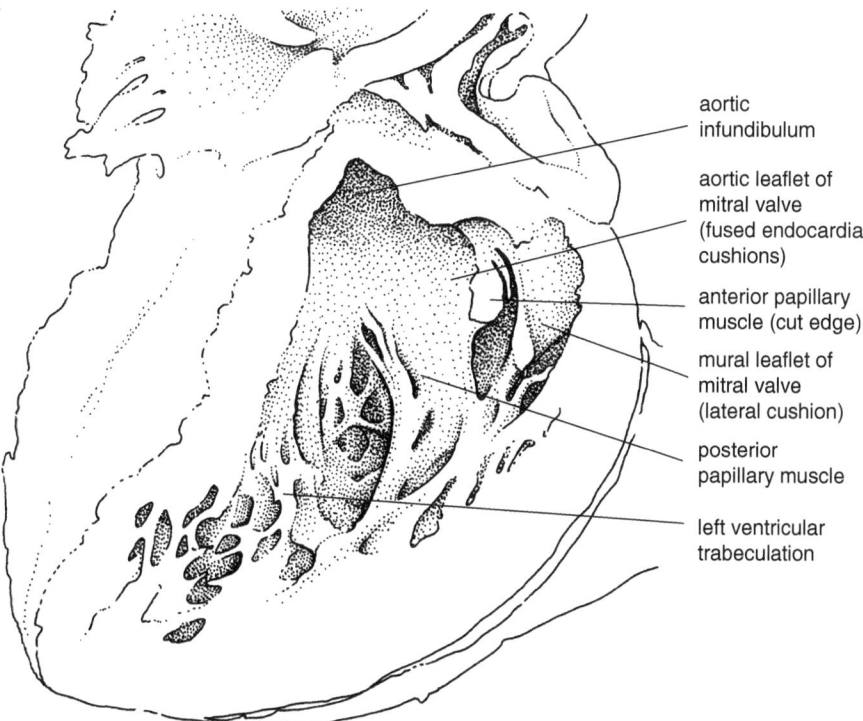

aortic
infundibulum

aortic leaflet of
mitral valve
(fused endocardial
cushions)

anterior papillary
muscle (cut edge)

mural leaflet of
mitral valve
(lateral cushion)

posterior
papillary muscle

left ventricular
trabeculation

FIGURES 4.61–4.63   Opened LV, outflow tract and great arteries (stage 21), left lateral and detailed views.

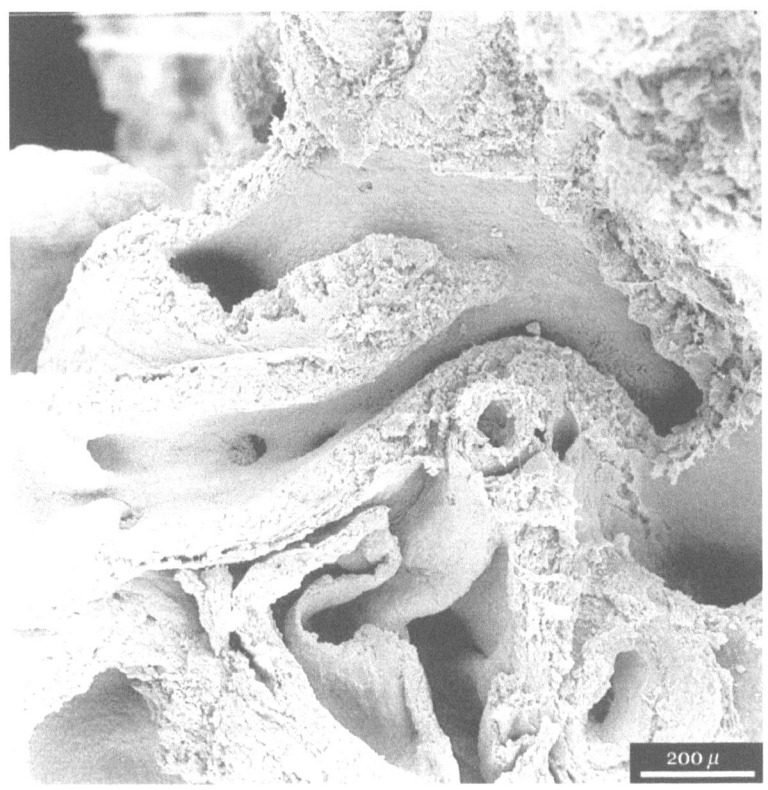

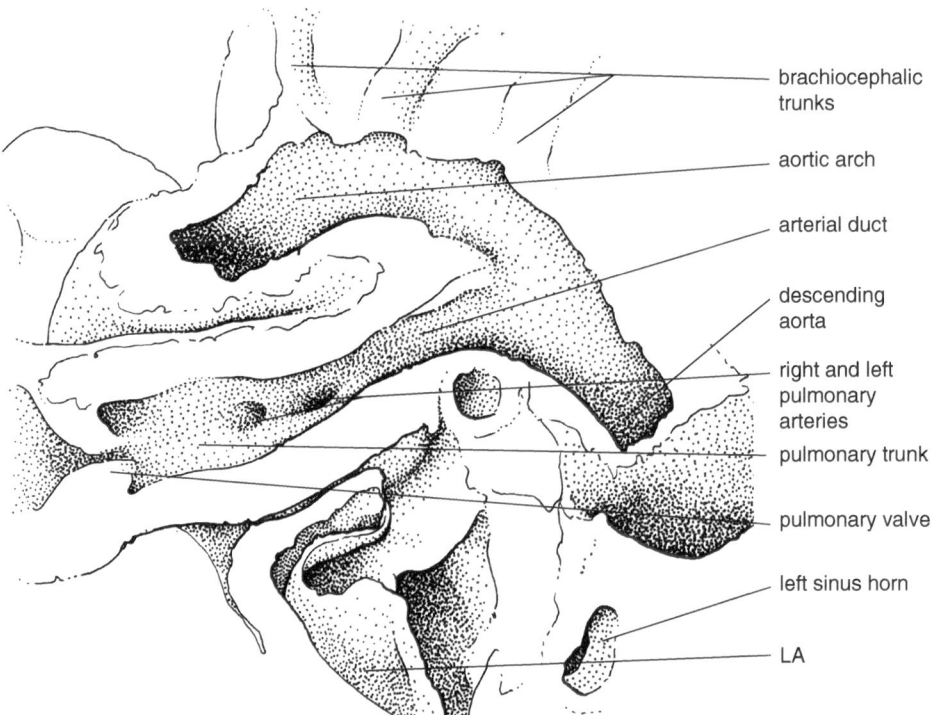

brachiocephalic
trunks

aortic arch

arterial duct

descending
aorta

right and left
pulmonary
arteries

pulmonary trunk

pulmonary valve

left sinus horn

LA

FIGURES 4.61–4.63   *Continued*

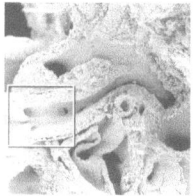

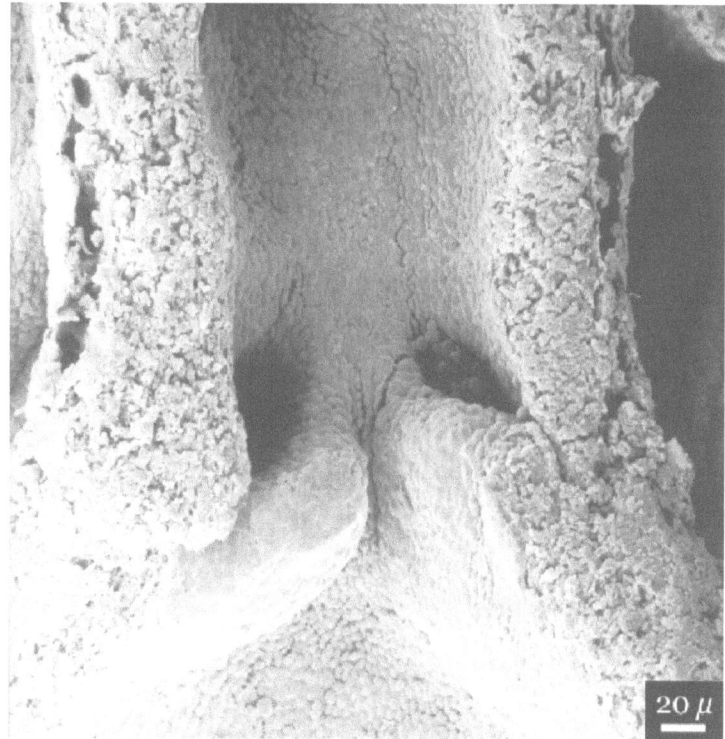

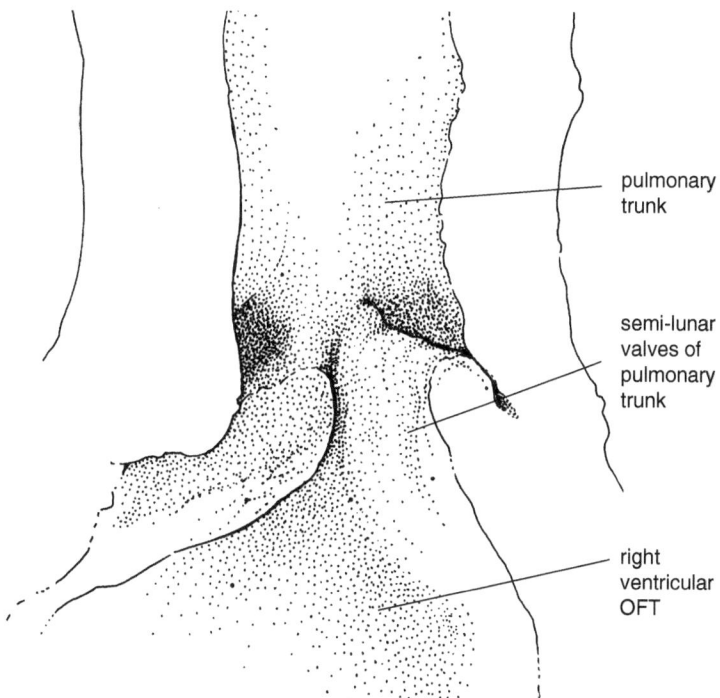

FIGURES 4.61–4.63   *Continued*

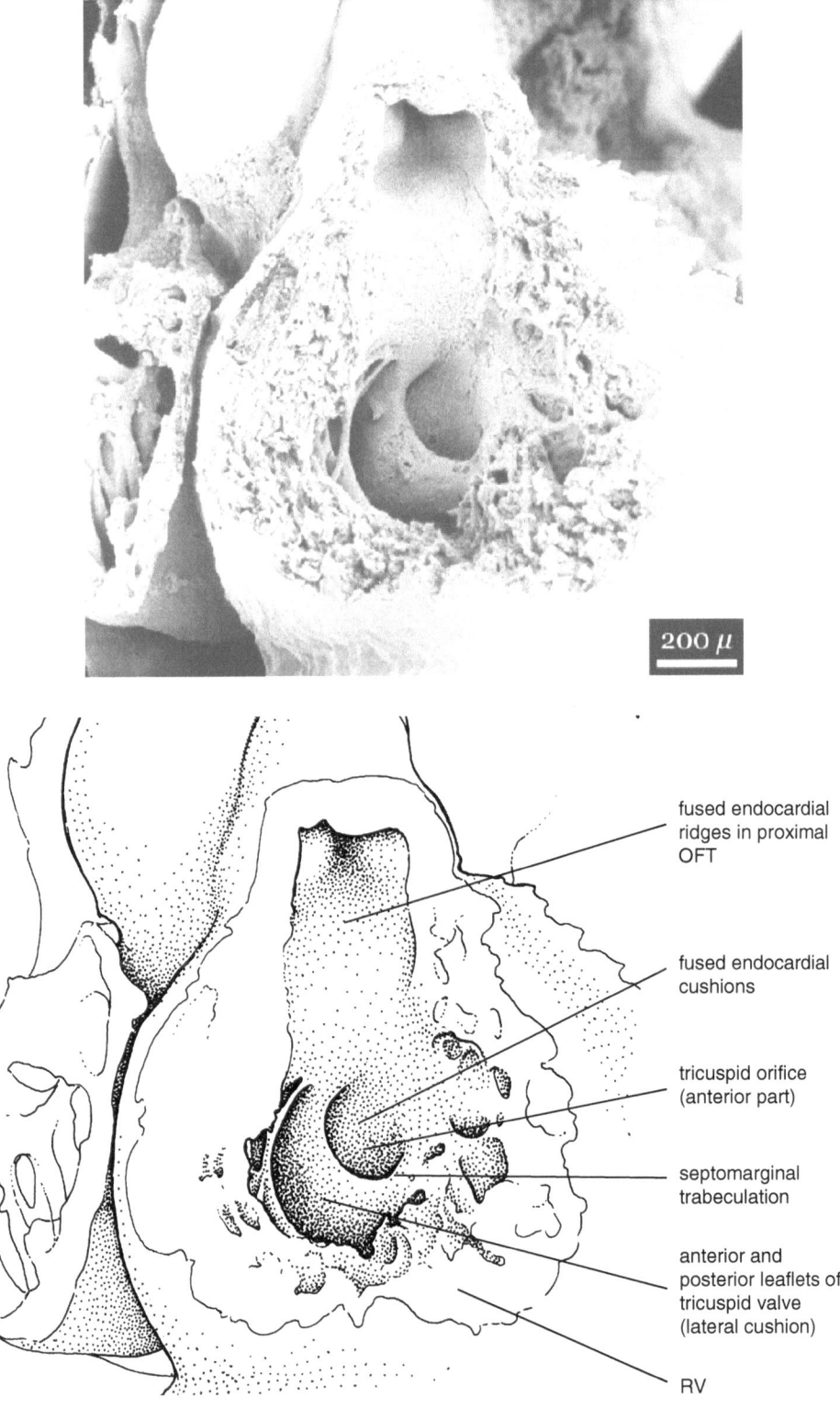

FIGURE 4.64   Opened RV (stage 21), right lateral view.

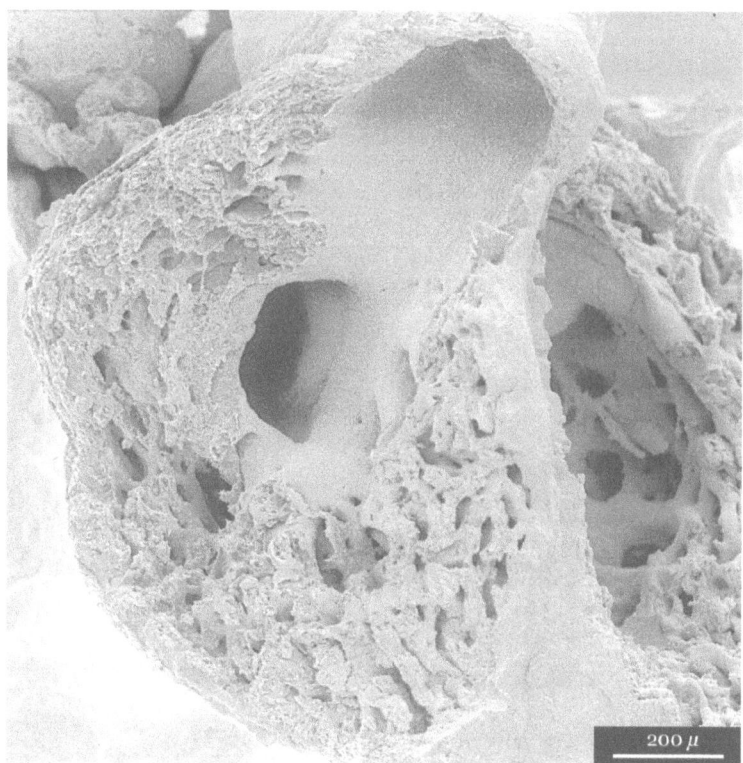

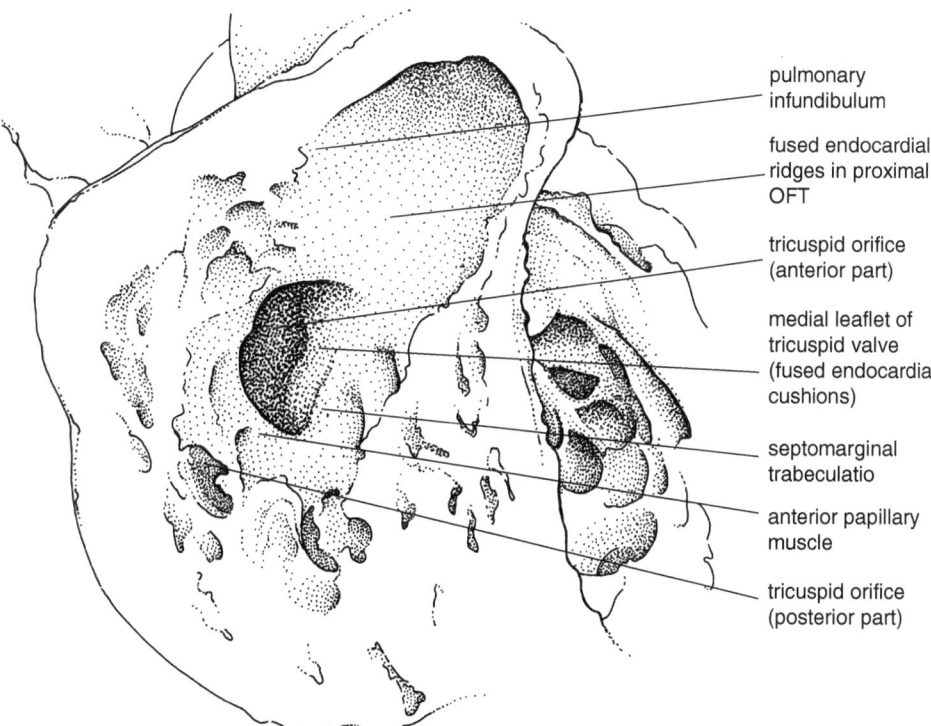

pulmonary
infundibulum

fused endocardial
ridges in proximal
OFT

tricuspid orifice
(anterior part)

medial leaflet of
tricuspid valve
(fused endocardial
cushions)

septomarginal
trabeculatio

anterior papillary
muscle

tricuspid orifice
(posterior part)

FIGURE 4.65   Opened RV (stage 23), right lateral view.

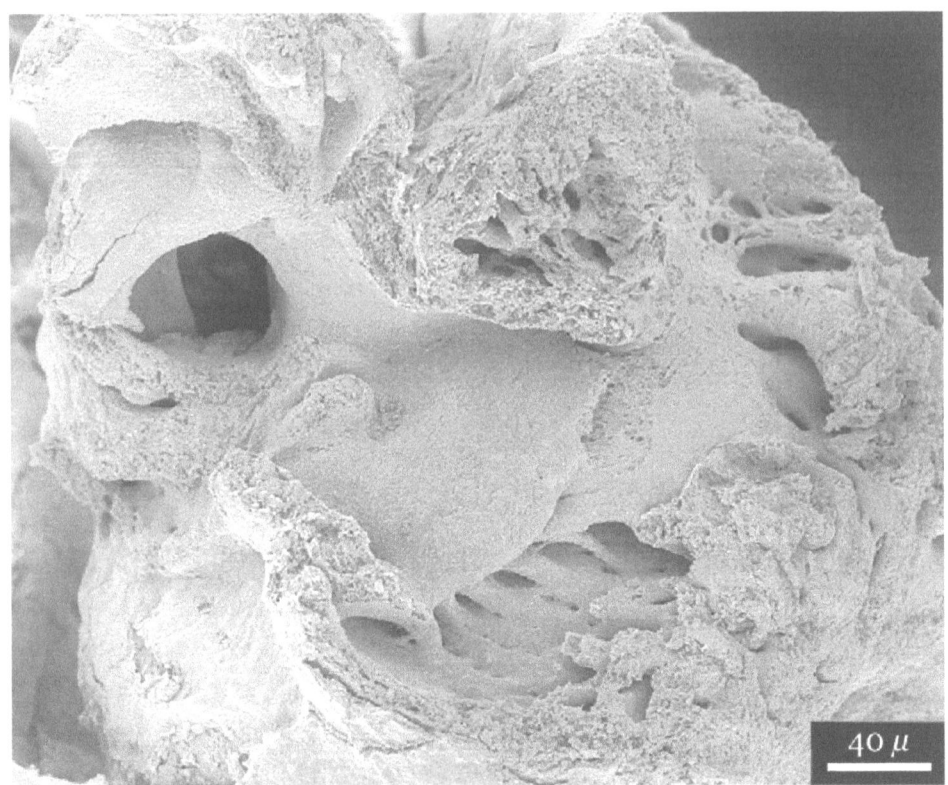

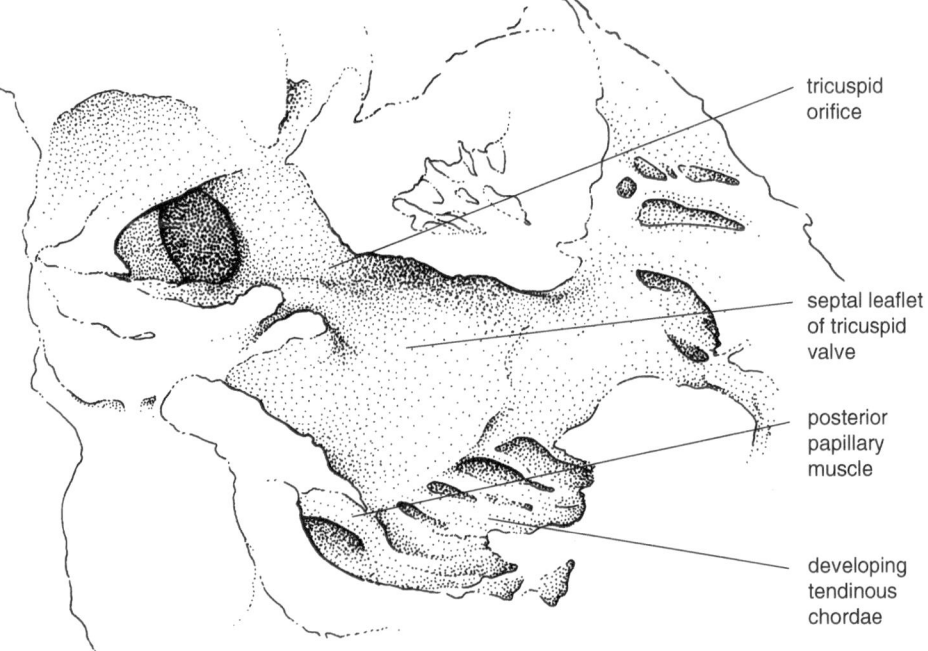

tricuspid
orifice

septal leaflet
of tricuspid
valve

posterior
papillary
muscle

developing
tendinous
chordae

FIGURE 4.66   Opened RV (stage 23), right lateral view.

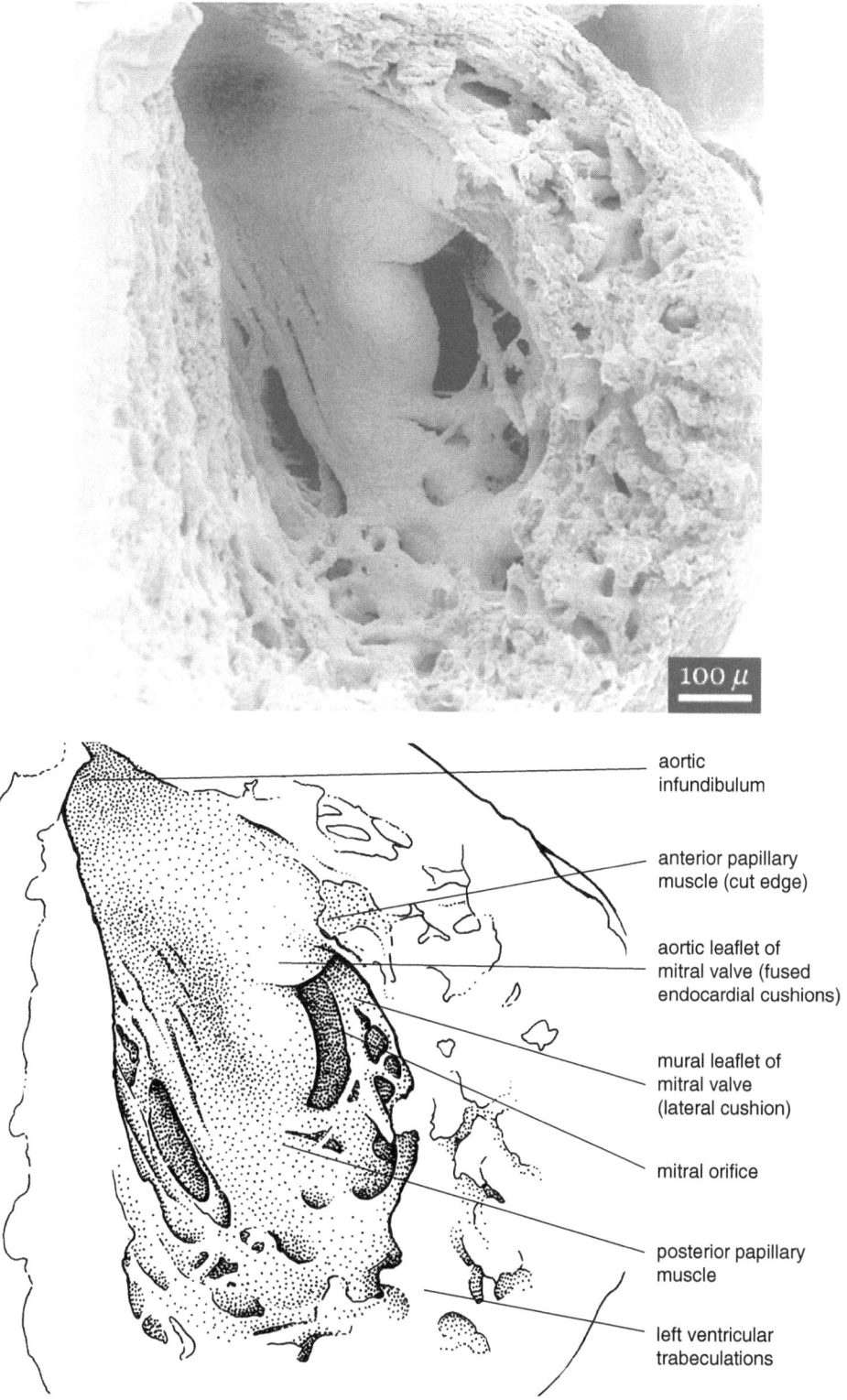

aortic
infundibulum

anterior papillary
muscle (cut edge)

aortic leaflet of
mitral valve (fused
endocardial cushions)

mural leaflet of
mitral valve
(lateral cushion)

mitral orifice

posterior papillary
muscle

left ventricular
trabeculations

FIGURE 4.67   Opened LV (stage 23), left lateral view.

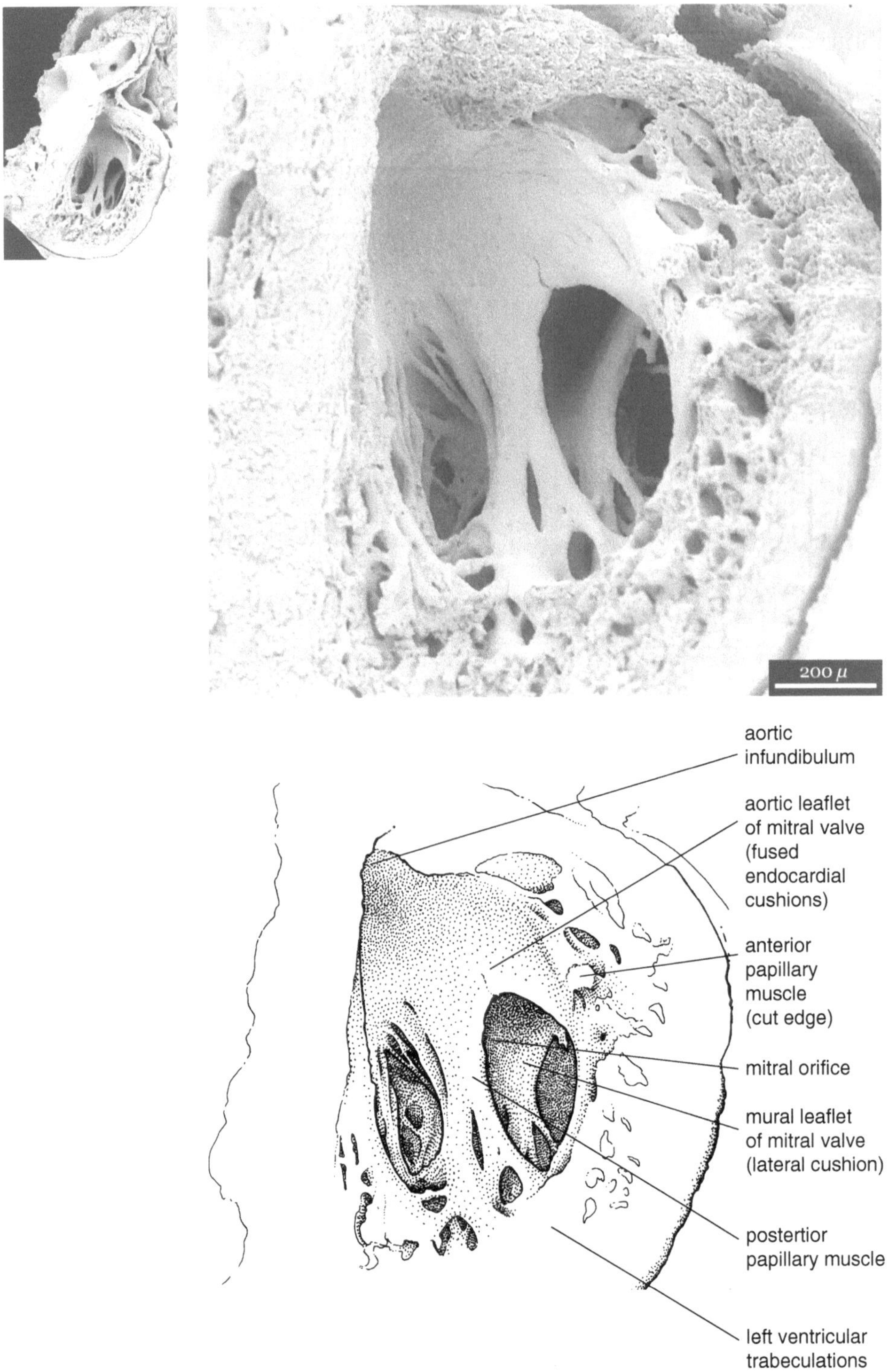

aortic
infundibulum

aortic leaflet
of mitral valve
(fused
endocardial
cushions)

anterior
papillary
muscle
(cut edge)

mitral orifice

mural leaflet
of mitral valve
(lateral cushion)

postertior
papillary muscle

left ventricular
trabeculations

FIGURE 4.68   Opened LV (stage 23), left lateral view. Due to fixation artifact, the line of fusion of the endocardial cushions is partly reopened.

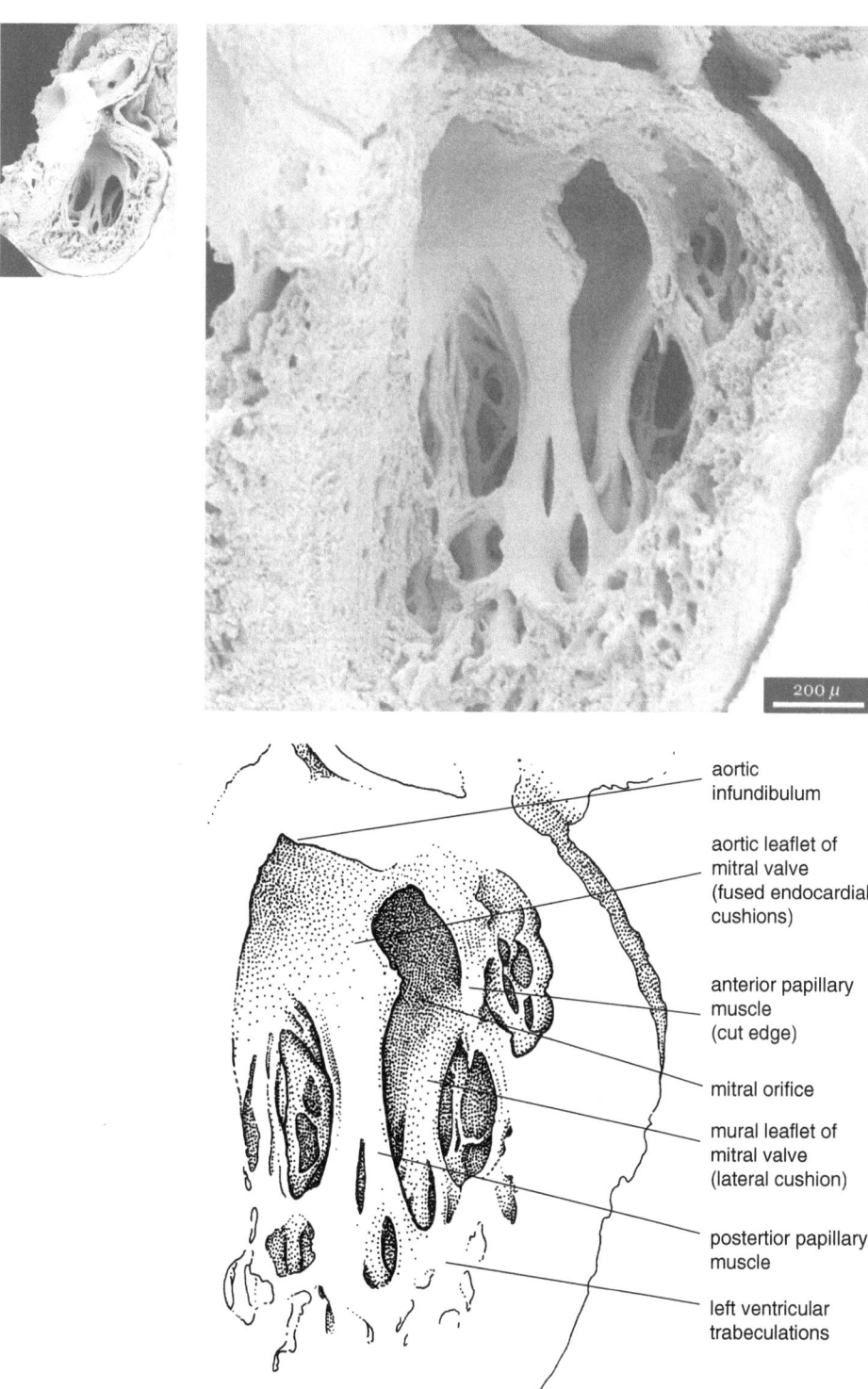

aortic
infundibulum

aortic leaflet of
mitral valve
(fused endocardial
cushions)

anterior papillary
muscle
(cut edge)

mitral orifice

mural leaflet of
mitral valve
(lateral cushion)

postertior papillary
muscle

left ventricular
trabeculations

FIGURES 4.69 and 4.70   Opened LV, outflow tract and great arteries (stage 23), left lateral
and detailed views. The aortic leaflet is partly removed.

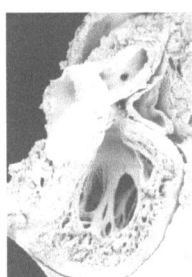

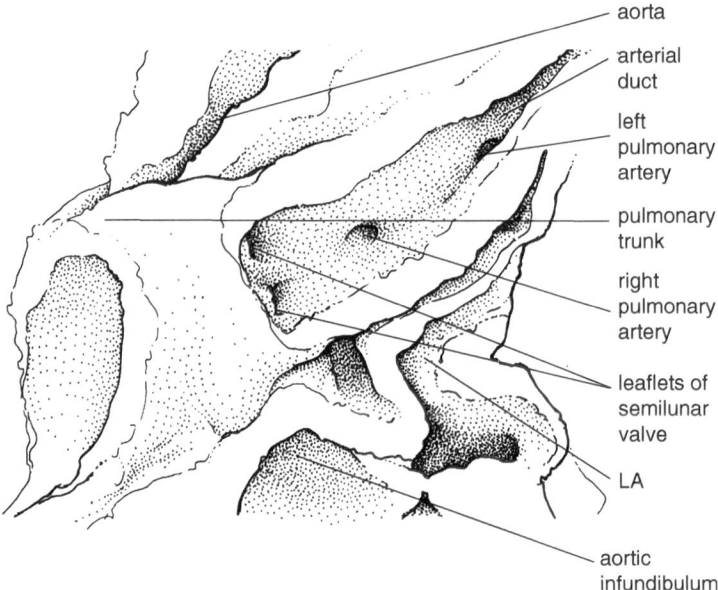

aorta

arterial
duct

left
pulmonary
artery

pulmonary
trunk

right
pulmonary
artery

leaflets of
semilunar
valve

LA

aortic
infundibulum

FIGURES 4.69 and 4.70   *Continued*

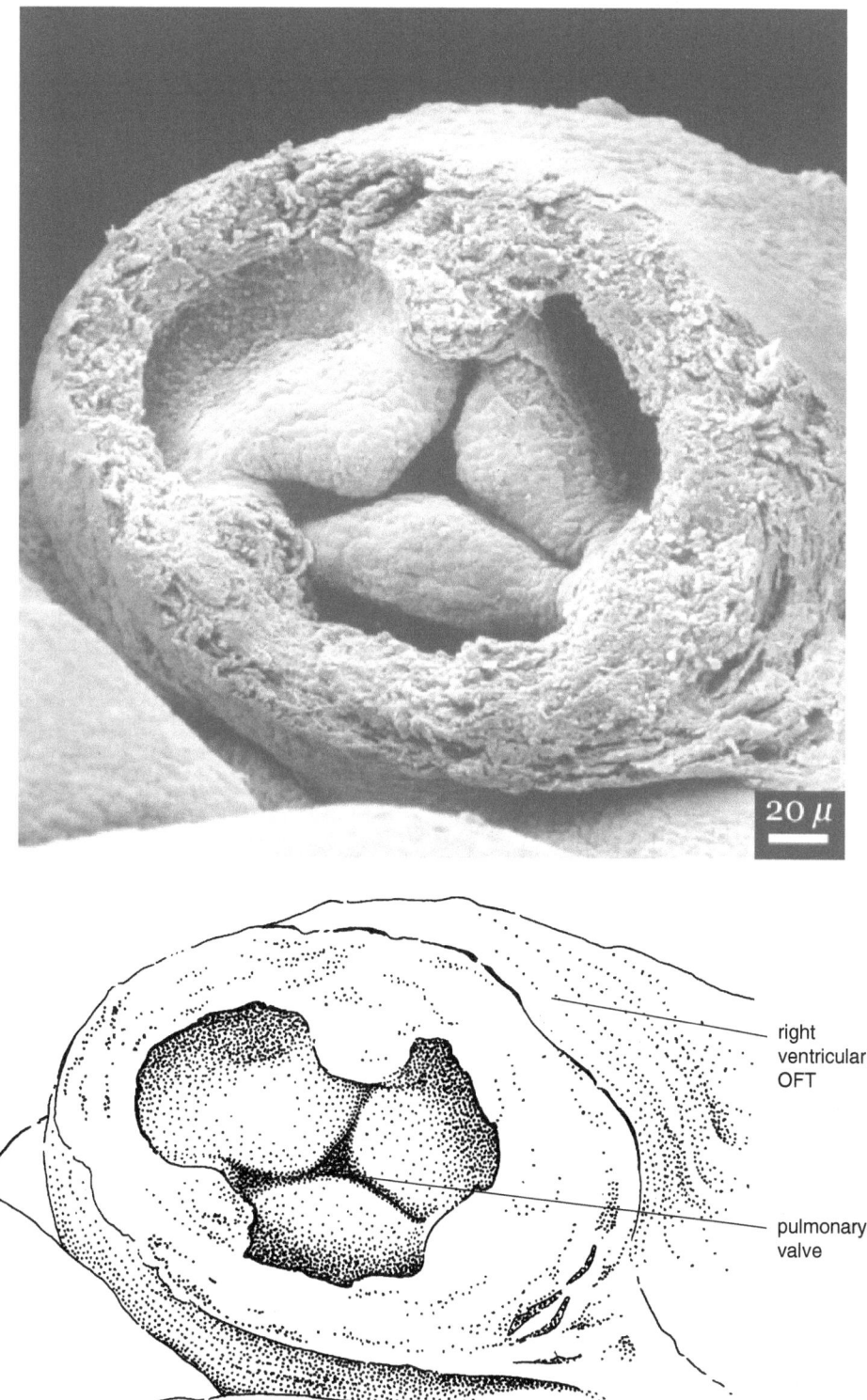

FIGURE 4.71   Transversely sectioned pulmonary trunk (stage 23), cranial view.

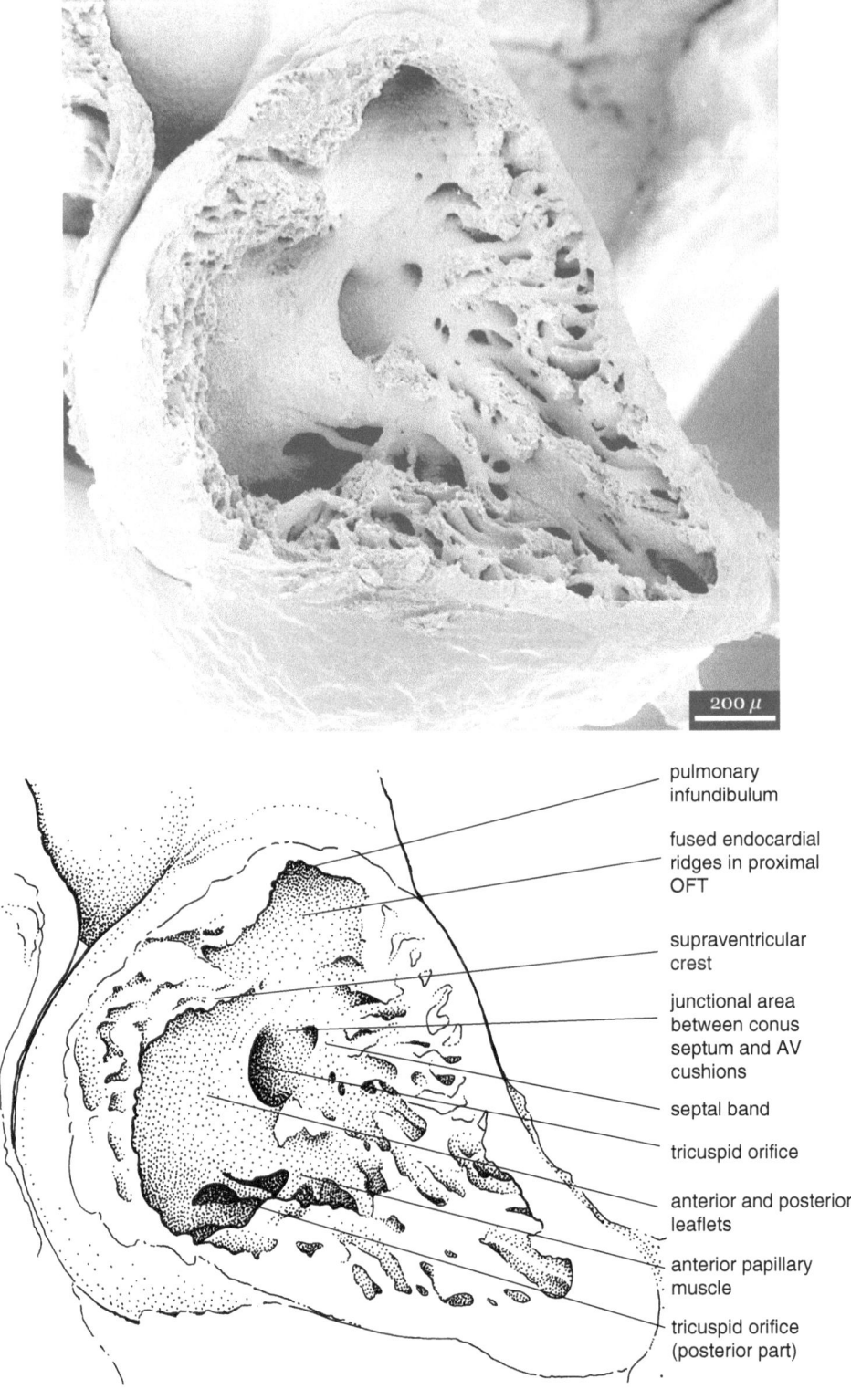

pulmonary
infundibulum

fused endocardial
ridges in proximal
OFT

supraventricular
crest

junctional area
between conus
septum and AV
cushions

septal band

tricuspid orifice

anterior and posterior
leaflets

anterior papillary
muscle

tricuspid orifice
(posterior part)

FIGURE 4.72   Opened RV (9 weeks), right lateral view.

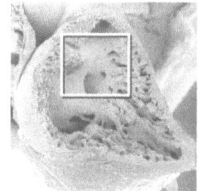

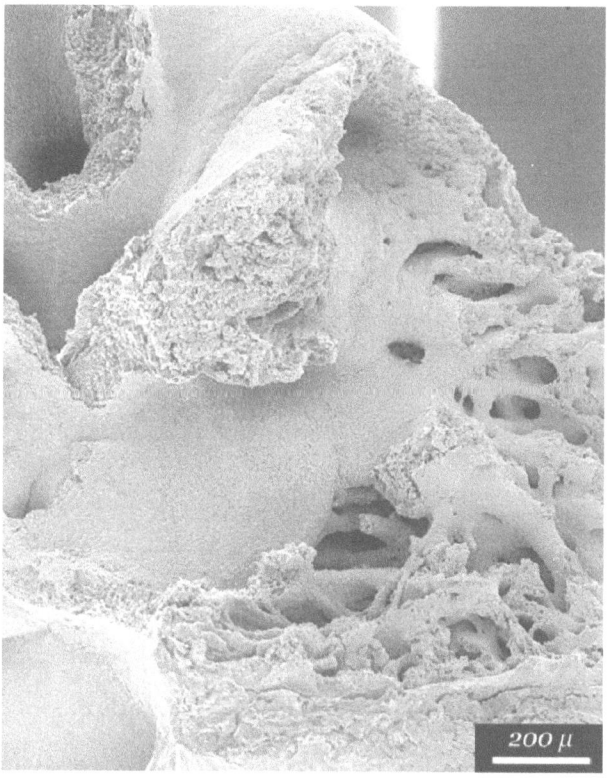

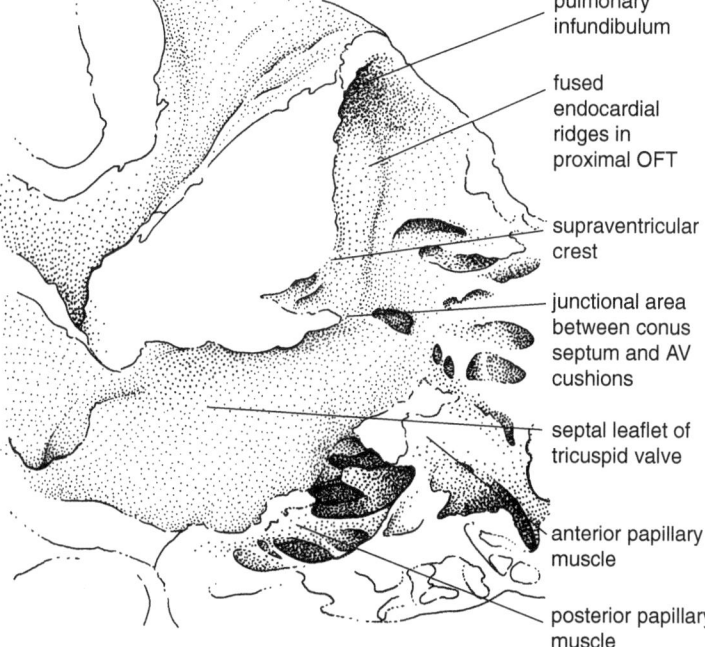

pulmonary
infundibulum

fused
endocardial
ridges in
proximal OFT

supraventricular
crest

junctional area
between conus
septum and AV
cushions

septal leaflet of
tricuspid valve

anterior papillary
muscle

posterior papillary
muscle

FIGURES 4.73 and 4.74   Opened RV (9 weeks), right and left lateral and detailed views. The right lateral wall, including the developing mural leaflets of the tricuspid valve, are removed.

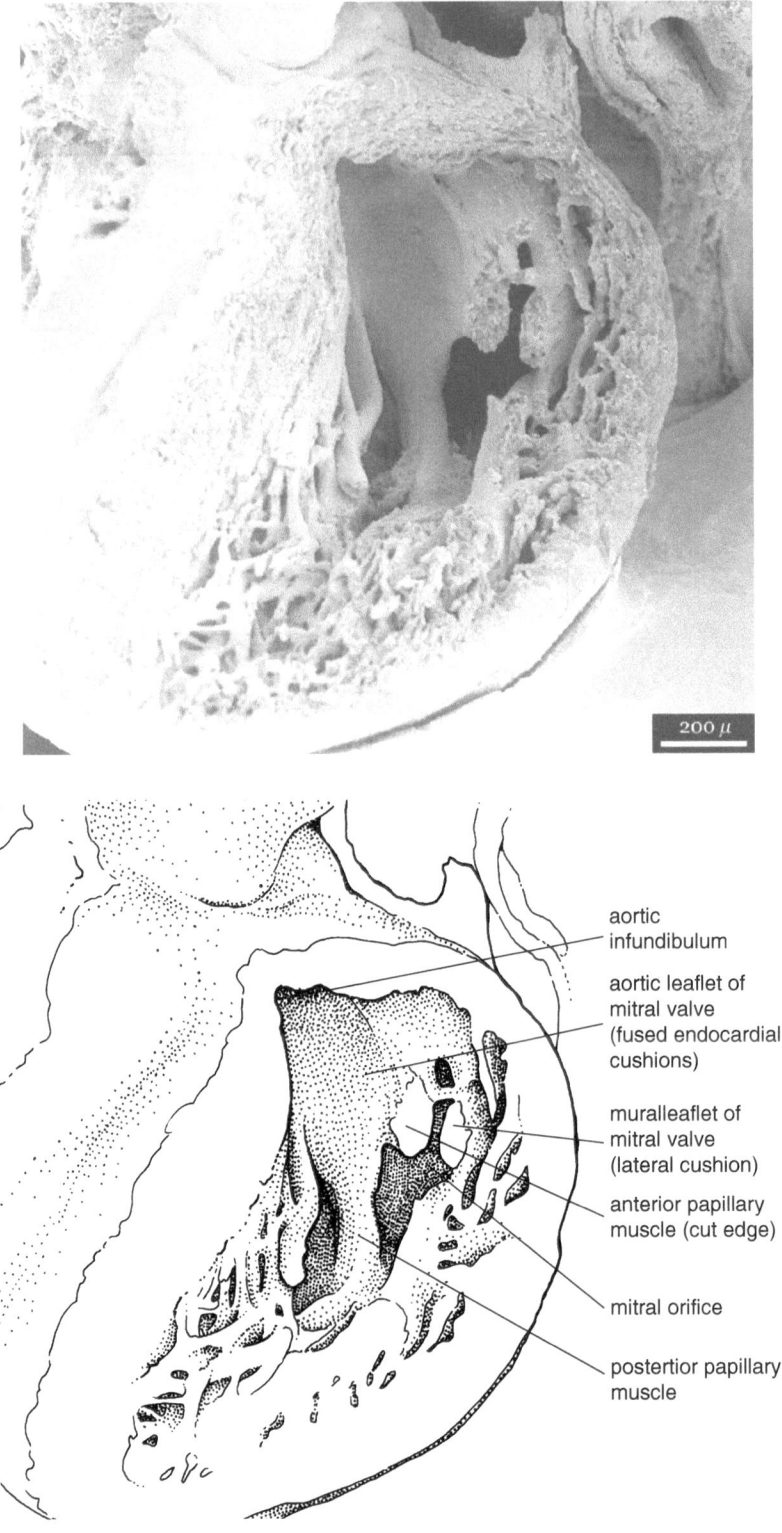

aortic
infundibulum

aortic leaflet of
mitral valve
(fused endocardial
cushions)

muralleaflet of
mitral valve
(lateral cushion)

anterior papillary
muscle (cut edge)

mitral orifice

postertior papillary
muscle

FIGURES 4.73 and 4.74   *Continued*

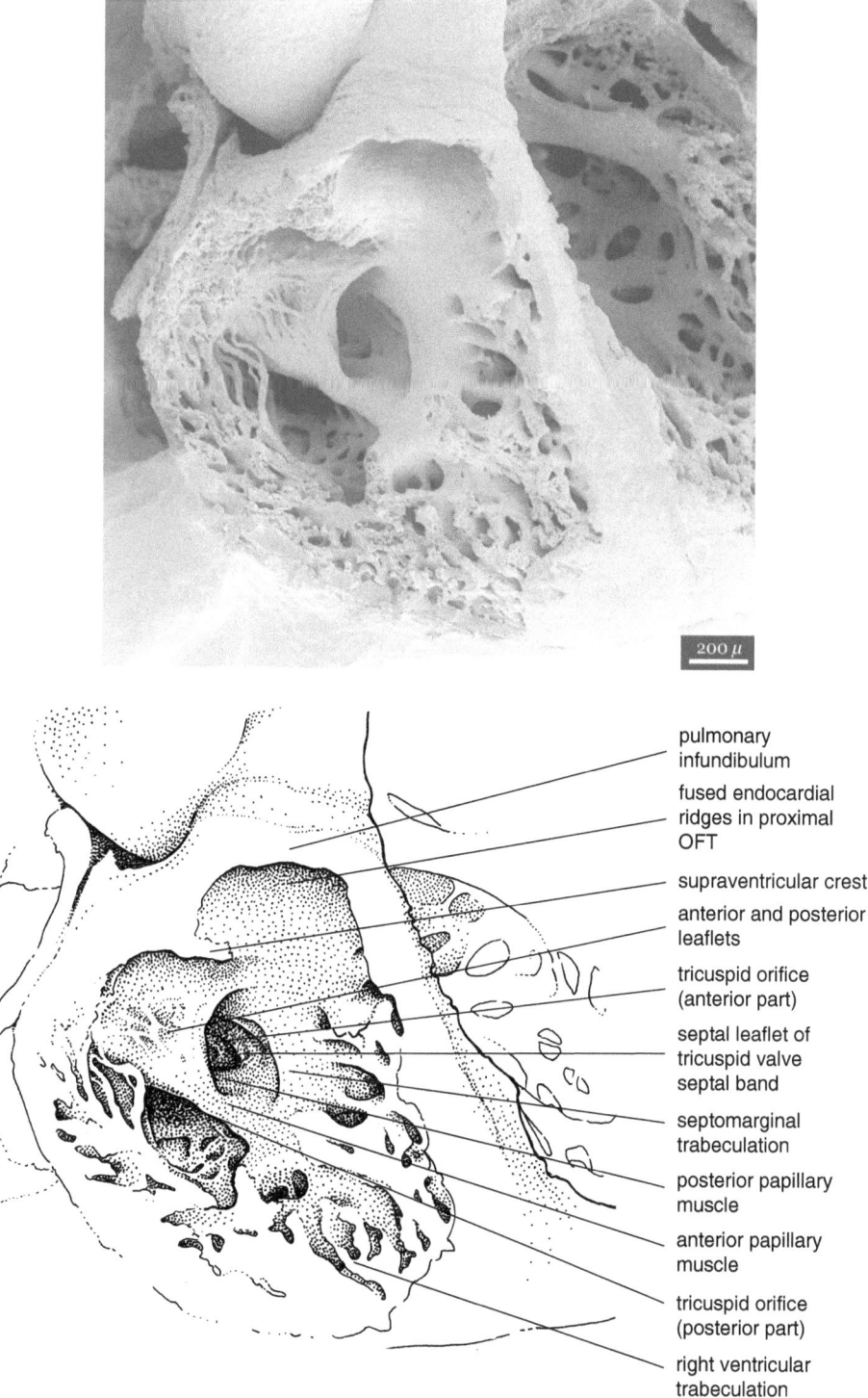

pulmonary
infundibulum

fused endocardial
ridges in proximal
OFT

supraventricular crest

anterior and posterior
leaflets

tricuspid orifice
(anterior part)

septal leaflet of
tricuspid valve
septal band

septomarginal
trabeculation

posterior papillary
muscle

anterior papillary
muscle

tricuspid orifice
(posterior part)

right ventricular
trabeculation

FIGURES 4.75–4.77   Opened RV and LV (9 weeks), left lateral and detailed views. In detail the posterior papillary muscle shows development of the tendinous chordae which commences at the end of the embryonic period.

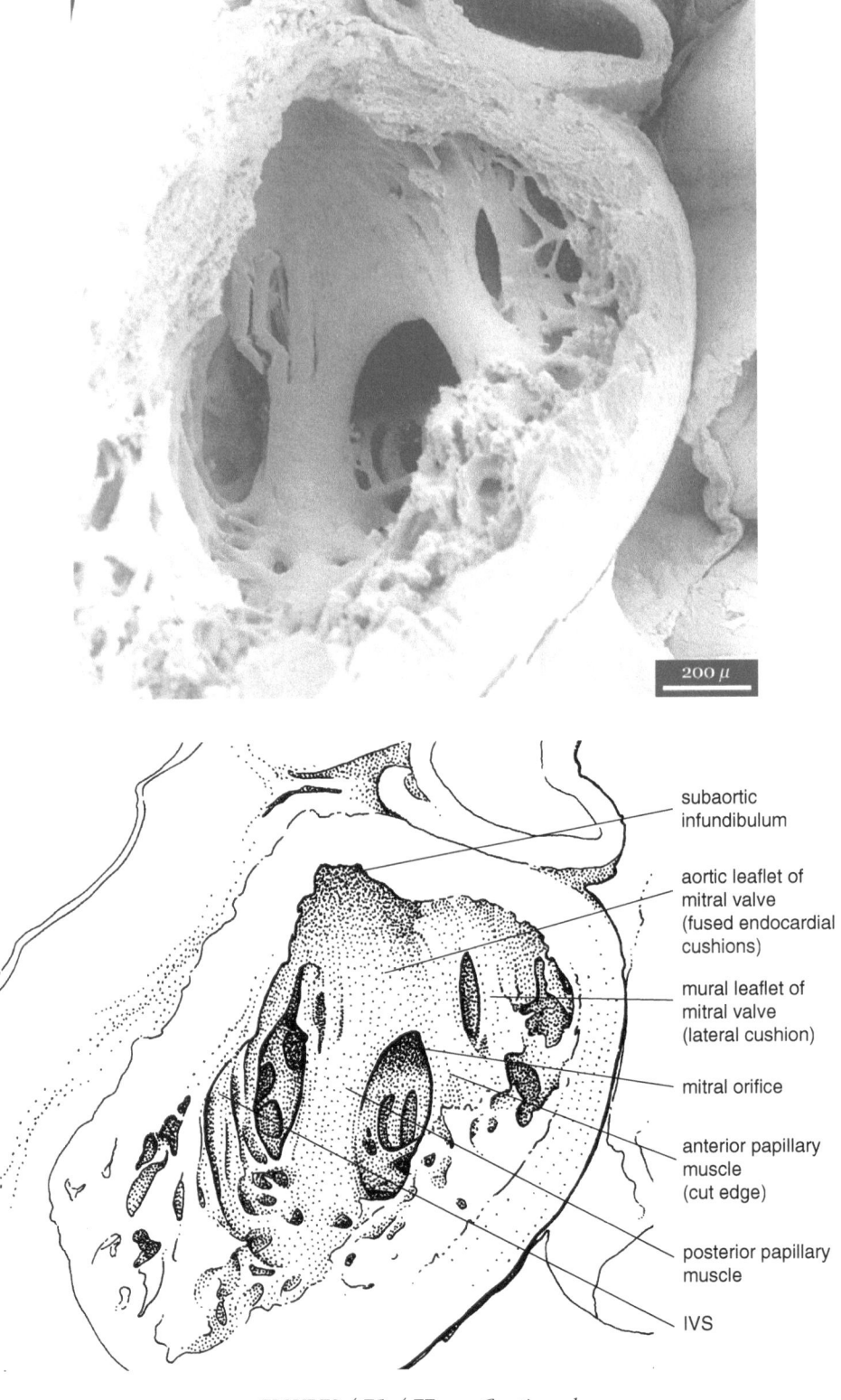

subaortic
infundibulum

aortic leaflet of
mitral valve
(fused endocardial
cushions)

mural leaflet of
mitral valve
(lateral cushion)

mitral orifice

anterior papillary
muscle
(cut edge)

posterior papillary
muscle

IVS

FIGURES 4.75–4.77   *Continued*

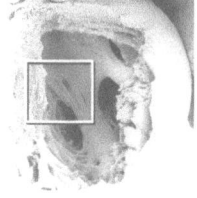

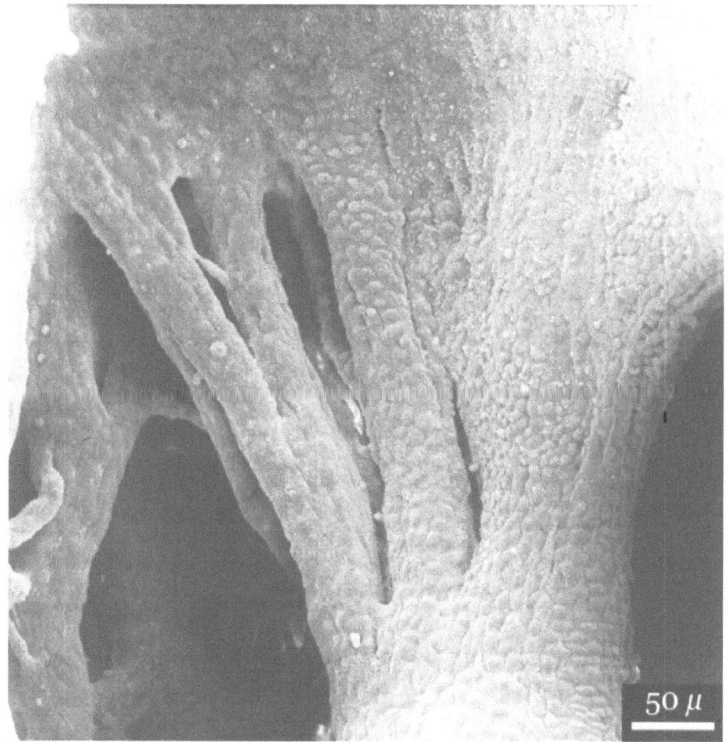

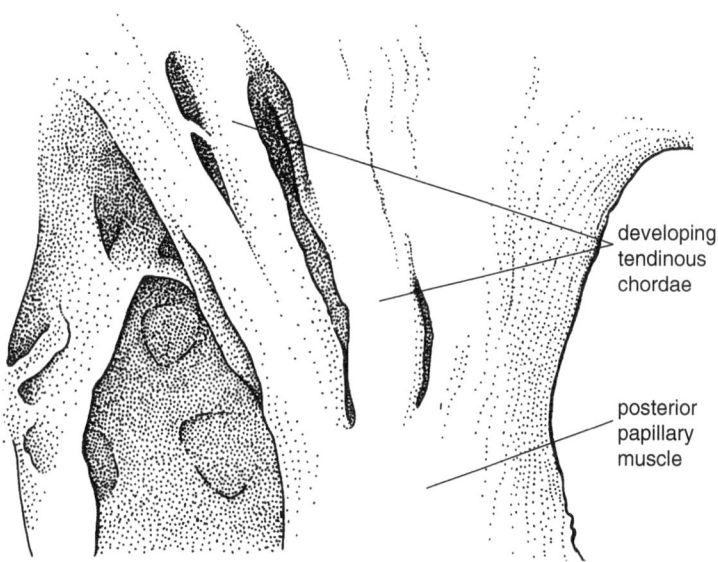

developing
tendinous
chordae

posterior
papillary
muscle

FIGURES 4.75–4.77   *Continued*

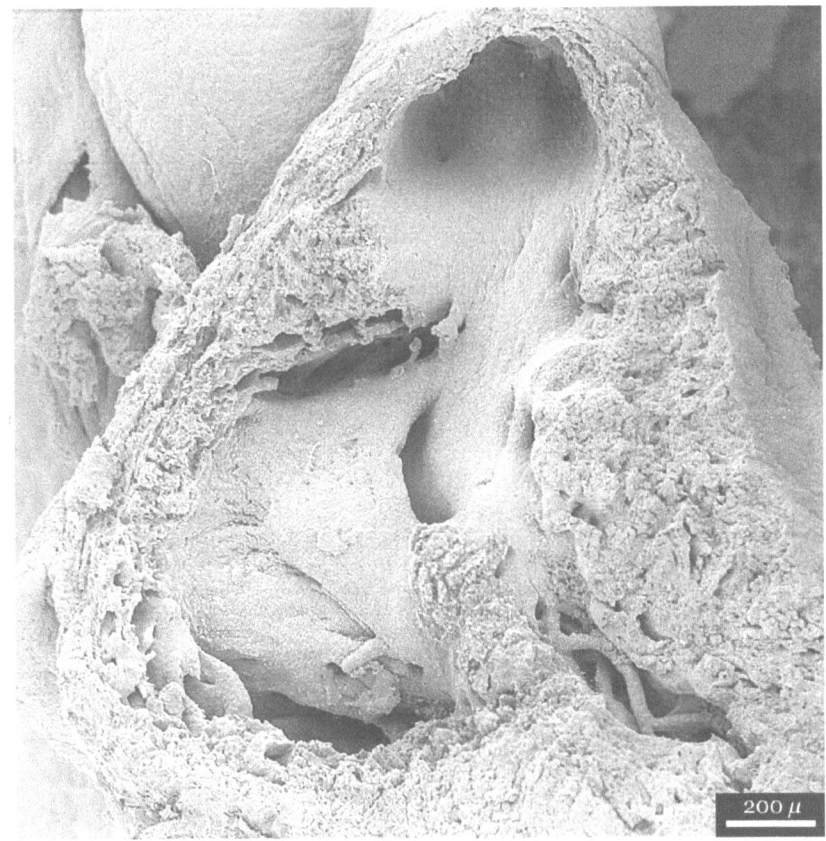

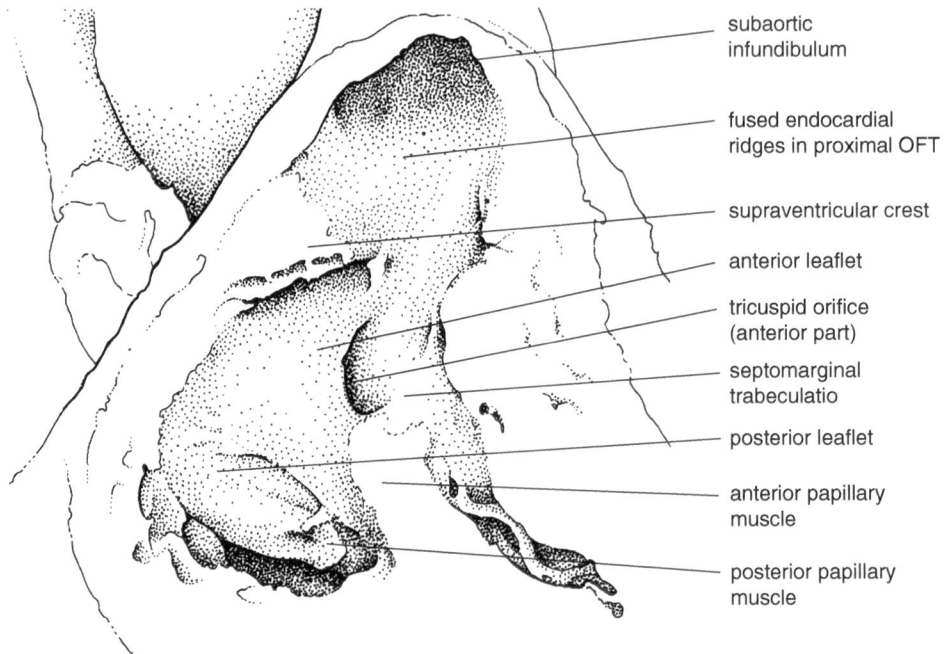

subaortic
infundibulum

fused endocardial
ridges in proximal OFT

supraventricular crest

anterior leaflet

tricuspid orifice
(anterior part)

septomarginal
trabeculatio

posterior leaflet

anterior papillary
muscle

posterior papillary
muscle

FIGURE 4.78   Opened RV (10 weeks), right lateral view.

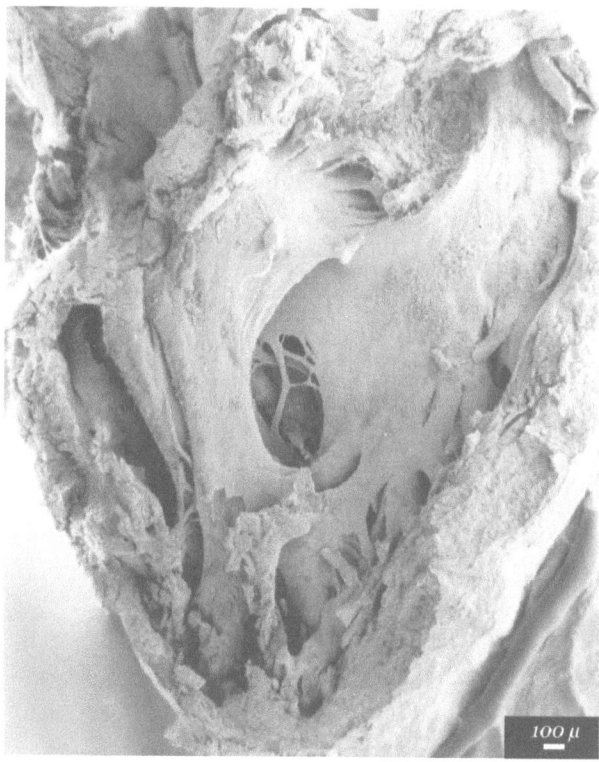

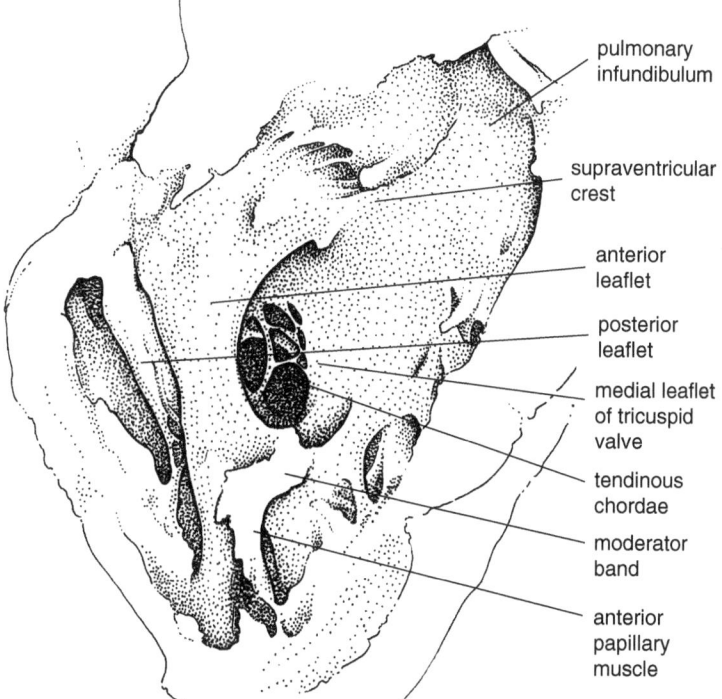

pulmonary
infundibulum

supraventricular
crest

anterior
leaflet

posterior
leaflet

medial leaflet
of tricuspid
valve

tendinous
chordae

moderator
band

anterior
papillary
muscle

FIGURES 4.79 and 4.80   Opened RV (11 weeks), right lateral and detailed views.

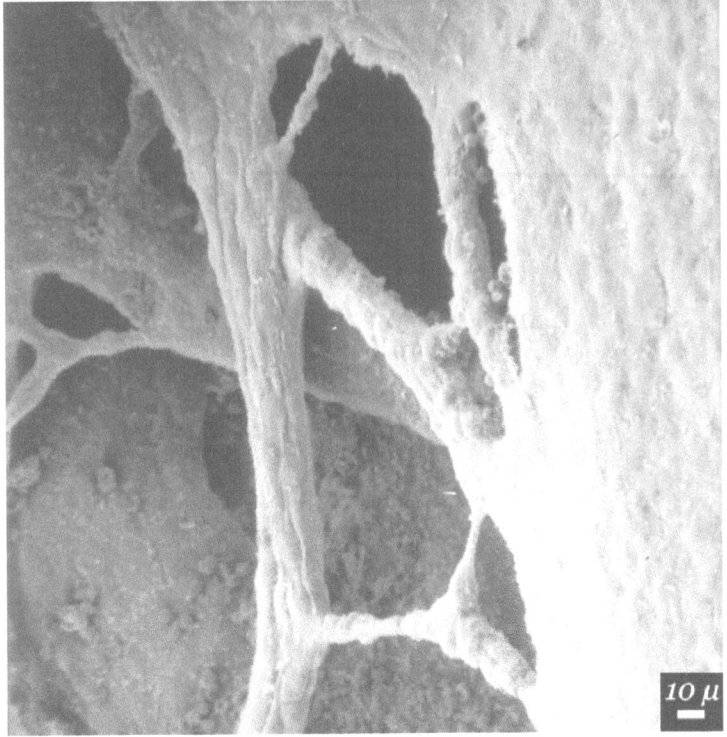

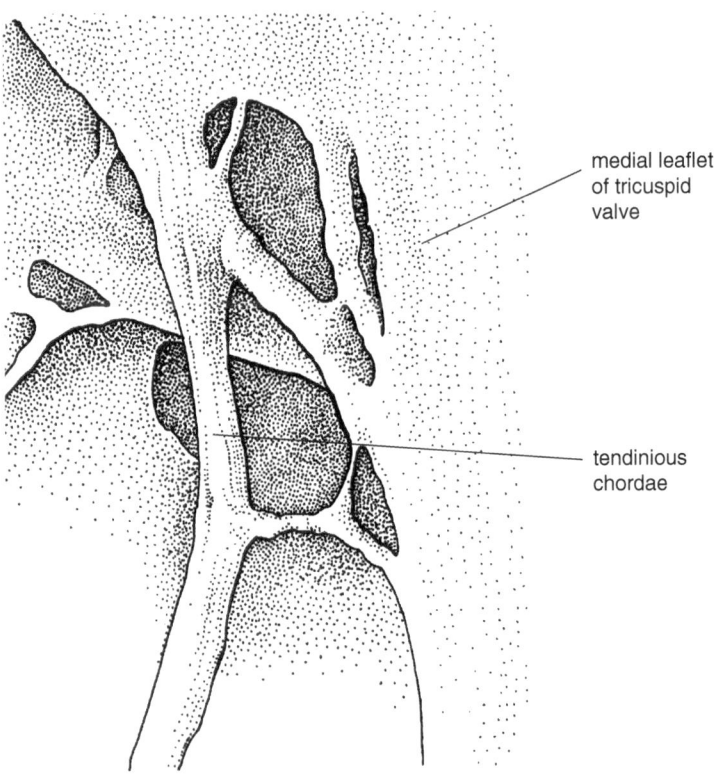

medial leaflet
of tricuspid
valve

tendinious
chordae

FIGURES 4.79 and 4.80   *Continued*

Development of endocardial, myocardial, epicardial layers and derivatives

DEVELOPMENT OF THE PRIMARY, TRABECULATED AND COMPACT MYOCARDIUM

As stated before, the cardiac compartments develop as progressively enlarging balloon-shaped distensions at the outer curvature of the atrial and ventricular loops. In the ventricular region this ballooning is accompanied by the formation of myocardial trabeculae, visible from stage 12 onward, which allows the ventricles to increase in size in the absence of a coronary circulation [Van Mierop & Kutsche, 1984]. Moreover, they enhance contractility [Challice & Virágh, 1973] and play an important role in the coordination of intraventricular conduction [De Jong et al., 1992]. Growth of the ballooning ventricles is achieved by tissue proliferation in the outer (compact) myocardium, which initially is only a few cell layers thick [Rumyantsev, 1977; Thompson et al., 1995; Henderson & Copp, 1998]. It is hypothesized that, as a result, the inner myocardial and endocardial layers, that do not contribute to this expansion, "crack open". The tissue bridges between the thus formed excavations, that become subsequently recoated with endocardium, are to become the primary trabecula. This "craking open" may be facilitated by the peristaltoid contraction patterns [Thompson et al., 2000] as well as the ballooning process itself [Sedmera et al., 2000]. This process repeats itself continuously during development, leading to a radially thickening layer of trabecula, with a proliferating outer layer that retains its compact structure [Steding & Seidl, 1980; Mikawa et al., 1992].

The early stages of trabecular proliferation are considered to be necessary to meet the increasing haemodynamic demand of the growing embryonic body in the absence of adequate coronary perfusion of the outermost myocardial layers [Sedmera et al., 1997]. The invasion of epicardially derived angioblasts that will give rise to the coronary vasculature (see below) is therefore likely to be hypoxia-driven. The vascularization of the outer layers allows the compact myocardium to become increasingly voluminous and to surpass the trabeculated myocardium in its contribution to the total myocardial mass by far [Blausen et al., 1990]. The thickening of the outer layers, which results from compression and compactions of trabeculations [Rychterova, 1971; Sedmera et al., 1997], is more pronounced in the left ventricle and proceeds well beyond the fetal period [Hirokawa, 1972]. Morphological differences between the right and left ventricular trabeculation patterns become apparent with the initiation of septation but remain quite unremarkable in mammalian embryos until the end of the embryonic period. It could be argued that the characteristically coarse right ventricular trabeculation results from the growth acceleration of the initially smaller right ventricle during the fetal period, in order to measure up with the left ventricular capacity.

Although the ballooning of the atrial and ventricular compartments commences more or less at the same time (stage 11), the atria, in contrast to the ventricles, are initially smooth-walled. It is not until stage 16 that these walls start to develop reliefs known as carneous trabeculae or pectinate muscles. This trabeculation remains restricted to those parts of the atria that become the auricles. It is the size and shape of these auricles and the extent of their trabeculation that determines the specific right and left atrial morphology [Anderson and Becker, 1980]. The function of these trabeculae is unknown but it is suggested that they play a role both in contractility enhancement [Sedmera et al., 1999] and impulse conduction.

The development of fast-contracting compartments has profound haemodynamic implications because the principle of a peristaltic pump that characterizes the early embryonic heart can no longer be maintained. Nevertheless, the residual presence of slowly conducting and relaxating primary myocardium at the sites of the inflow tract, atrioventricular canal and outflow tract is of great importance for proper functioning of the heart at this stage. After contraction of the primary myocardium of the inflow tract, relaxation of this part of the heart tube has not yet occurred when the atria contract. As a result the blood will be propelled exclusively in the direction of the atrioventricular canal. Subsequently, the primary myocardium of the atrioventricular canal contracts when the atria start to relaxate and it will still be in contracted state by the time the ventricles contract, thereby, again, avoiding retrograde bloodflow. For the same reason, the primary myocardium of the outflow tract contracts when the ventricles relax. Therefore, in stead of being primarily involved in blood propulsion, the derivatives of the primary heart tube (being the inflow tract, atrioventricular canal and outflow tract) start to act as sphincters in the chambered but still valveless heart [De Jong et al., 1992].

The ballooning of the embryonic compartments matches with molecular alterations. Already in the straight heart tube stages, genes involved in the differentiation of trabeculated myocardium, e.g. Chisel, ANF, connexin 43 and Irx5 [Moorman et al., 2000; Christoffels et al., 2000], are expressed along the future outer curvature of the areas that will form the atrial and ventricular loops. Later on expression of these genes is restricted to the ballooning part of the heart tube. With respect to histochemical and physiological properties the newly formed trabeculated myocardium of the compartments differs considerably from the original primary myocardium of the heart tube. In contrast to the low-voltaged depolarizations, slow conduction velocities and peristaltoid contraction waves of the primary myocardium, the trabeculated myocardium shows high-voltaged and fast-propagating discharges resulting in synchronous contractions of the compartments. In line with this, the cells of the compartment myocardium have much more gap junctions and express higher levels of conduction-related proteins, e.g. connexin 43 [Moorman et al., 1998] and SERCA2a [Moorman et al., 2000], compared to primary myocardium. At the same time an electrocardiogram can be derived which shows remarkable resemblance with that of a mature heart, despite the absence of a specific conduction system [Van Mierop, 1967]. In fact, the primary myocardium of the inflow tract and atrioventricular canal functions as equivalent of the future sinu-atrial and atrioventricular nodes. The inflow tract generates an impulse which, after rapid depolarization of the atria, is delayed in the atrioventricular canal, prior to a rapid depolarization of the ventricles.

DEVELOPMENT OF THE EPICARDIUM AND THE CORONARY VASCULATURE

The epicardium, in contrast to the endocardium and myocardium, is not a derivative of the heart tube. It originates from an epithelially lined mass of mesenchymal cells with villous protrusions, called the pro-epicardium [Viragh et al., 1993]. This structure is derived from the pericardium and mesothelial lining that covers the sinus venosus and the transverse septum and appears during the looping stages [Virágh and Challice, 1981; Hirakow, 1992]. In subsequent stages, these cells are transferred to the myocardial surface of the atria, atrioventricular canal, ventricles, and proximal part of the outflow tract, by means of adhesion of the mesothelial protrusions to the cardiac surface and/or shedding of cells in the pericardial space [reviewed by Männer et al., 2001; Muñoz-Chápuli et al., 2002a], whereas the distal part of the outflow tract, beyond the myocardial border, is covered by an outgrowth of the pericardial mesothelium [Männer, 1999; Perez-Pomares et al., 2003]. Subsequent to the formation of the epicardium a space is formed between the developing epicardium and the outer myocardial layer, especially in the atrioventricular and conoventricular furrows of the heart tube [Virágh and Challice, 1981; Hirakow, 1992], which is named the subepicardial space or subepicardium. Subsequently, this space becomes populated by mesenchymal cells that appear to be mostly derived from the epicardium by means of epithelial to mesenchymal transition [Perez-Pomares et al., 1997]. These epicardium-derived cells play an important role in the formation of the coronary vasculature. The precursors of the coronary fibroblasts, smooth muscle cells and endothelium are derived from these apparently pluripotent cells [Mikawa and Gourdie; 1996; Vrancken-Peeters et al., 1999], which possibly also play roles in the development of non-coronary tissues, including atrioventricular cushion mesenchyme and myocardium [Muñoz-Chápuli et al., 2002b; Wessels and Perez-Pomares, 2004]. The remnants of the pro-epicardium can still be found in the sinus venosus area up to stage 15.

The processes involved in development of the coronary system, as reviewed extensively by Bernanke and Velkey [2002], have been poorly understood until a few years ago. Before then, coronary arteries were assumed to form by means of angiogenesis, like endothelial evaginations that sprout from the aortic root [e.g. Hutchins et al., 1988]. However, it appeared that coronary vessels developed prior to the formation of coronary orifices in the aortic sinuses [Bogers et al., 1988] and could, therefore, never originate from the aortic root. Moreover, since angiogenesis cannot initiate from non-capillary vessels (i.c. the aorta) the developing coronary arteries must invade the aorta rather than sprout from it [Waldo et al., 1990]. Although the association of epicardial formation and the appearance of blood-island-like structures in the subepicardial space was known at the time [Hiruma and Hirakow, 1989], it took several years before the essential role of the epicardially derived mesenchyme in the formation of the coronary vasculature became established as such. By means of vasculogenesis [Poole and Coffin, 1989], the mesenchymal cells in the subepicardial space transform into angioblasts, in a manner comparable to what happens in the lateral plate mesoderm of the early post-gastrulation embryo (see Chapter 1). The angioblasts generate primitive vessels that elongate and branch by means of angiogenesis, thus creating a capillary plexus, which invades the myocardium and spreads over the myocardial surface in the directions in which the epicardium develops. On approaching the base of the outflow tract several sprouts connect to the sinuses of the aortic root by means of apoptosis [Velkey en Bernanke, 2001], although in the end only a single right and left coronary artery will remain [Bernanke and Velkey, 2002]. This explains why rudimentary coronary orifices are found in no less than 35% of human hearts [Turner and Navaratnam, 1996]. The remaining vessels will acquire a media of smooth muscle cells, and an adventitia, whereas those that do not form a tunica media will go into regression [Poelmann et al., 1993]. The coronary veins develop in a similar way, i.e. like a subepicardially sprouting capillary plexus that penetrates the coronary sinus. In most species this occurs prior to the invasion of the aorta. With remodelling of the capillary plexus and reducing the number of arteriovenous anastomoses the outlines of the mature coronary artery pattern are laid down [Vrancken-Peeters et al., 1997].

DEVELOPMENT OF THE ENDOCARDIUM AND CARDIAC JELLY

As mentioned in Chapter 1, the primary heart tube consists of two cell layers: the myocardium and the endocardium. In between, an extra-cellular matrix is present, dubbed the cardiac jelly, which is initially acellular [Markwald et al., 1975, 1977]. This matrix, which is synthesized by the myocardium [Krug et al., 1985, 1987], can be considered as a fusion between a myocardial basement membrane, with a dense and a reticular layer, and a thin endocardial basement membrane, comprising only a dense layer [Kitten et al., 1987]. The myocardial basement membrane contains various proteins, including collagen types I and IV, fibrillin, fibulin, laminin, and proteoglycans [reviewed by Nakajima et al., 2000; Schroeder et al., 2003]. While the heart tube starts to loop, there is sudden rise in the concentration of the glycosaminoglycan molecule hyaluronan [Markwald et al., 1978] in the cardiac jelly at the sites of what become the atrioventricular canal and the distal and proximal parts of the outflow tract. This event, which is crucial for the local volume increase [Nakamura and Manasek, 1981], is followed by epithelial to mesenchymal transdifferentiation of a subset of endocardial cells which subsequently invade the cardiac jelly [Markwald et al., 1975, 1977]. These local expansions of the initially homogenously distributed cardiac jelly are to become the endocardial cushions and ridges. Transdifferentiation of endocardial cells, which is mediated by transforming growth factor (TGF)-beta [Nakajima et al., 1997], is specifically induced by the overlying myocardium of the atrioventricular and outflow tract regions. The inducing signal consists of secreted glycoproteins, including fibronectin [Kitten et al., 1987; Mjaatvedt et al., 1987; Ffrench-Constant and Hynes, 1988]. Only those endothelial cells that express the JB3 antigen (fibrillin) will undergo epithelial to mesenchymal transdifferentiation [Wunsch et al., 1994]. The precursors of these cells can already been differentiated from the myocardial lineage in the cardiogenic plate during gastrulation, whereas non JB3 expressing endothelial precursors will later migrate into this area [Coffin and Poole, 1991; Wunsch et al., 1994; Sugi and Markwald, 1996].

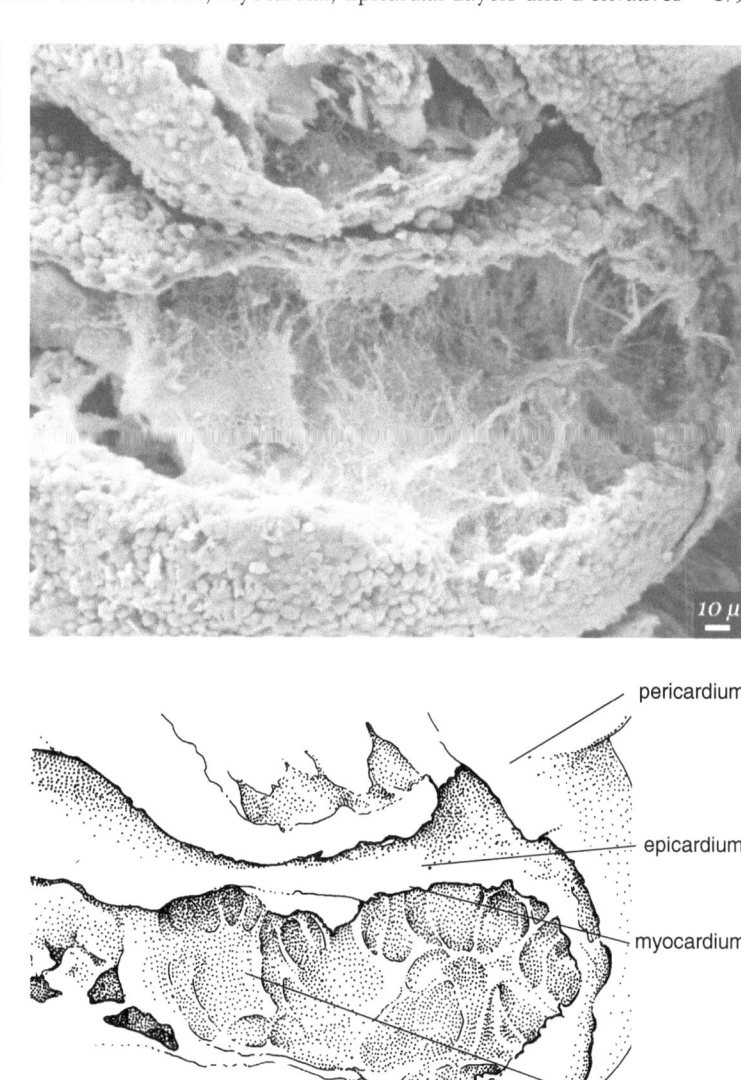

FIGURE 5.1   Partially openened heart tube (stage 11), ventral view.

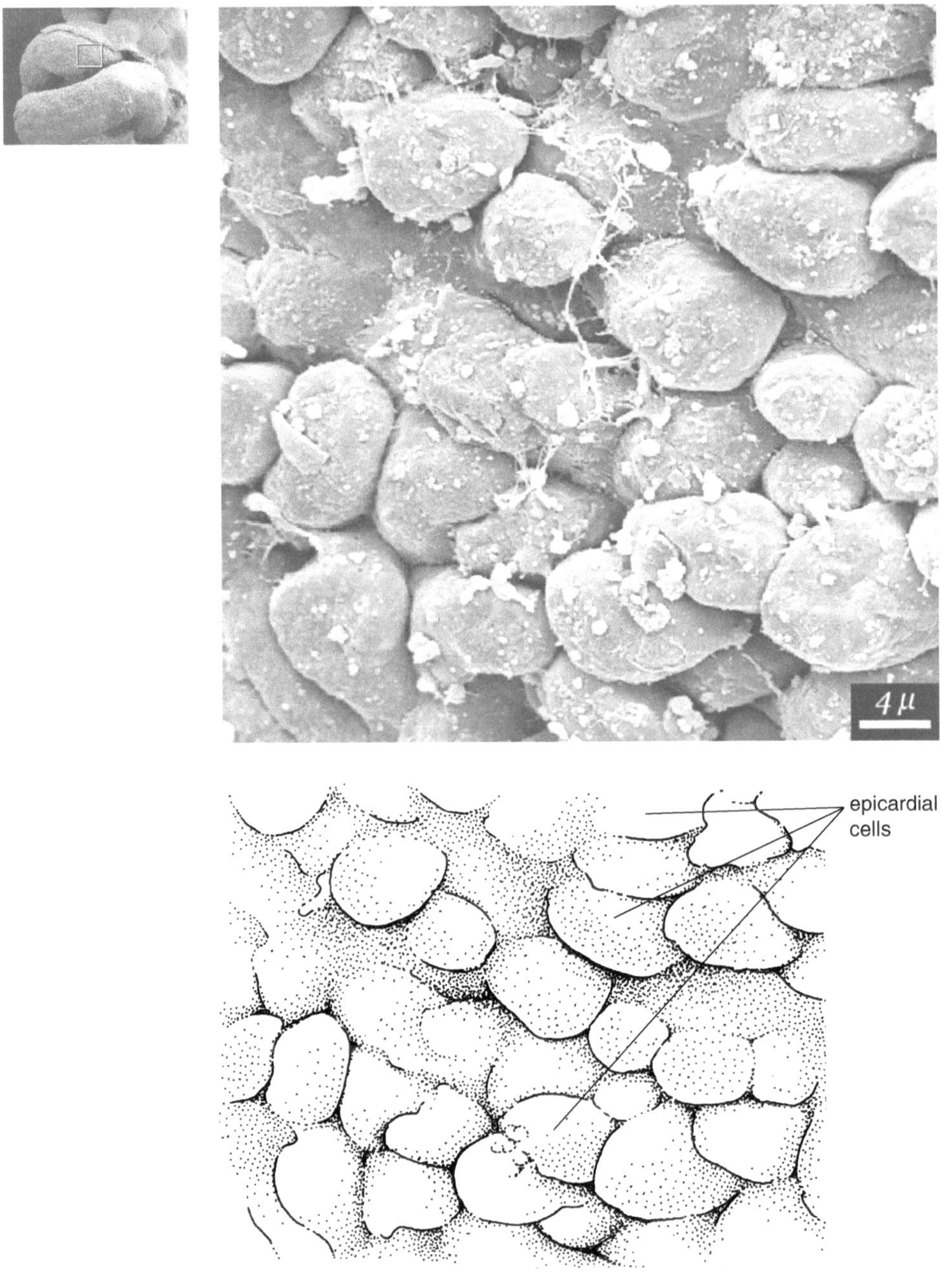
4 µ
epicardial
cells

FIGURE 5.2 Detail of the surface of the outflow tract (stage 11).

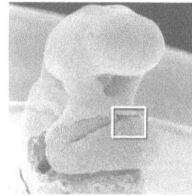

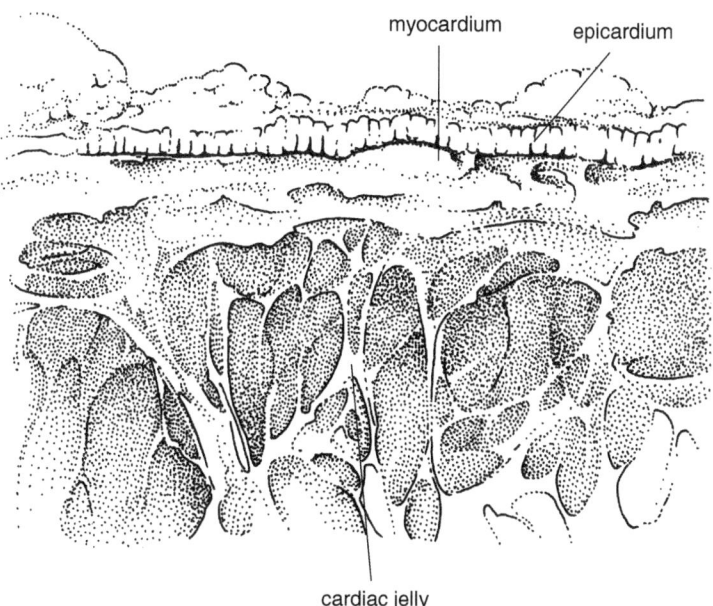

FIGURES 5.3 and 5.4   Section through the ventricular part of the heart tube (stage 11).

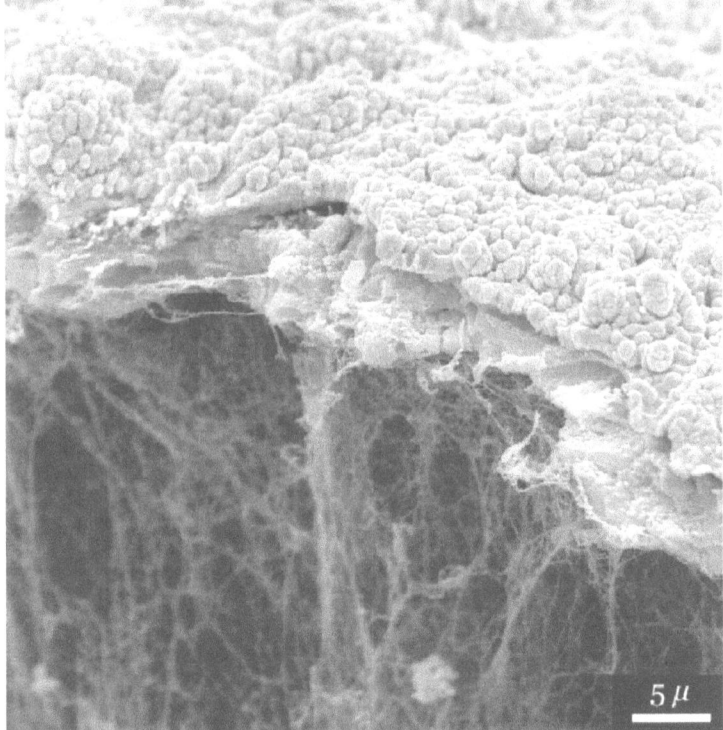
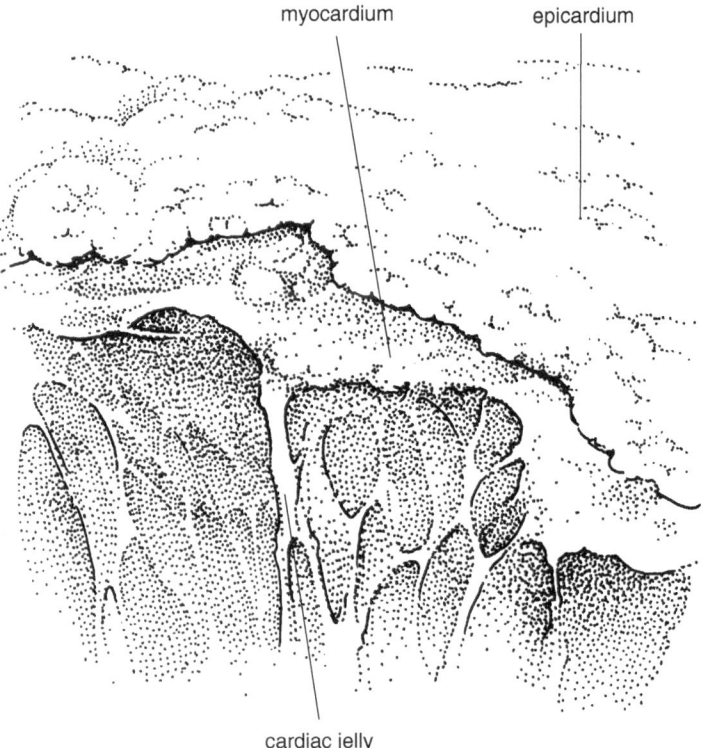

FIGURES 5.3 and 5.4   *Continued*

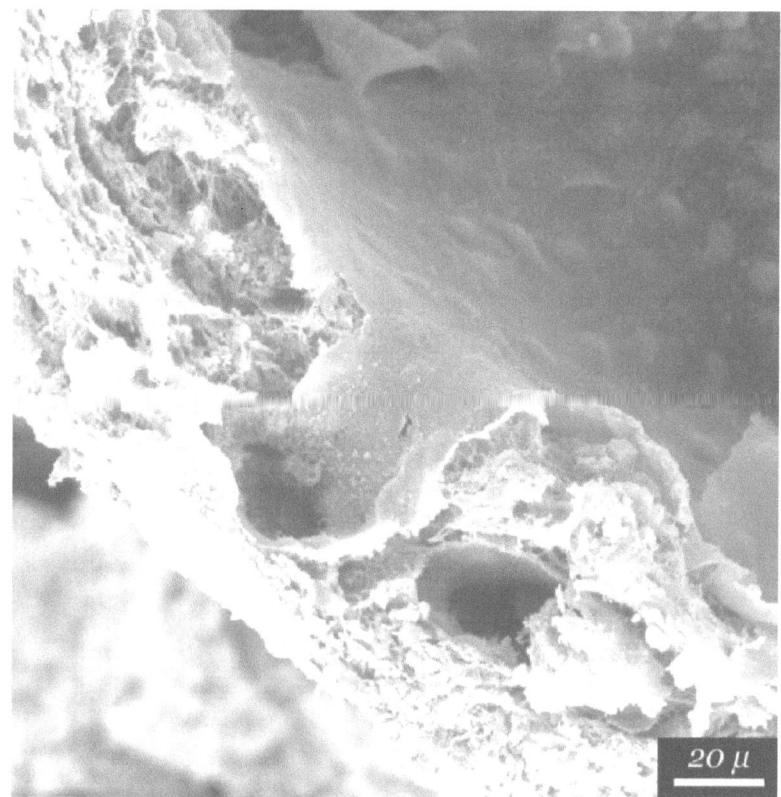

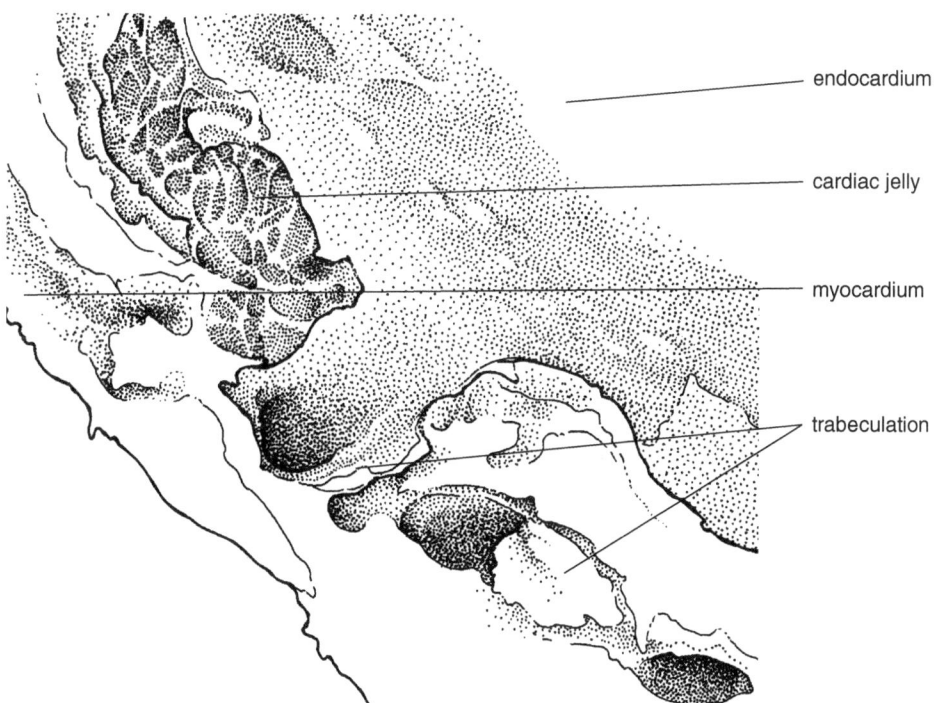

FIGURES 5.5–5.7   Transversely sectioned RV (stage 12).

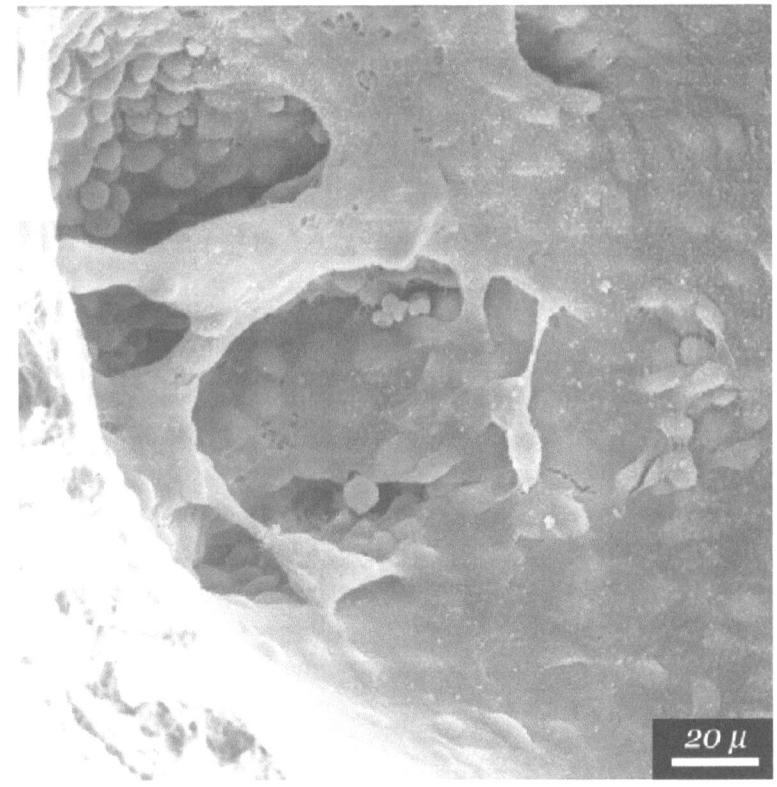

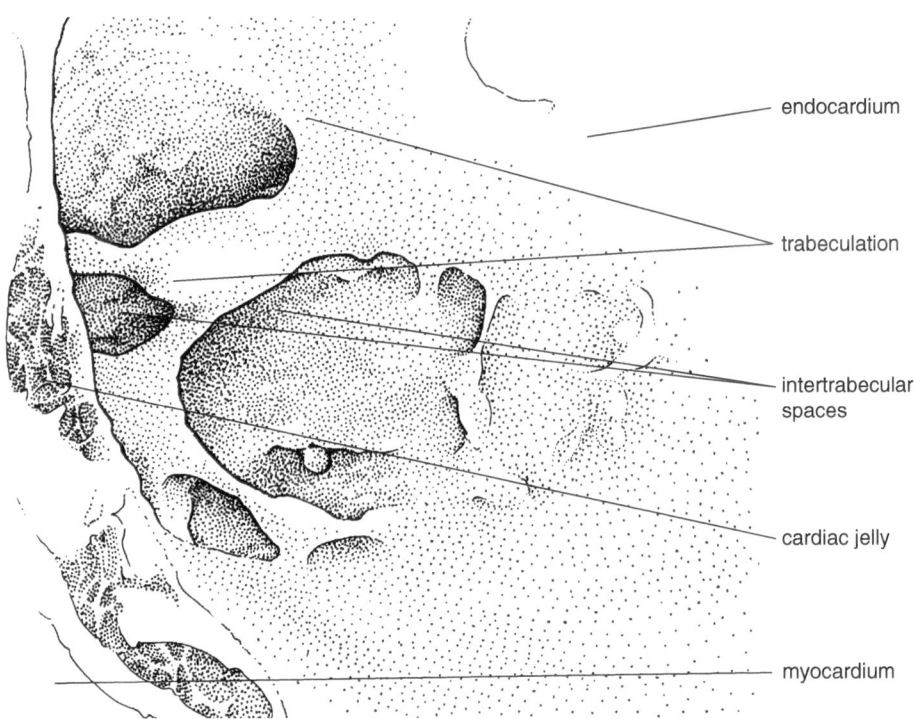

FIGURES 5.5–5.7   *Continued*

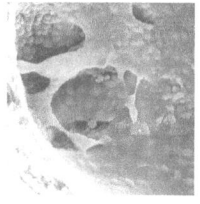

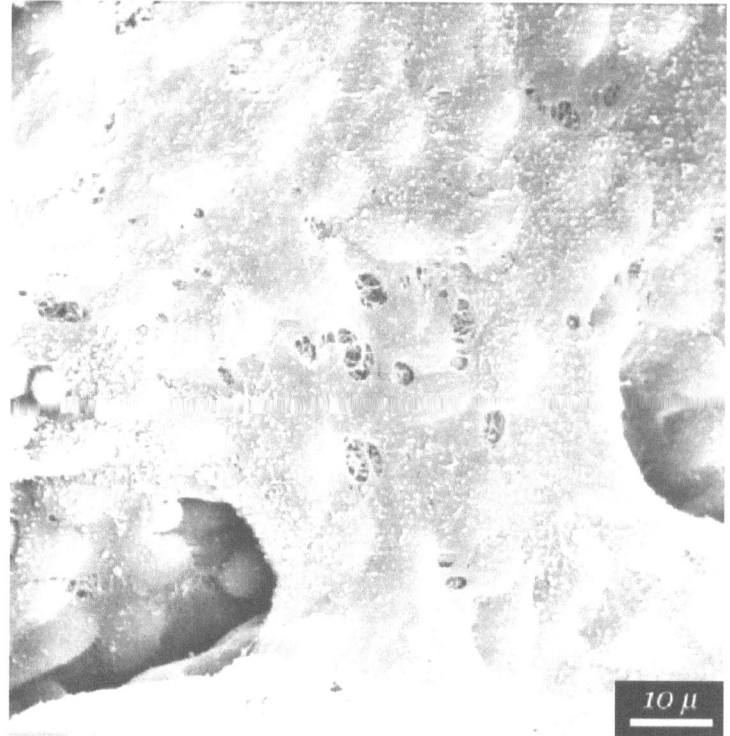

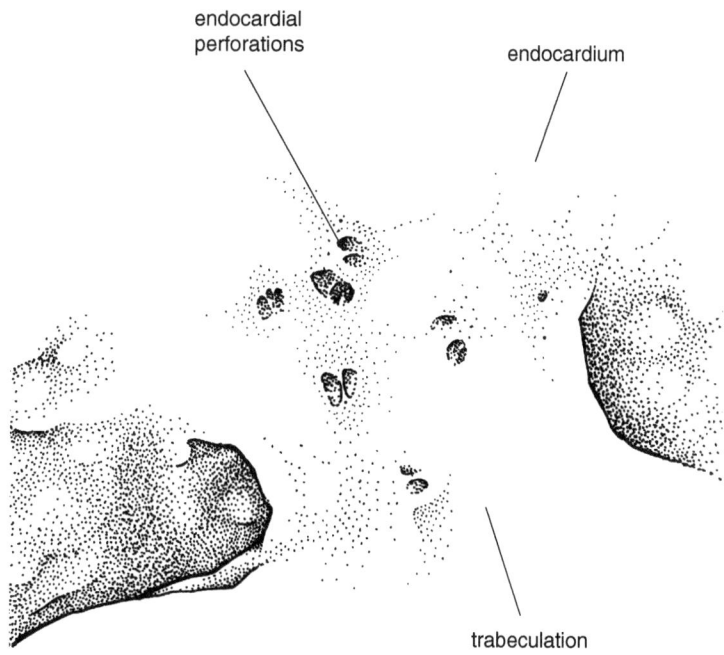

endocardial
perforations

endocardium

trabeculation

FIGURES 5.5–5.7   *Continued*

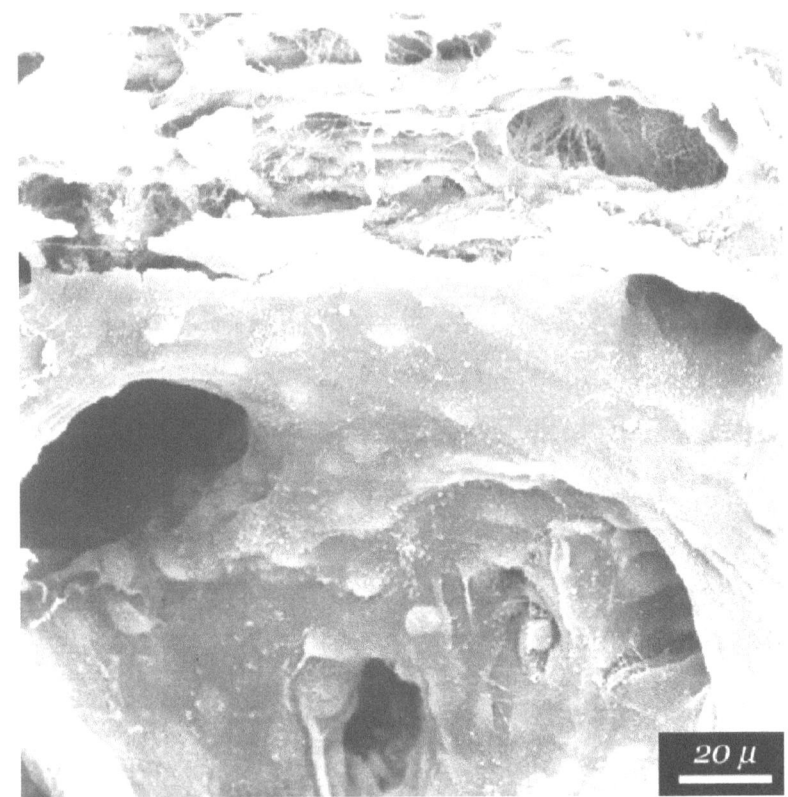

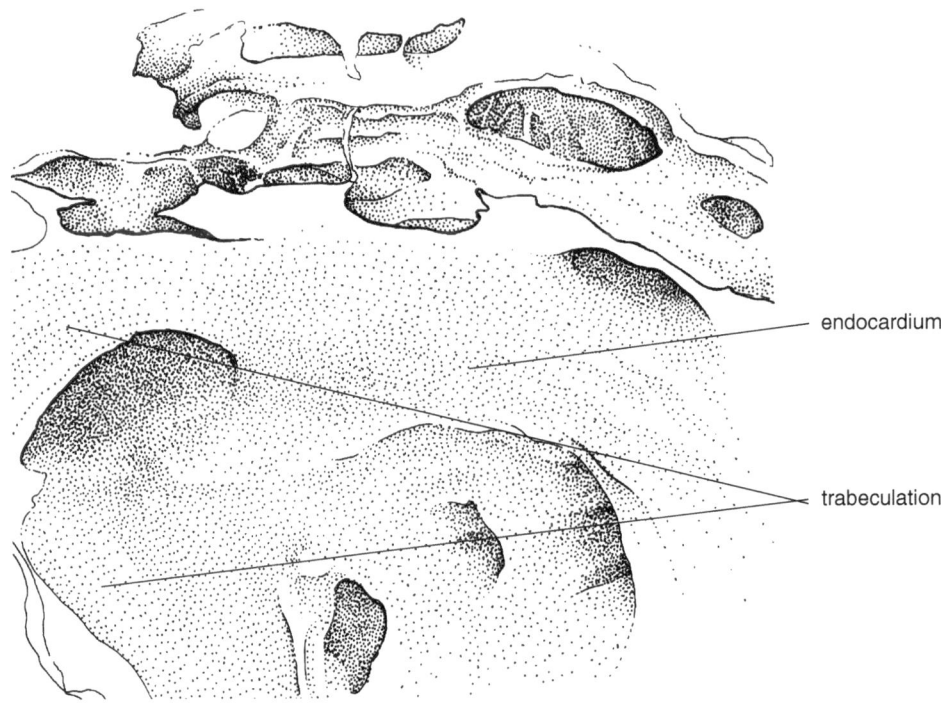

FIGURE 5.8   Transversely sectioned LV (stage 12).

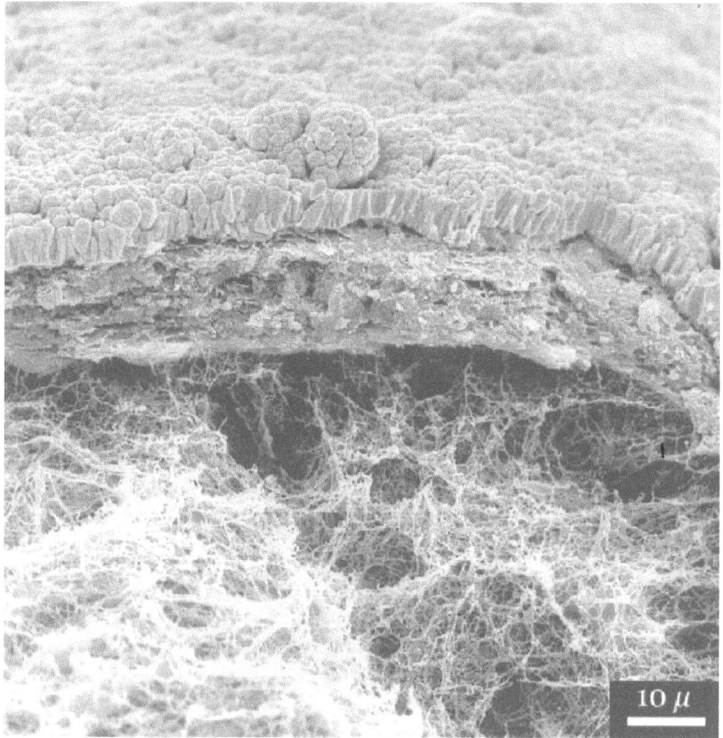

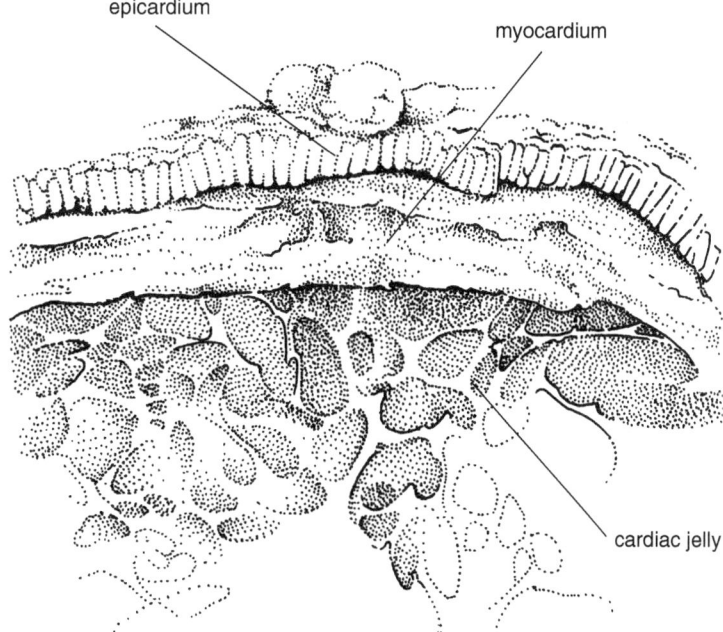

FIGURES 5.9 and 5.10   Transversely sectioned outflow tract (stage 13).

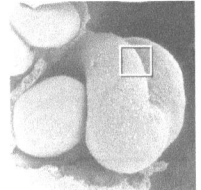

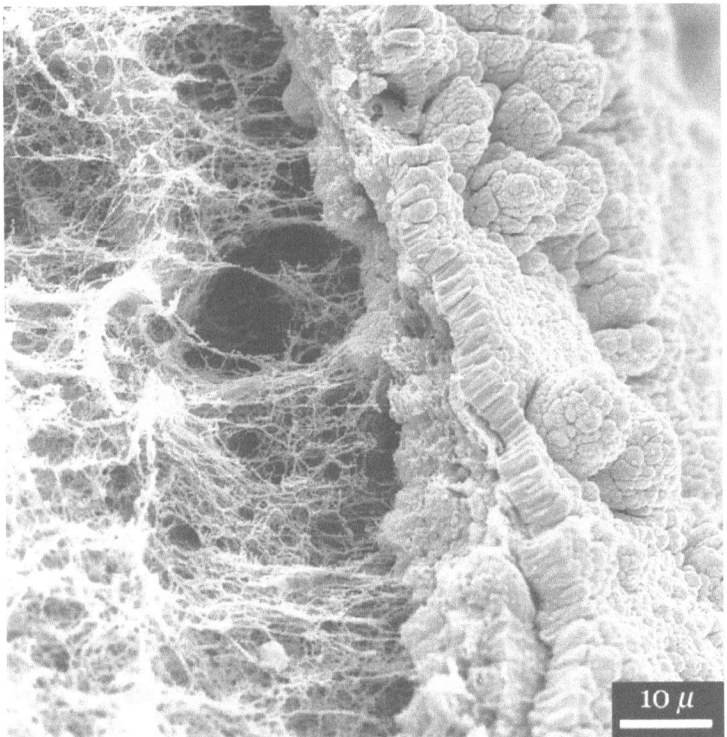

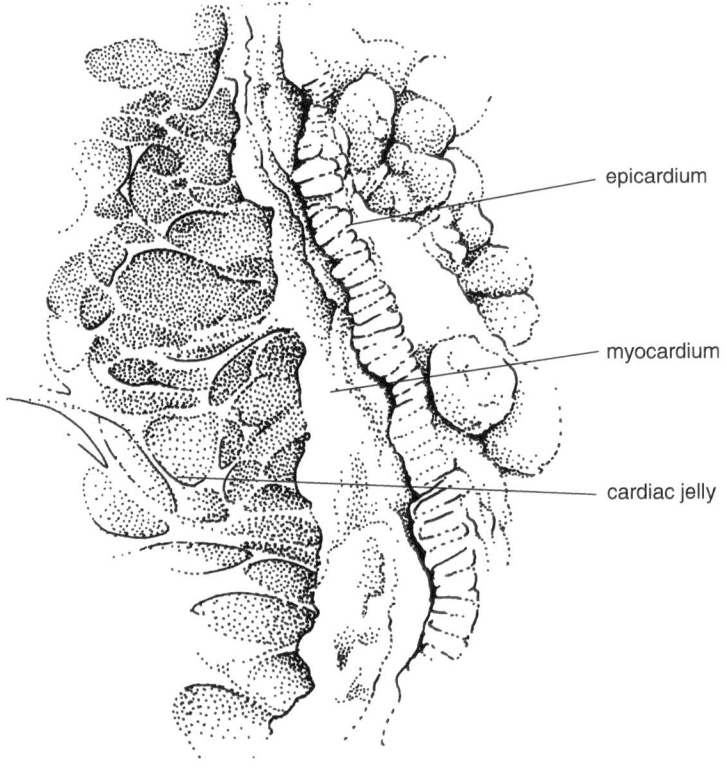

FIGURES 5.9 and 5.10   *Continued*

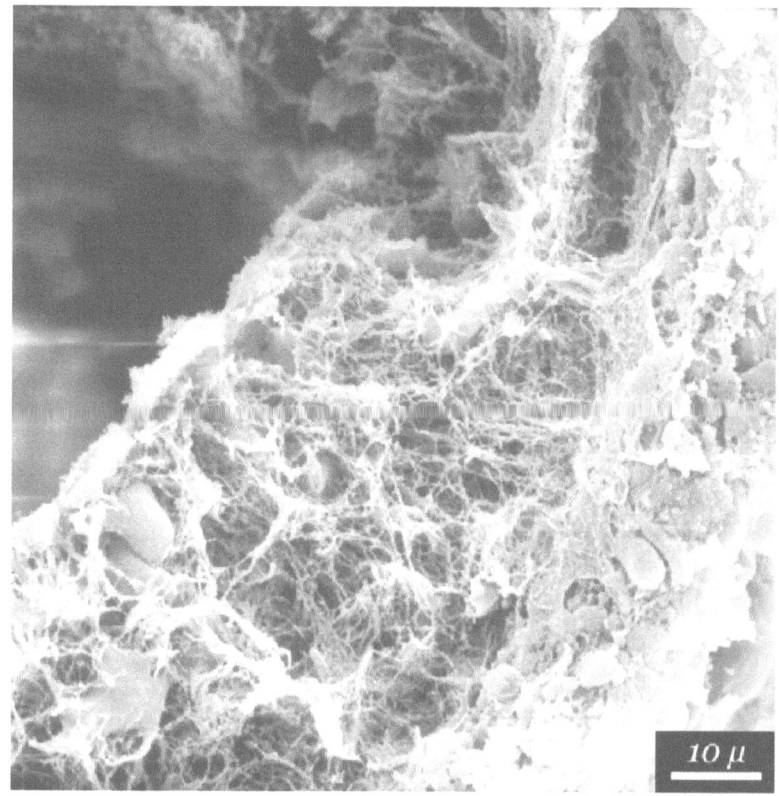

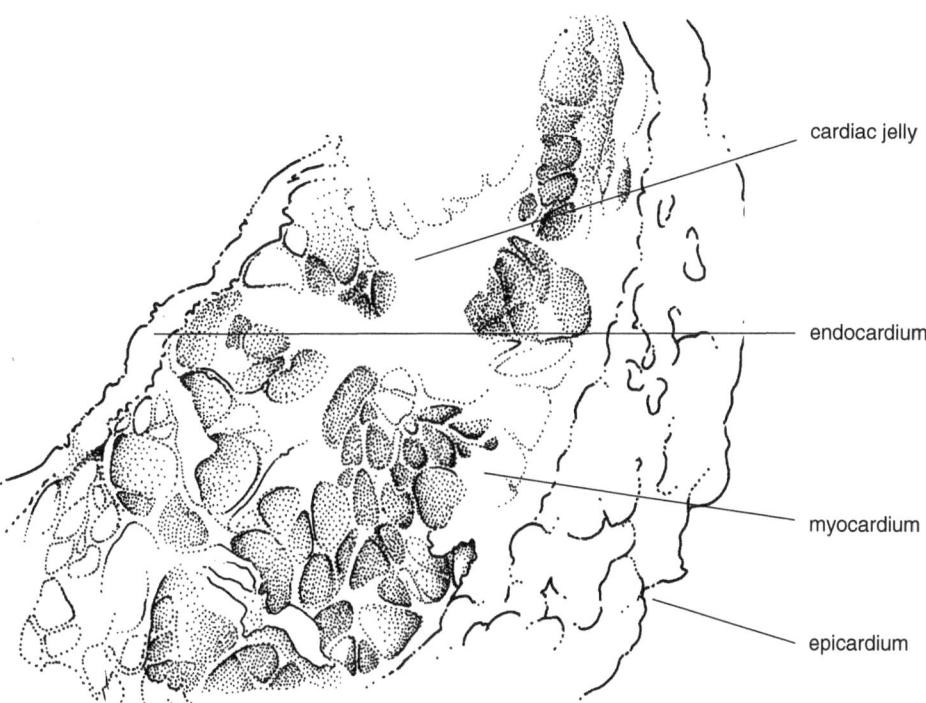

FIGURE 5.11   Transversely sectioned outflow tract (stage 14).

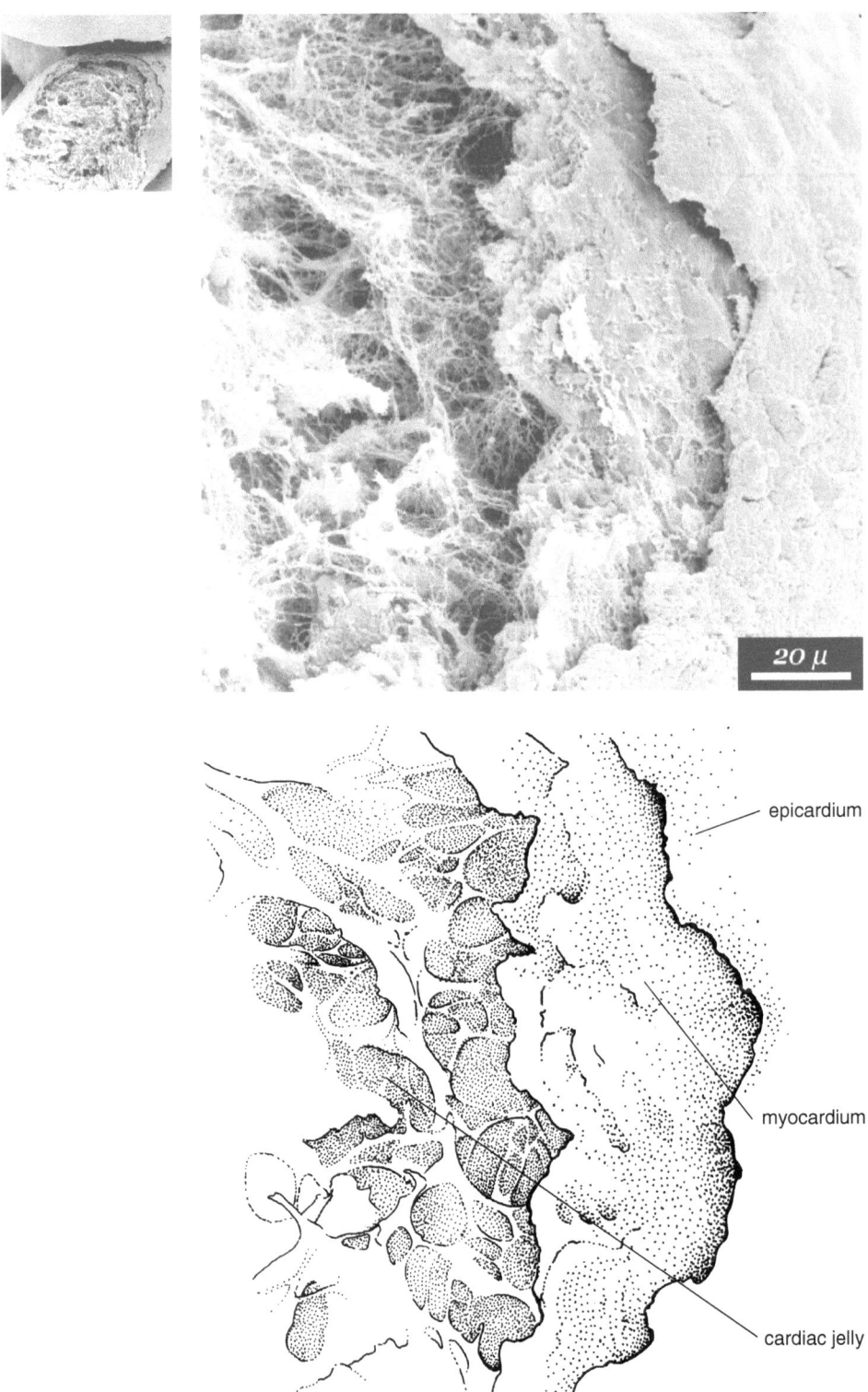

FIGURE 5.12   Partially opened distal outflow tract (stage 14).

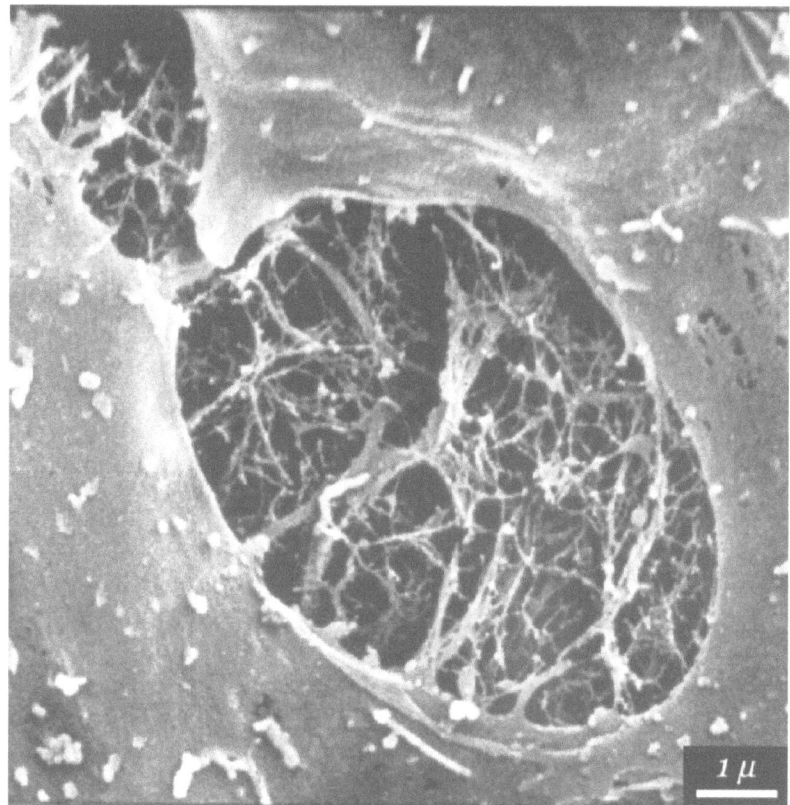

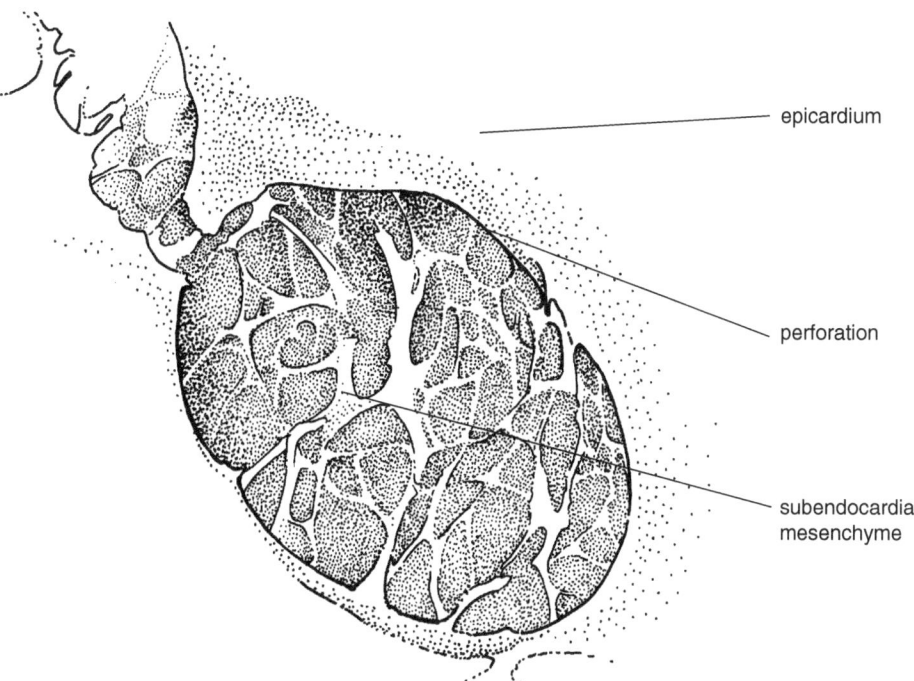

FIGURE 5.13   Detail of the lumenal surface of the LV (stage 14).

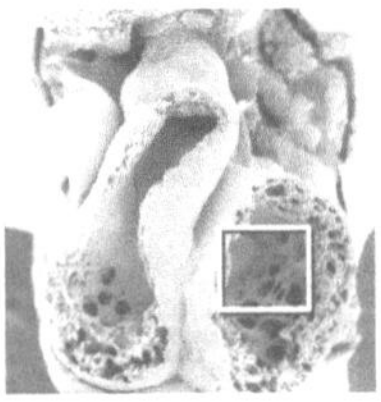

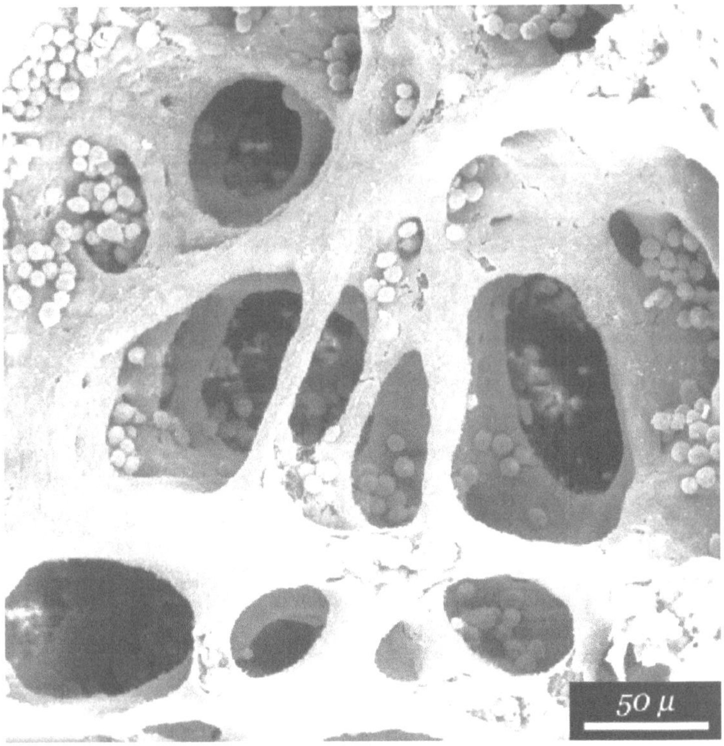

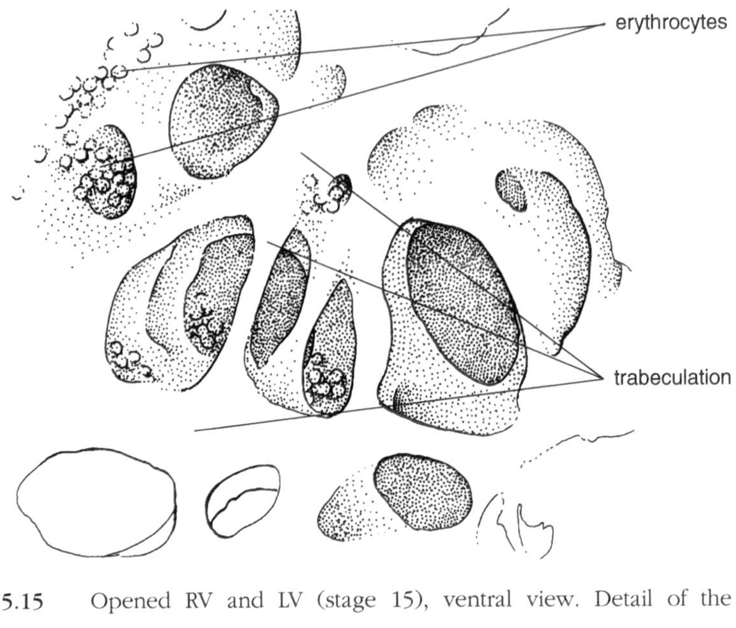

FIGURES 5.14 and 5.15   Opened RV and LV (stage 15), ventral view. Detail of the trabeculation.

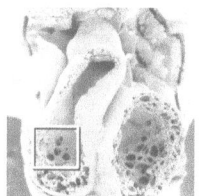

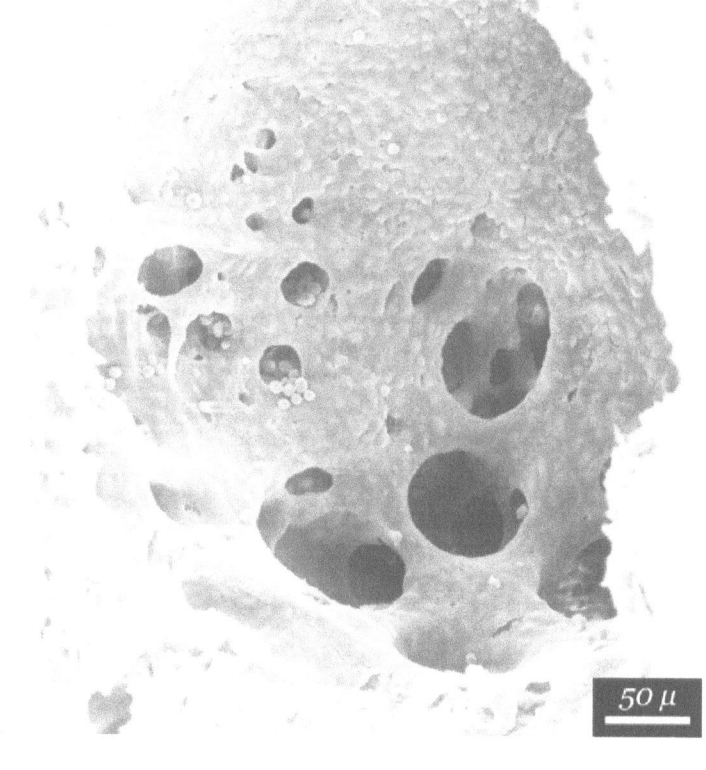

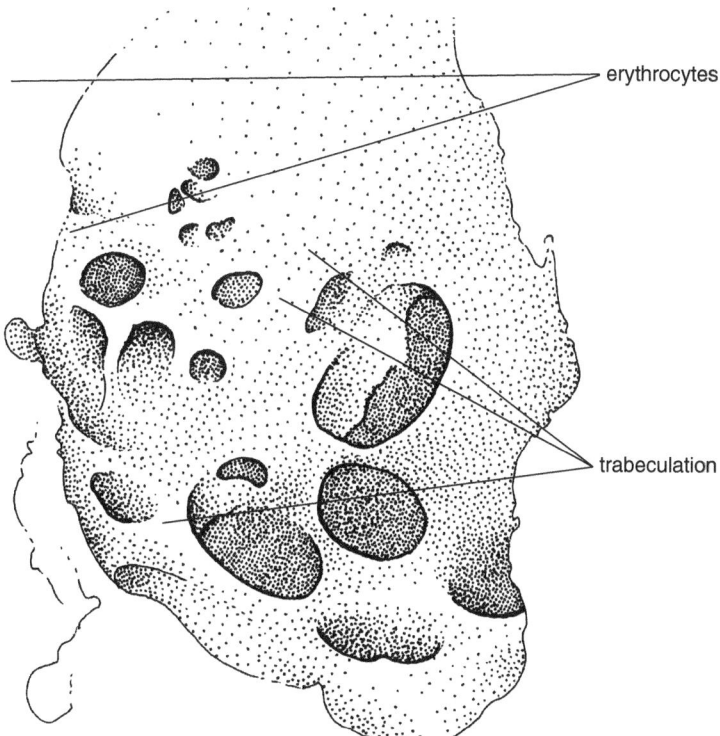

FIGURES 5.14 and 5.15   *Continued*

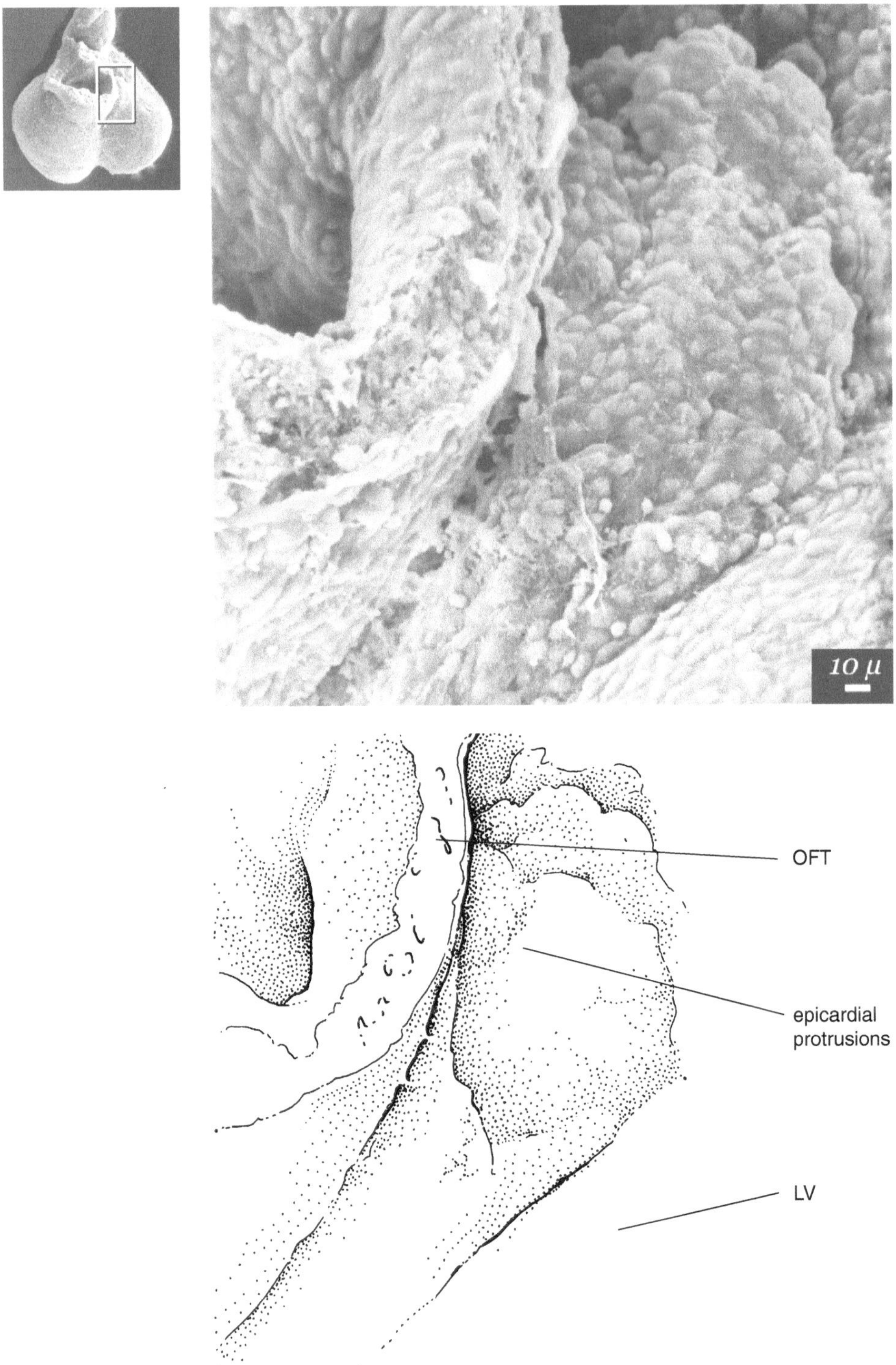

FIGURE 5.16   Atrioventricular canal and ventricles (stage 15), dorsal view.

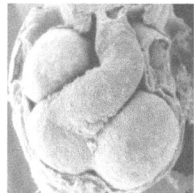
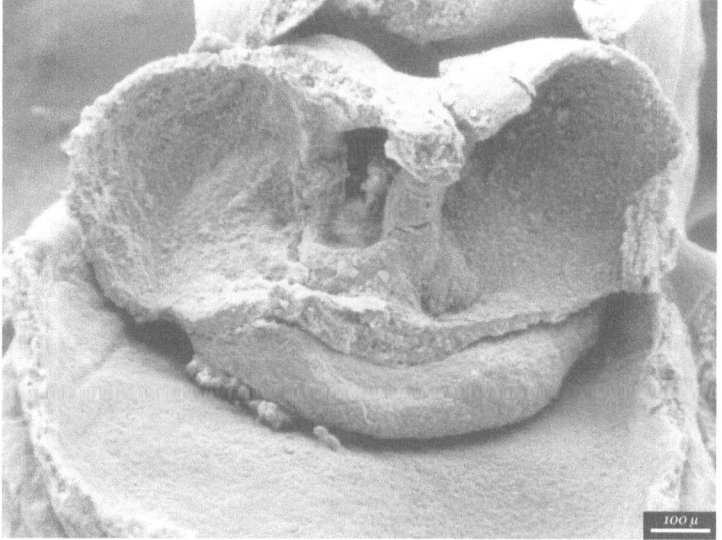
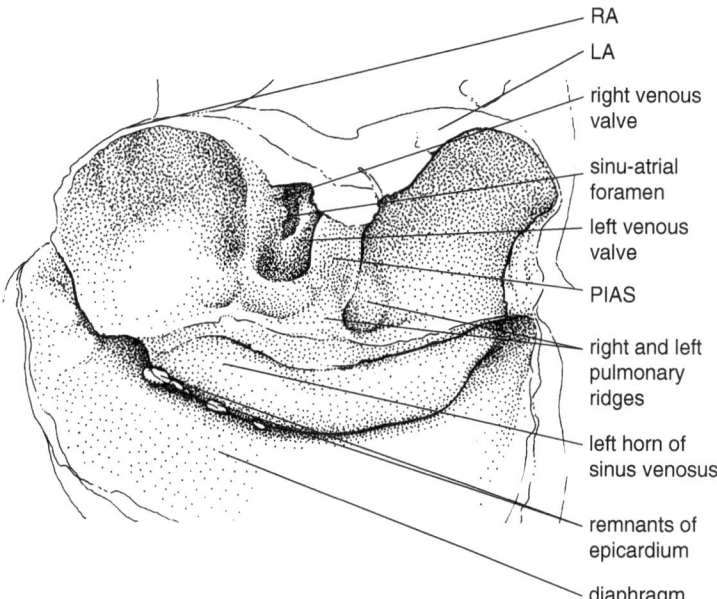

FIGURES 5.17 and 5.18   Opened RA and LA (stage 15), ventral view. The ventricles and outflow tract are removed. (See also Figs. 3.7–3.9)

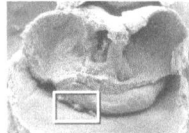

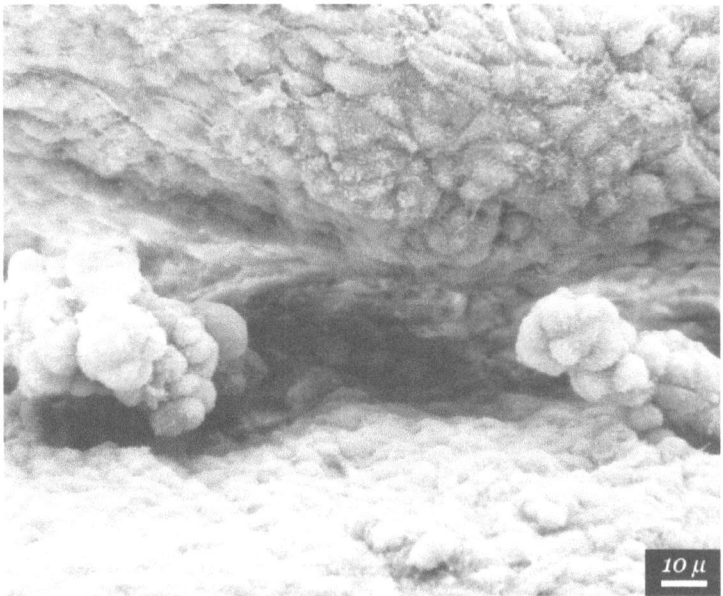

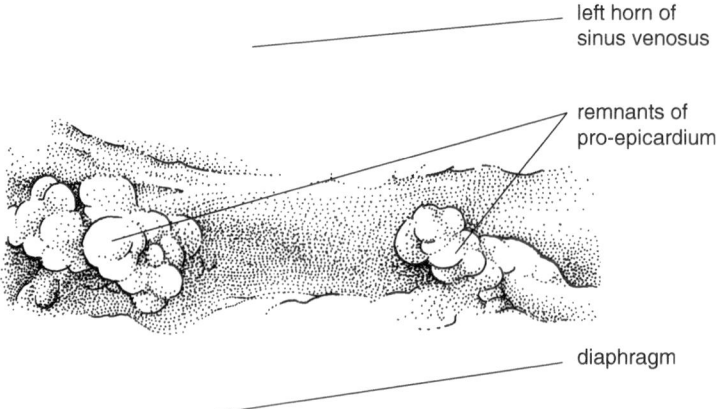

left horn of
sinus venosus

remnants of
pro-epicardium

diaphragm

FIGURES 5.17 and 5.18   *Continued*

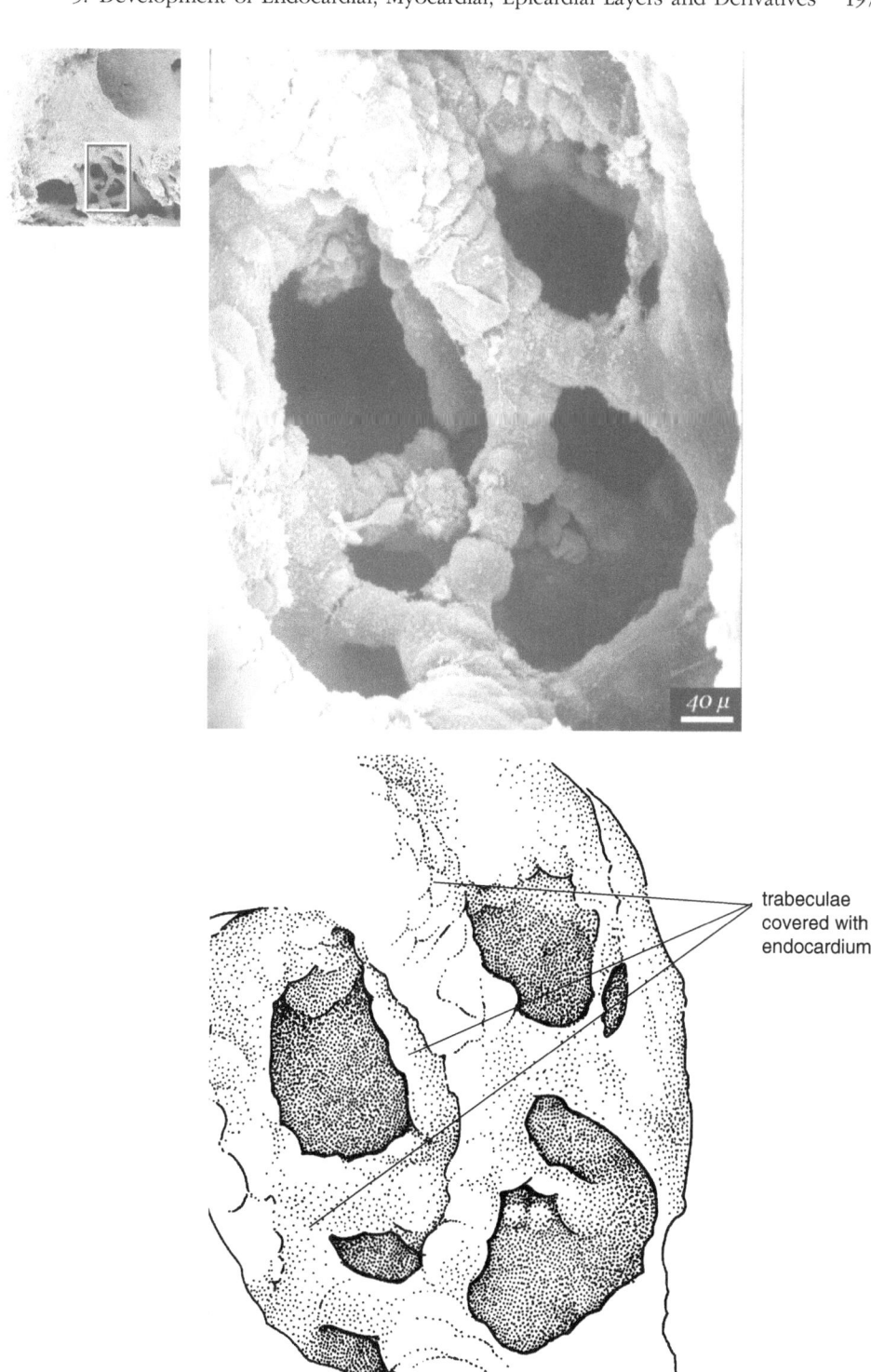

FIGURES 5.19 and 5.20   Opened RV (stage 19), ventral view. Detail of the trabeculae.

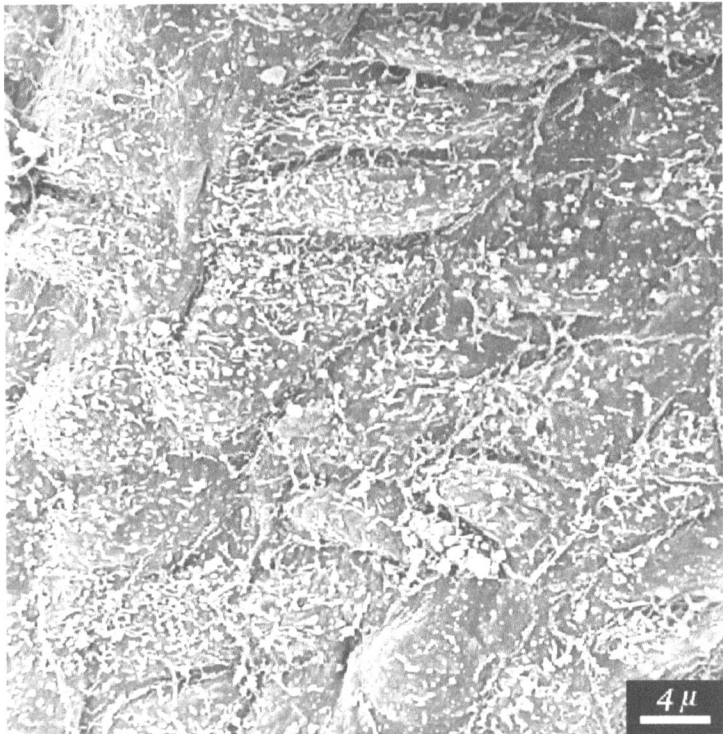

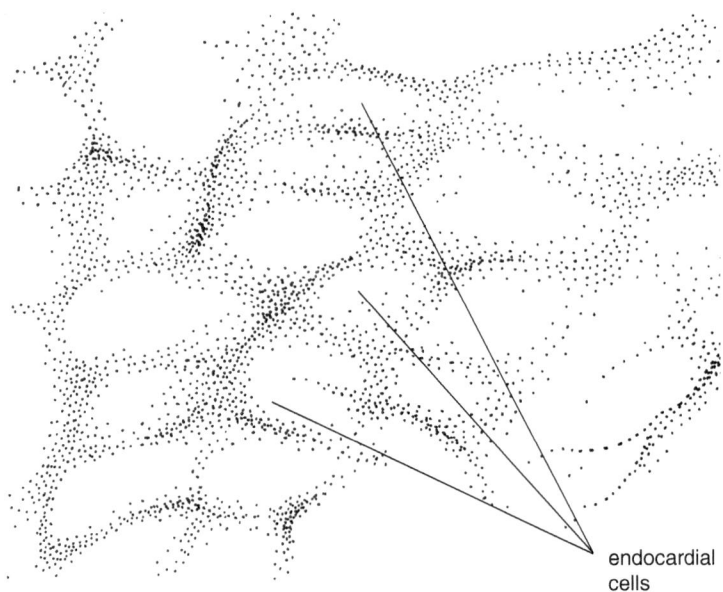

endocardial cells

FIGURES 5.19 and 5.20   *Continued*

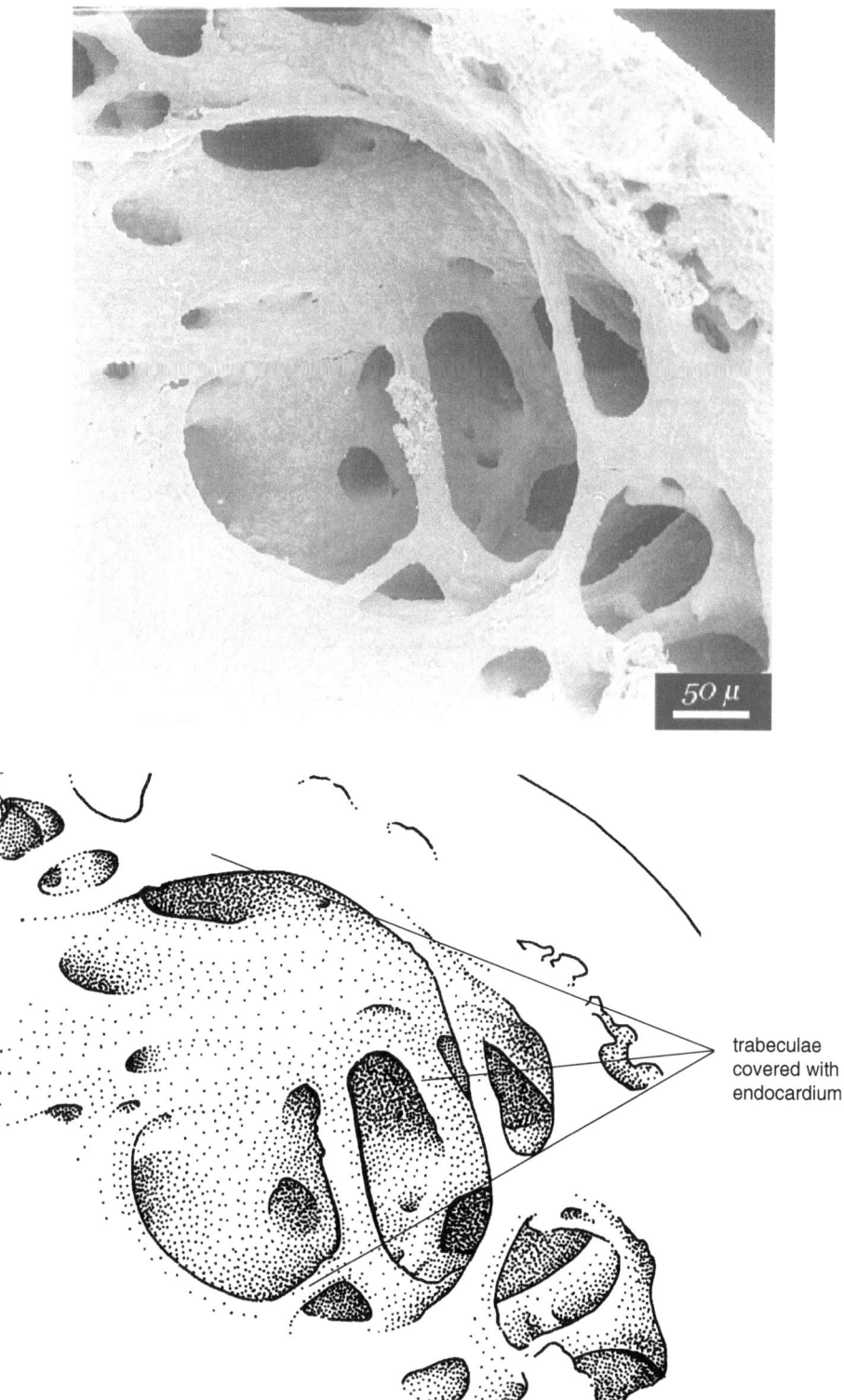

FIGURE 5.21   Opened RV (stage 22), ventral view. Detail of the trabeculae.

References

Anderson RH, Becker AE, Wenink ACG. The development of the conducting tissues. In: Roberts EA, ed. Cardiac Arrhythmias in the Neonate Infant and Child. New York, NY: Appleton-Century-Crofts; 1978.

Anderson RH, Becker RA. Cardiac anatomy: an integrated text and colour atlas. London: Gower Medical Publishing, Churchill Livingstone; 1980.

Anderson RH, Webb S, Brown NA. Clinical anatomy of the atrial septum with reference to its developmental components. Clin Anat 1999;12:362–374.

Anderson RH, Brown NA, Webb S. Development and structure of the atrial septum. Heart 2002;88:104–110.

Arguello C, Alanis J, Pantoja O, Valenzuela B. Electrophysiological and ultrastructural study of the atrioventricular canal during the development of the chick embryo. J Mol Cell Cardiol 1986;18:499–510.

Bernanke DH, Velkey JM. Development of the coronary blood supply: changing concepts and current ideas.

Anat Rec 2002;269:198–208.

Blausen BE, Johannes RS, Hutchins GM. Computer-based reconstructions of the cardiac ventricles of human embryos. Am J Cardiovasc Pathol 1990;3:37–43.

Bliss DF, Hutchins GM. The dorsal mesocardium and development of the pulmonary veins in human embryos. Am J Cardiovasc Pathol 1994;5:55–67.

Bogers AJJC, Gittenberger-de-Groot AC, Dubbeldam JA, Huysmans HA. The inadequacy of existing theories on development of the proximal coronary arteries and their connexions with the arterial trunks. Int J Cardiol 1988;20:117–123.

Bremer JL. The presence and influence of two spiral sterams in the heart of the chick embryo. Am J Anat 1932;49:409–440.

Challice CE, Viragh S. The architectural development of the early mammalian heart. Tissue Cell 1973;6:447–462.

Christoffels VM, Habets PE, Franco D, Campione M, de Jong F, Lamers WH, Bao ZZ, Palmer S, Biben C, Harvey RP, Moorman AF. Chamber formation and morphogenesis in the developing mammalian heart. Dev Biol 2000;223:266–278.

Coffin JD, Poole TJ. Endothelial cell origin and migration in embryonic heart and cranial blood vessel development. Anat Rec 1991;231:383–395.

De la Cruz MV, Sanchez Gomez C, Arteaga MM, Arguello C. Experimental study of the development of the truncus and the conus in the chick embryo. J Anat 1977;123:661–686.

De la Cruz MV, Sanchez-Gomes C. Straight heart tube. Primitive cardiac cavities vs. primitive cardiac segments. In: De la Cruz MV, Markwald RR (eds). Living Morphogenesis of the Heart. Bosto: Birkhäuser. 1999; pp 85–98.

De Jong F, Opthof T, Wilde AA, Janse MJ, Charles R, Lamers WH, Moorman AF. Persisting zones of slow impulse conduction in developing chicken hearts. Circ Res 1992;71:240–250.

De Lange FJ, Moorman AF, Anderson RH, Manner J, Soufan AT, de Gier-de Vries C, Schneider MD, Webb S, van den Hoff MJ, Christoffels VM. Lineage and morphogenetic analysis of the cardiac valves. Circ Res 2004;95:645–654.

De Ruiter MC, Gittenberger-de Groot AC, Poelmann RE, VanIperen L, Mentink MM. Development of the pharyngeal arch system related to the pulmonary and bronchial vessels in the avian embryo. With a concept on systemic-pulmonary collateral artery formation. Circulation 1993;87:1306–1319.

De Ruiter MC, Gittenberger-De Groot AC, Wenink AC, Poelmann RE, Mentink MM. In normal development pulmonary veins are connected to the sinus venosus segment in the left atrium. Anat Rec 1995;243(1):84–92.

Franco D, Lamers WH, Moorman AF. Patterns of expression in the developing myocardium. Towards a morphologically integrated transcriptional model. Cardiovasc Res 1998;38:25–53.

Franco D, Campione M, Kelly R, Zammit PS, Buckingham M, Lamers WH, Moorman AF. Multiple transcriptional domains, with distinct left and right components, in the atrial chambers of the developing heart. Circ Res 2000;87:984–991.

Ffrench-Constant C, Hynes OR. Patterns of fibronectin gene expression and splicing during cell migration in chicken embryos. Development 1988;104:369–382.

Harh JY, Paul MH. Experimental cardiac morphogenesis. I. Development of the ventricular septum in the chick. J Embryol Exp Morphol 1975;33:13–28.

Henderson DJ, Copp AJ. Versican expression is associated with chamber specification, septation, and valvulogenesis in the developing mouse heart. Circ Res 1998;83:523–532.

Hirakow R. Epicardial formation in staged human embryos. Acta Anat Nippon 1992;67:616–622.

Hirokawa K. A quantitative study on pre- and postnatal growth of human heart. Acta Path Jpn 1972;22:613–624.

Hiruma T, Hirakow R. Epicardial formation in embryonic chick heart: Computer-aided reconstruction, scanning, and transmission electron microscopic studies. Am J Anat 1989;184:129–138.

Hogers B, DeRuiter MC, Baasten AM, Gittenberger-de Groot AC, Poelmann RE. Intracardiac blood flow patterns related to the yolk sac circulation of the chick embryo. Circ Res 1995;76:871–877.

Hogers B, De Ruiter MC, Gittenberger-de Groot AC, Poelmann RE. Unilateral vein ligation alters intracardiac blood flow patterns and morphogenesis in the chick embryo. Circ Res 1997;80:473–481.

Hogers B, De Ruiter M, Gittenberger-de Groot AC, Poelmann RE. Extraembryonic venous obstructions lead to cardiovascular malformations and can be embryolethal. Cardiovasc Res 1999;41:87–99.

Hutchins GM, Kessler-Hanna A, Moore GW. Development of the coronary arteries in the embryonic human heart. Circulation 1988;77:1250–1257.

Jaffee OC. Hemodynamic factors in the development of the chick embryo heart. Anat Rec 1965;151:69–76.

Kelly RG, Brown NA, Buckingham ME. The arterial pole of the mouse heart forms from Fgf10-expressing cells in pharyngeal mesoderm. Dev Cell 2001;1:435–440.

Kitten GT, Markwald RR, Bolender DL. Distribution of basement membrane antigens in cryopreserved early embryonic hearts. Anat Rec 1987;217:379–390.

Knauth A, McCarthy KP, Webb S, Ho SY, Allwork SP, Cook AC, Anderson RH. Interatrial communication through the mouth of the coronary sinus. Cardiol Young 2002;12:364–372.

Kosaki K, Mendoza A, Jones KL. Cervical flexion: its contribution to normal and abnormal cardiac morphogenesis. Teratology 1996;54:135–144.

Krug EL, Runyan RB, Markwald RR. Protein extracts from early embryonic hearts initiate cardiac endothelial cytodifferentiation. Dev Biol 1985;112:414–426.

Krug EL, Mjaatvedt CH, Markwald RR. Extracellular matrix from embryonic myocardium elicits an early morphogenetic event in cardiac endothelial differentiation. Dev Biol 1987;120:348–355.

Lamers WH, Wessels A, Verbeek FJ, Moorman AFM, Viragh S, Wenink ACG, Gittenberger-de Groot AC, Anderson RH. New findings concerning ventricular septation in the human heart. Circulation 1992;86:1194–1205.

Lamers WH, Viragh S, Wessels A, Moorman AF, Anderson RH. Formation of the tricuspid valve in the human heart. Circulation 1995;91:111–121.

Leyhane JC. Visualization of blood streams in the developing chick heart. Anat Rec 1969;163:312–313.

Los JA. De embryonale ontwikkeling van de venae pulmonales en de sinus coronarius bij de mens. Thesis. Leiden: University of Leiden. 1958; p 131.

Manasek FJ, Monroe RG. Early cardiac morphogenesis is independant of function. Dev Biol 1972;27:584–588.

Männer J, Seidl W, Steding G. Correlation between the embryonic head flexures and cardiac development. An experimental study in chick embryos. Anat Embryol 1993:188:269–285.

Männer J, Seidl W, Steding G. The role of extracardiac factors in normal and abnormal development of the chick embryo heart. Anat Embryol 1995;191:61–72.

Männer J. Does the subepicardial mesenchyme contribute myocardioblasts to the myocardium of the chick embryo heart? A quail-chick chimera study tracing the fate of the epicardial primordium. Anat Rec 1999;255:212–226.

Männer J, Perez-Pomares JM, Macias D, Munoz-Chapuli R. The origin, formation and developmental significance of the epicardium: a review. Cells Tissues Organs 2001;169:89–103.

Manning A, McLachlan JC. Looping of chick embryo hearts in vitro. J Anat 1990;168: 257–263.

Markwald RR, Fitzharris TP, Adams-Smith WN. Structural analysis of endocardial cytodifferentiation. Dev Biol 1975;42:160–180.

Markwald RR, Fitzharris TP, Manasek FJ. Structural development of endocardial cushions. Amer J Anat 1977;148:85–120.

Markwald RR, Fitzharris TP, Bank H, Bernanke DH. Structural analyses on the matrical organization of glycosaminoglycans in developing endocardial cushions. Dev Biol 1978;62: 292–316.

Mikawa T, Borisov A, Brown AM, Fischman DA. Clonal analysis of cardiac morphogenesis in the chicken embryo using a replication-defective retrovirus: I. Formation of the ventricular myocardium. Dev Dyn 1992;193:11–23.

Mikawa T, Gourdie RG. Pericardial mesoderm generates a population of coronary smooth muscle cells migrating into the heart along with ingrowth of the epicardial organ. Dev Biol 1996;174:221–232.

Mjaatvedt CH, Lepera RC, Markwald RR. Myocardial specificity for initiating endothelial-mesenchymal cell transition in embryonic chick heart correlates with a particulate distribution of fibronectin. Dev Biol 1987;119:59–67.

Mjaatvedt CH, Nakaoka T, Moreno-Rodriguez R, Norris RA, Kern MJ, Eisenberg CA, Turner D, Markwald RR. The outflow tract of the heart is recruited from a novel heart-forming field. Dev Biol 2001;238:97–109.

Moorman AF, de Jong F, Denyn MM, Lamers WH. Development of the cardiac conduction system. Circ Res 1998;82:629–644.

Moorman AF, Schumacher CA, de Boer PA, Hagoort J, Bezstarosti K, van den Hoff MJ, Wagenaar GT, Lamers JM, Wuytack F, Christoffels VM, Fiolet JW. Presence of functional sarcoplasmic reticulum in the developing heart and its confinement to chamber myocardium. Dev Biol 2000;223:279–290.

Moorman AF, Christoffels VM. Cardiac chamber formation: development, genes, and evolution. Physiol Rev 2003;83:1223–1267.

Munoz-Chapuli R, Macias D, Gonzalez-Iriarte M, Carmona R, Atencia G, Perez-Pomares JM. The epicardium and epicardial-derived cells: multiple functions in cardiac development. Rev Esp Cardiol 2002a;55:1070–1082.

Munoz-Chapuli R, Gonzalez-Iriarte M, Carmona R, Atencia G, Macias D, Perez-Pomares JM. Cellular precursors of the coronary arteries. Tex Heart Inst J 2002b;29:243–249.

Nakajima Y, Miyazono K, Kato M, Takase M, Yamagishi T, Nakamura H. Extracellular fibrillar structure of latent TGF beta binding protein-1: role in TGF beta-dependent endothelial-mesenchymal transformation during endocardial cushion tissue formation in mouse embryonic heart. J Cell Biol 1997;136:193–204.

Nakajima Y, Yamagishi T, Hokari S, Nakamura H. Mechanisms involved in valvuloseptal endocardial cushion formation in early cardiogenesis: roles of transforming growth factor (TGF)-beta and bone morphogenetic protein (BMP). Anat Rec 2000;258:119–127.

Nakamura A, Manasek FJ. An experimental study of the relation of cardiac jelly to the shape of the early chick embryonic heart. J Embryol Exp Morphol 1981;65:235–256.

Neill CA. Development of the pulmonary veins. Pediatrics 1956;18:880–887.

Oosthoek PW, Wenink AC, Vrolijk BC, Wisse LJ, DeRuiter MC, Poelmann RE, Gittenberger-de Groot AC. Development of the atrioventricular valve tension apparatus in the human heart. Anat Embryol (Berl) 1998;198:317–329.

Qayyum SR, Webb S, Anderson RH, Verbeek FJ, Brown NA, Richardson MK. Septation and valvar formation in the outflow tract of the embryonic chick heart. Anat Rec 2001;264: 273–283.

Perez-Pomares JM, Macias D, Garcia-Garrido L, Munoz-Chapuli R. Contribution of the primitive epicardium to the subepicardial mesenchyme in hamster and chick embryos. Dev Dyn 1997;210:96–105.

Perez-Pomares JM, Phelps A, Sedmerova M, Wessels A. Epicardial-like cells on the distal arterial end of the cardiac outflow tract do not derive from the proepicardium but are derivatives of the cephalic pericardium. Dev Dyn 2003;227:56–68.

Poelmann RE, Gittenberger-de-Groot AC, Mentink MMT, Bökenkamp R, Hogers B. Development of the cardiac coronary vascular endothelium, studied with antiendothelial antibodies, in chick/quail chimeras. Circ Res 1993;73:559–568.

Poole TJ, Coffin JD. Vasculogenesis and angiogenesis: Two distinct morphogenetic mechanisms establish embryonic vascular pattern. J Exp Zool 1989;251:224–231.

Rammos S, Gittenberger-de Groot AC, Oppenheimer-Dekker A. The abnormal pulmonary venous connexion: a developmental approach. Int J Cardiol 1990;29:285–295.

Rumyantsev PP. Interrelations of the proliferation and differentiation processes during cardiac myogenesis and regeneration. Int Rev Cytol 1977;51:186–273.

Rychter Z, Lemez L. Changes in localization in aortic arches of laminar blood streams of main venous trunksto the heart after exclusion of vitelline vessels on the second day of incubation. Fed Proc Transl Suppl 1965;24:815–820.

Rychterova V. Principle of growth in thickness of the heart ventricular wall in the chick embryo. Folia Morphol Praha 1971;19:262–272.

Schroeder JA, Jackson LF, Lee DC, Camenisch TD. Form and function of developing heart valves: coordination by extracellular matrix and growth factor signaling. J Mol Med 2003;81:392–403.

Sedmera D, Pexieder T, Hu N, Clark EB. Developmental changes in the myocardial architecture of the chick. Anat Rec 1997;248:421–432.

Sedmera D, Pexieder T, Rychterova V, Hu N, Clark EB. Remodeling of chick embryonic ventricular myoarchitecture under experimentally changed loading conditions. Anat Rec 1999;254:238–252.

Sedmera D, Pexieder T, Vuillemin M, Thompson RP, Anderson RH. Developmental patterning of the myocardium. Anat Rec 2000;258:319–337.

Soufan AT, van den Hoff MJ, Ruijter JM, de Boer PA, Hagoort J, Webb S, Anderson RH, Moorman AF. Reconstruction of the patterns of gene expression in the developing mouse heart reveals an architectural arrangement that facilitates the understanding of atrial malformations and arrhythmias. Circ Res 2004;95:1207–1215.

Steding G, Seidl W. Contribution to the development of the heart. Part 1: normal development. Thorac Cardiovasc Surg 1980;28:386–409.

Steding G, Xu JW, Seidl W, Manner J, Xia H. Developmental aspects of the sinus valves and the sinus venosus septum of the right atrium in human embryos. Anat Embryol (Berl) 1990;181:469–475.

Steding G, Seidl W. Morphology and physiology of the early embryonic heart: the correlations between blood flow and septation. In: Clark EB, Takao A (eds). Developmental cardiology. Morphogenesis and function. Futura Publishing Company, Inc., Mount Kisco, 1990.

Sugi Y, Markwald RR. Formation and early morphogenesis of endocardial endothelial precursor cells and the role of endoderm. Dev Biol 1996;175:66–83.

Thompson RP, Sumida H, Abercrombie V, Satow Y, Fitzharris TP, Okamoto N. Morphogenesis of Human Cardiac Outflow. Anat Rec 1985;213:578–586.

Thompson RP, Kanai T, Germroth PG, Gourdie RG, Thomas PC, Barton PJR, Mikawa T, Anderson RH. Organization and function of early specialized myocardium. In: Clark EB, Markwald RR, Takao A (eds). Developmental Mechanisms of Heart Disease. Armonk, NY: Futura Publishing Co Inc; 1995:269–279.

Thompson RP, Soles-Rosenthal P, Cheng G. Origin and fate of cardiac conduction tissue. In: Clark EB, Takao A (eds). Fifth International Symposium on Etiology and Morphogenesis of Congenital Heart Disease. New York: Futura. 2000.

Turner K, Navaratnam V. The positions of the coronary arterial ostia. Clin Anat 1996;9:76–380.

Van den Hoff MJB, Moorman AFM, Ruiiter IM, Lamers WH, Bennington RW, Markwald RR, et al. Myocardialisation of the cardiac outflow tract. Dev Biol 1999;212:477–490.

Van den Hoff MJB, Kruithof BP, Moorman AF. Making more heart muscle. Bioessays 2004;26:248–261.

Van Gils FA. The fibrous skeleton in the human heart: embryological and pathogenetic considerations. Virchows Arch A Pathol Anat Histol 1981;393:61–73.

Van Mierop LHS, Alley RD, Kausel HW, Stranahan A. The anatomy and embryology of endocardial cushion defects. J Thorac Cardiovasc Surg 1962;43:71–83.

Van Mierop LHS. Localization of pacemaker in chick embryo heart at the time of initiation of heartbeat. Am J Physiol 1967;212:407–415.

Van Mierop LHS, Kutsche LM. Comparative anatomy and embryology of the ventricles and arterial pole of the vertebrate heart. In: Nora JJ, Takao A (eds). Congenital heart disease: causes and processes. New York: Futura. 1984; pp 459–479.

Velkey JM, Bernanke DH. Apoptosis during coronary artery orifice development in the chick embryo. Anat Rec 2001;262(3):310–317.

Vernall DG. The human embryonic heart in the seventh week. Am J Anat 1962;111:17–24.

Viragh S, Challice CE. The origin of the epicardium and the embryonic myocardial circulation in the mouse. Anat Rec 1981;201:157–168.

Viragh S, Szabo E, Challice CE. Formation of the primitive myo- and endocardial tubes in the chicken embryo. J Mol Cell Cardiol 1989;21:123–137.

Viragh S, Gittenberger-de Groot AC, Poelman RE, Kalman F. Earyly development of the quail heart epicardium and associated vascular and glandular structures, Anat Embryol 1993;188:381–393.

Vrancken Peeters MPFM, Gittenberger-de-Groot AC, Mentink MMT, Hungerford JE, Little CD, Poelmann RE. The development of the coronary vessels and their differentiation into arteries and veins in the embryonic quail heart. Dev Dyn 1997;208:338–348.

Vrancken Peeters MP, Gittenberger-de Groot AC, Mentink MM, Poelmann RE. Smooth muscle cells and fibroblasts of the coronary arteries derive from epithelial-mesenchymal transformation of the epicardium. Anat Embryol (Berl) 1999;199:367–378.

Waldo KL, Willner W, Kirby ML. Origin of the proximal coronary artery stems and a review of ventricular vascularization in the chick embryo. Am J Anat 1990;188:109–120.

Waldo K, Miyagawa-Tomita S, Kumiski D, Kirby ML. Cardiac neural crest cells provide new insight into septation of the cardiac outflow tract: aortic sac to ventricular septal closure. Dev Biol 1998;196:129–144.

Waldo KL, Kumiski DH, Wallis KT, Stadt HA, Hutson MR, Platt DH, Kirby ML. Conotruncal myocardium arises from a secondary heart field. Development 2001;128:3179–3188.

Webb S, Brown NA, Wessels A, Anderson RH. Development of the murine pulmonary vein and its relationship to the embryonic venous sinus. Anat Rec 1998;250(3):325–334.

Webb S, Brown NA, Anderson RH. Formation of the atrioventricular septal structures in the normal mouse. Circ Res 1998b;82:645–656.

Webb S, Kanani M, Anderson RH, Richardson MK, Brown NA. Development of the human pulmonary vein and its incorporation in the morphologically left atrium. Cardiol Young 2001;11:632–642.

Webb S, Qayyum SR, Anderson RH, Lamers WH, Richardson MK. Septation and separation within the outflow tract of the developing heart. J Anat 2003;202:327–342.

Wenink AC, Gittenberger-de Groot AC, Brom AG. Developmental considerations of mitral valve anomalies. Int J Cardiol 1986;11:85–101.

Wessels A, Vermeulen JLM, Virágh S, Kálmán F, Lamers WH, Moorman AFM. Spatial distribution of "tissue-specific" antigens in the developing human heart and skeletal muscle, II: an immunohistochemical analysis of myosin heavy chain isoform expression patterns in the embryonic heart. Anat Rec 1991;229:355–368.

Wessels A, Vermeulen JL, Verbeek FJ, Viragh S, Kalman F, Lamers WH, Moorman AF. Spatial distribution of "tissue-specific" antigens in the developing human heart and skeletal muscle. III. An immunohistochemical analysis of the distribution of the neural tissue antigen G1N2 in the embryonic heart; implications for the development of the atrioventricular conduction system. Anat Rec 1992;232:97–111.

Wessels A, Markman MW, Vermeulen JL, Anderson RH, Moorman AF, Lamers WH. The development of the atrioventricular junction in the human heart. Circ Res 1996;78:110–117.

Wessels A, Anderson RH, Markwald RR, Webb S, Brown NA, Viragh S, Moorman AF, Lamers WH. Atrial development in the human heart: an immunohistochemical study with emphasis on the role of mesenchymal tissues. Anat Rec 2000;259:288–300.

Wessels A, Perez-Pomares JM. The epicardium and epicardially derived cells (EPDCs) as cardiac stem cells. Anat Rec A Discov Mol Cell Evol Biol 2004;276:43–57.

Wunsch A, Little CD, Markwald RR. Cardiac endothelial heterogeneity is demonstrated by the diverse expression of JB3 antigen, a fibrillin-like protein of the endocardial cushion tissue. Dev Biol 1994;165:585–601.

Xavier-Neto J, Rosenthal N, Silva FA, Matos TG, Hochgreb T, Linhares VL. Retinoid signaling and cardiac anteroposterior segmentation. Genesis 2001;31:97–104.

Ya J, Van Den Hoff MJB, De Boer PAJ, Tesink-Taekema Franco D, Moorman AFM, Lamers WH Normal development of the outflow tract in the rat. Circ Res 1998;82:464–472.

Yoshida H, Manasek F, Archilla RA. Intracardiac flow patterns in early embryonic life. A reexamination. Circ Res 1983;53:363–371.

Terminology

Below is a list of terms used to denominate the depicted structures. Frequently used synonyms and abbreviations are between brackets.

sinus venosus (venous sinus)
sinus septum
sinu-atrial fold
right sinus horn (right horn of the sinus venosus)
right sinus (venous) valve
left sinus (venous) valve
right anterior cardinal vein
right common cardinal vein
right posterior cardinal vein
left sinus horn (left horn of the sinus venosus)
left anterior cardinal vein
left common cardinal vein
left posterior cardinal vein
inferior caval vein
superior caval vein
coronary sinus

right atrium
right auricle
crista terminalis (terminal crest)
pectinate muscles
secondary (inter)atrial septum

left atrium
left auricle
primary (inter)atrial septum
primary interatrial foramen
secondary interatrial foramen
pulmonary pit
right pulmonary ridge (spina vestibuli / vestibular spine)
left pulmonary ridge
pulmonary veins

atrioventricular canal
superior (dorsal, upper) endocardial cushion
inferior (ventral, inferior) endocardial cushion
right lateral endocardial cushion

left lateral endocardial cushion
tricuspid orifice
mitral orifice

right ventricle
septomarginal trabeculation
moderator band
anterior papillary muscle
posterior papillary muscle
tendinous chordae
tricuspid valve
medial (septal) leaflet of the tricuspid valve
anterior (antero-superior) leaflet op the tricuspid valve
posterior (inferior) leaflet op the tricuspid valve
inner heart curvature (conoventricular flange)
supraventricular crest (crista supraventricularis)
pulmonary infundibulum

interventricular septum
primary interventricular foramen

left ventricle
anterior papillary muscle
posterior papillary muscle
tendinous chordae
mitral valve
arterial (septal) leaflet of the mitral valve
mural (parietal) leaflet of the mitral valve
aortic infundibulum

outflow tract
proximal (part of the) outflow tract (conus)
parietal (right) endocardial ridge in the proximal (part of the) outflow tract (right
    conus ridge)
fused endocardial ridges in the proximal outflow tract (conus septum)
septal (left) endocardial ridge in the proximal (part of the) outflow tract (left conus
    ridge)
distal part of the outflow tract (truncus)
superior endocardial ridge in the distal (part of the) outflow tract (superior truncus
    ridge)
inferior endocardial ridge in the distal (part of the) outflow tract (inferior truncus
    ridge)
intercalated endocardial ridges
aortic (semi-lunar) valve
pulmonary (semi-lunar) valve

aortic sac
aortico-pulmonary septum
superior limb of the aortico-pulmonary septum
inferior limb of the aortico-pulmonary septum

aortico-pulmonary window
pharyngeal arch arteries

pericardial cavity
transverse pericardial sinus
pericardial fold
pro-epicardium

cardiogenic crescent
intraembryonic coelom
heart tube

Table of human embryonic stages in relation to cardiac development

Carnegie stage	Age (dpc)	CRL (mm)	Cardiac developmental hall marks
8	18	1–1.5	pericephalic coelom appears cardiogenic plate, pericardial
9	20	1.5–2.5	cavity and endocardial plexus form and starts to curve ventrally; myocardium and cardiac jelly appear
10	22	2–3.5	endocardial tubes fuse and start to loop; dorsal mesocardium is formed; ballooning commences and 2 pairs of PAAs present; first heart beats
11	24	2.5–4.5	heart is beating; peristaltic flow commence; dorsal mesocardium is perforated; sinus venosus drains on RA; additional PAAs are formed
12	26	3–5	closed circulation; right venous valve and PIAS appear; IVS and fist ventricular trabeculations recognizable; cells appear in cardiac jelly
13	28	4–6	left venous valve, pulmonary pit, AV-cushions appear
14	32	5–7	AV-cushions start to approach; OFT ridges and sinuatrial node are distinguishable
15	33	7–9	secondary foramen in PIAS appears; distal OFT becomes septated and meets APS
16	37	8–11	auricles and AV node become recognizable; AV-cushions meet; proximal OFT ridges approach each other and IVS
17	41	11–14	tricuspid and mitral orifices become separated; semi-lunar valves are formed; proximal OFT becomes septated; PIF narrows
18	44	13–17	AV valves start to form; remainder of PIF starts to close; papillary muscles appear
19	47	16–18	remainder of PIF may close; left venous valve merges with atrial septum; delamination of AV valve leaflets commences
20	50	18–22	primary foramen is obliterated; SIAS may appear
21	52	22–24	
22	54	23–28	chordae tendiniae start to form
23	56	27–31	septal leaflet of tricuspid valve starts to delaminate